THE ACCIDENTAL TERRORIST

ALSO BY WILLIAM SHUNN

Cast a Cold Eye (with Derryl Murphy)
An Alternate History of the 21st Century

For Chris —
A terrific writer and reader
who saw and helped with a lot
of parts of this book.
Thank you!
All best,
Bill

THE ACCIDENTAL TERRORIST

CONFESSIONS OF A RELUCTANT MISSIONARY

• A MEMOIR BY •

WILLIAM SHUNN

SINISTER REGARD
New York
2015

ISBN 978-1-941-92855-4 (hardcover)
ISBN 978-1-941-92856-1 (trade paperback)

First edition: November 2015

www.sinisterregard.com
www.accidentalterrorist.com
www.shunn.net

For my podcast listeners,
who made this book seem possible.

But especially for Laura,
who makes everything seem possible.

NOTE

THIS BOOK IS NOT A WORK OF FICTION. IT IS A MEMOIR, A CHRONI-cle of a specific period in my life as I recall it. In some instances I've made small changes to the chronology of events for the sake of narrative clarity. Dialogue is intended not as a transcription but as a representative amalgam of real conversations. Otherwise, I've attempted to reconstruct these events as accurately as possible, as I experienced them. I've been aided by church papers, legal documents, newspaper articles, e-mail exchanges, maps, calendars, weather reports, and my own earlier written or recorded versions of this story, but for the most part my own memory has served as my most important resource.

Some of the participants in these events behaved in ways that, while innocuous enough to outsiders, might cause them some measure of embarrassment within the Mormon community today. I've tried to conceal their identities as best I can without distorting the story. The only contemporary characters who appear under their own names are the members of my immediate family and one classmate from a university summer writing program.

A man's memory is bound to be a distortion of his past in accordance with his present interests, and the most faithful autobiography is likely to mirror less what a man was than what he has become.

—Fawn M. Brodie, *No Man Knows My History*

THE ACCIDENTAL TERRORIST

PRELUDE

2/23/1987

THE DETECTIVE UNLOCKS MY TINY ROOM AND DRAGS A PLASTIC chair in from the hallway.

"Mister Shunn," she says, "I'd like to ask you some questions now, if you have a few minutes."

"I'm not going anywhere," I say, narrowing my eyes. My stinging eyes.

There's no one but the detective and me in this consultation booth, no knob on the inside of the door. The detective locks us in, sits down, crosses her legs, and smooths her short, short skirt.

I squirm in my chair. She's disconcertingly blond, mid-thirties. I'm nineteen years old, and I haven't been alone so close to a woman in five months. With no table between us, our knees nearly touch. This is against mission rules in so many ways, I can't even count. She arranges a steno pad atop her bare thigh, pencil sharpened and poised.

"Should I call you, what is it, 'Elder' instead?"

I try to breathe easy and keep my eyes above her neck. "Either way."

"Your name, please, Elder?"

I'm confused. "You used it a minute ago."

"For the record." Her green eyes don't blink. "Full name."

I touch the spot on my sweater where the black name tag should have been. "Donald William Shunn. The Second."

"Age?"

"Nineteen."

"Are you a Canadian citizen?"

"No, I'm American."

"And you've been in Canada for how long?"

"Five months, about."

"Any previous criminal record?"

"No."

She takes sharp, efficient notes in shorthand, a skill I didn't know still existed.

"Okay, Elder," she says, crossing her legs the other way. "Let's talk about your activities today."

I keep my eyes up, up. "I've been through this already, with the constable at the airport."

She shrugs. "Now you're going through it with me, and you'll probably go through it with someone else after that. That's how these things go."

"I'd like to talk to my mission president."

"So would we, Elder. We take terrorism very seriously."

The word knocks the wind out of me. "What?"

"Terrorism, conspiracy . . ."

"Conspiracy? There's no conspiracy."

She taps her pencil against the pad. "Imagine what it looks like from here."

I'm going to prison. I'm going to prison, and I'm going to die there.

"I'm not a terrorist." The words grate in my throat. "I already explained what happened."

"Explain it to *me*. Help me out here. We can't get any of your people on the phone. All we have is you. All *you* have is you."

I close my eyes, trying to work my frozen lungs. How many times was Joseph Smith in scrapes like this? Plenty, and *he* got through it.

Well, no. Actually, they shot him in the end. But I try not to think about that. *I* can get through this.

"Elder Shunn, tell me," says the detective. "Tell me how you ended up here."

My impulse is to blurt out everything. I take a deep breath. I choose my details with care.

BOOK I

THE MISSIONARY IMPOSITION

9/24/1986 - 12/3/1986

And it came to pass that many of the Lamanites did go into the land northward; and also Nephi and Lehi went into the land northward, to preach unto the people.

—Helaman 6:6, *The Book of Mormon*

CHAPTER 1

AT THE TAP ON MY SHOULDER I JERKED MY HEAD. "ELDER SHUNN, you're up," whispered Elder Rosenberg.

Time for my intake interview.

I stood and picked my way through the cluster of folding chairs in the darkened front room. The apes—a.p.'s, or assistants to the president—had drawn the heavy drapes and were nattering on about mission procedures, with transparency sheets and an overhead projector as aids. Elder Fearing and Elder Hardy had cheerfully announced that each of us would have 70 proselytizing hours a week to look forward to, at least eighteen of them knocking on doors. Ten solid Book of Mormon placements would be the minimum weekly goal, along with six first discussions. The monthly goal would be two convert baptisms.

I hated talking to strangers, let alone about religion. Two *years* of this? Who was I kidding? I'd be lucky to last two weeks.

Near the doorway watching the proceedings sat Sister Tuttle, a short, round woman in her late fifties with carefully coiffed hair in store-bought auburn. She smiled up at me and took my hand.

"He loves missionaries, Elder Shunn," she whispered, meaning her husband. "You'll be fine."

I looked back at the other ten greenies—nine elders and one sister—mostly teenagers like me, indistinct and unformed in the grainy gray light. The boys wore dark suits and ties, Sister Crowley a pullover sweater, conservative skirt, and low-heeled shoes. Black plastic name tags adorned our chests. We had just spent three intense weeks together in the spiritual boot camp that was the Missionary Training Center in Provo, Utah—living in dorms, eating cafeteria food, and being drilled in the arts of preaching, persuasion, and conversion. After solemn farewells to family and friends that morning at Salt Lake International, we had boarded our flight north to Calgary with backslapping bravado. Two hours later we stood on Canadian ground, clutching work visas in our sweaty, anxious hands. It was real. We were missionaries now.

I ghosted down a hallway of whitewashed cinder block. Outside it might be sunny, but gloom ruled this dim limbo. Soft voices murmured from cubicles nearby as the elderly office staff kept business rolling. I touched my back pocket with longing but didn't take out my wallet. I was trying to ration the time I spent staring at Katrina, and at the special scrap of chewing-gum foil stashed behind her photos.

I passed the front foyer, with its framed painting of Jesus Christ. How disconnected from the accompanying photographs of the prophet and his counselors it seemed, how much less real than those three old men with their mild smiles and expensive suits. Like a television program shot part on film and part on tape, the elements didn't quite harmonize.

But Christ in heaven was the living, breathing head of our church, however difficult I found it to imagine. A straight line ran from him to our new prophet, Ezra Taft Benson, then down through the apostles and other General Authorities directly to J. Matheson Tuttle, mission president. Outside whose office door, open a crack, I now stood.

My stomach knotted. Deep breath. "Remember, always obey your mission president," my father had told me at the airport. "He's a man of God."

I straightened my suit jacket, arranged my face into a mask, and knocked.

"Come in," President Tuttle chirped. He stood as I entered, reaching over his desk, a round man of sixty or so. His hand was soft but his grip firm. "Let's kneel, Elder Shunn. Will you offer the prayer?"

The office was small, crowded with bookshelves and filing cabinets. Despite the open blinds behind him, the space felt oppressively shadowed and intimate. He hitched up the legs of his black pinstriped trousers as he knelt beside the desk, where I joined him.

"Our dear Father which art in heaven," I fumblingly intoned, "we give thanks to thee this day for the many blessings thou hast given us, for our lives and our families and our knowledge of thy true gospel, and most of all this day for the opportunity to serve thee in the mission field. We ask thy Spirit to be with us during this meeting and through all our work, that we may be diligent and fruitful in bringing many souls unto the light of thy truth. These things we pray for in the name of thy Son, Jesus Christ, amen."

"Amen."

My ears burned as we rose and seated ourselves across the desk from each other. My words had rung hollow and rote, with no trace of the closeness to God I sometimes felt during my personal prayers. If this interview was a chess match, mine was hardly an impressive opening gambit.

"Shunn, Shunn," President Tuttle said absently, smiling. "From Kaysville, Utah. I know I've heard that name before. What does your father do?"

"He teaches school. Junior high, in Bountiful."

"We used to live there! What does he teach?"

"Wood and metal shop."

His mouth popped open in an O of wonder. "I think a couple of my boys might have had him for class."

Tuttle was not a handsome man, with his balding head and beaked nose, but he radiated a magnetic good cheer. I wanted to bask like a lizard in the warmth of his attention. At the same time, I needed desperately to conceal from him my true self, my inner infidel.

"Small world," I said.

"Small church. But that's what's we're here to change, eh, Elder?" he said, eyes twinkling behind large wire-rimmed glasses. He indicated the neat stacks of papers and folders on his desk. "You've made quite an impression on your leaders back home, you know. Your bishop and stake president both wrote highly complimentary letters about you. They seem to think you're a natural leader."

"Thank you." I hungered for a glimpse of those letters, those warm words of praise. I could have read them upside-down as we talked, given the opportunity. "That's very kind."

Tuttle's eyes crinkled but not his mouth. "Oh, don't thank me. Their opinions are helpful, but I keep my own counsel." Before the sting had sunk in, he lowered his voice and asked, "Are you glad to be here, Elder Shunn?"

I had endured interviews with church leaders for most of my life, like all Mormon boys—before baptism at eight, before ordination as a deacon at twelve, before admission to the temple at eighteen, and at least once a year otherwise for routine checkups. The purpose was to assess my preparedness and moral worthiness for whatever milestone came next in my spiritual development.

But this was more than that. President Tuttle, a stranger to me, would use this brief interview to assess my potential as a missionary. On the basis of my responses and his perceptions, he would assign me my first companion and proselytizing area. My comportment here could spell the difference between a plum posting and miserable exile. A thousand miles from home, this interview would set the tone for the next two years of my life.

Of course, Tuttle would also rely on prayer in making his decisions. As Fearing and Hardy had told us more than once since picking us up at the airport, "Prez is inspired." It was a mantra I would hear time and again as a missionary, meaning our president was a man of God whose every decision was guided by the whisperings of the Holy Spirit. My fate might already be set, predetermined by the Lord, no matter what I said here.

But maybe not.

So, was I glad to be here? Of course not. I was nineteen. I had plans. I had stories and novels to write. I had Katrina. I had two years of college under my belt, and in two more years I could be done. The thought of all that lost time and opportunity made me ill. But I couldn't say that.

Solemnly I bobbed my head. "Oh, yes. Very glad."

Tuttle tilted his head like a great bird of prey. Was that a glint of suspicion in his eye? The Spirit might that moment be whispering to my inspired leader that I was a liar. My palms prickled. Which was worse for my soul, lying to the Lord or confessing the awful truth?

His brow furrowed. "Are you trunky at all, Elder? You know, homesick?"

"Well, sure," I said, shrugging. A partial truth for misdirection. "A little."

He nodded. "That's perfectly natural, and you'll get over it soon enough. Believe me, there's nothing like losing yourself in the work of the Lord to take your mind off home."

"I'm sure."

"You *are* his representative now. It'll help to remember that at all times."

Christ's representative. That made *me* part of the great church hierarchy too, heir to a portion of the same power possessed by President Tuttle and everyone above him. Another profundity I couldn't wrap my head around. I nodded as if in deep concentration.

Tuttle leaned forward, hands clasped on the desktop. "Now, what particular experience do you have that you think is going to help you be an effective missionary?"

"Well, I've studied a lot," I said, flailing for answers better than the ones that came to mind. "I know the scriptures fairly well. I do a pretty good job speaking in church."

"Any retail experience? Any door-to-door?"

"Uh, not really." I scratched my cheek, nonplussed. These were not the usual worthiness questions. "I sold candy to help us go to scout camp once."

"Hmm. Management experience?"

Management? I hadn't even finished *college* yet. "Deacons quorum president, I guess? And I was senior patrol leader in my scout troop."

"Eagle scout, right?"

"Yes. At thirteen."

He nodded, his tone encouraging. "That's good, that's something. Now, what do you think your weaknesses are as a missionary?"

"Oh . . . well." Besides not wanting to *be* a missionary? "I guess I'm pretty reserved. I don't really talk or relate all that well to people I don't know."

Tuttle waved a hand. "A few days in the field and you'll get over that. Now, judging from your school grades, you have quite an aptitude for languages. Are you sorry you ended up being sent to Canada?"

In this question lurked more traps than Indiana Jones had faced in any jungle tomb. "As opposed to . . . ?"

"Oh, maybe someplace more . . . exciting? Someplace you could learn a language?"

My closest friends had been called to places like Brazil, Japan, Norway, Thailand, Italy. I was a long way from Quebec, so my three years of French apparently counted for little to whoever made mission assignments at church headquarters. Either that or it was evidence that the Lord really *did* dictate mission calls to the prophet. Why squander my value in an English-speaking mission unless I was needed here for a reason?

I tried to erase all traces of resentment from my reply. "I was a little disappointed at first, sure. But I prayed about it, and . . . well, it's like something my mom pointed out. I'm a writer, and English is my tool. It's the language I'm best at."

"Good answer," Tuttle said, nodding. He was already speaking quietly but lowered his voice further. I had to lean forward to hear better. "Now, do you have a testimony of the gospel, Elder?"

There. The crux of any priesthood interview. To a Mormon, a testimony is one's inner conviction of the truthfulness of the church. Saying you *have* a testimony implies that diligent study and prayer have instilled in you an unshakeable assurance that the Book of Mormon and the gospel of Jesus Christ as restored by the prophet Joseph Smith are true, correct, and authored by God. Such a statement takes as given that spiritual inquiries, like the scientific, must yield in predictable fashion to empirical attack.

Did I have a testimony? After a lifetime of wrestling with that question, I still couldn't be certain. I had felt chills of awe many times at the power or beauty of a passage of scripture, or at a fellow Saint's spoken testimony, or during fervent prayer, but was that the same as the burning in the bosom, imparted by the Holy Ghost, that made truth known to man? How was I to tell?

When I was honest with myself, I had to admit I didn't *know* the church was true. No, I *feared* it was true. Most of the people I knew regarded their knowledge of the gospel as the greatest blessing and privilege that could ever have entered their lives, but to me that knowledge was a curse. I resented the burden it placed upon me, and I envied the less restrictive lives that less enlightened people lived. I wished fervently for ignorance, for the freedom that truth banished.

So. Did I have a testimony of the gospel?

"Yes," I said firmly. A testimony of the most perverse sort, rooted in pessimism and despair, but a testimony nonetheless.

"Good," said President Tuttle. "And do you have a testimony of Joseph Smith? Of the Book of Mormon?"

I hedged a little. Partial honesty would come across as more sincere. "A pretty good one, yes. I keep working on it."

"Do you love the Lord, Elder?"

Mouth dry. "Of course I do."

"You have a girlfriend at home?"

Though I didn't want to hear whatever he had to tell me on the subject, there was no point in lying. Like so much else, this tidbit was no doubt tucked away in one of those file folders.

Come to think of it, my father's occupation must have been in there too.

"Yes."

"Is it serious?"

It had always been serious for me, but I hadn't understood how seriously Katrina took it until that very morning, at Salt Lake International.

"Fairly serious," I admitted.

"Do you want to marry her?"

A pit yawned inside me. President Tuttle's attention had long since ceased to warm me. The wallet burned in my back pocket.

"Elder?" he prompted. "Do you plan to marry this girl?"

Was this his gift of discernment, peering at last into my lying soul?

I shook my head. "I don't think we've thought that far ahead," I said, keeping my face blank.

He looked at me hard without speaking. Maybe one of the other missionaries—Elder Vickers, for instance—had already told him otherwise, ratted me out. I held his gaze and volunteered nothing more.

At last he moved on. "Any unresolved transgressions you might have let slide in talking to your bishop back home, or to your branch president at the MTC?"

He meant sins of a sexual nature, which required confession and heavy penance. A serious enough sin might even get me sent back home until the repentance process was complete. But whether out of virtue or timidity, I'd never tried to go further than first base with any girl, not even Katrina. I might have committed a few furtive acts of onanism during my three weeks at the Missionary Training Center, but I didn't feel particularly inclined to admit this.

"No, nothing."

President Tuttle turned X-ray eyes upon me. For a moment I felt certain he was about to contradict me.

"Let me tell you something, Elder," he said, his voice a steel rail. "There are more ways to transgress with a girl than just physically, particularly when you're a missionary. This girl of yours—what's her name again?"

"Katrina." Answering felt like betraying a secret, but again I'm sure he had that information already.

"Write to Katrina once a week, and the rest of the time put all thoughts of her away. Let the Lord worry about her for you while you're gone. These two years are *his* time. Now that you've put on the black name tag, your only concern is saving souls. Dwelling on romantic feelings at this time in your life will rob you of your focus, rob you of the Spirit, and ultimately rob the Lord of the best work you can give him. This is why it's so vitally important that missionaries avoid all involvement with members of the opposite sex. The Adversary is sneaky and trips us up through our natural inclinations." He folded his hands on the desk and frowned. "Are you familiar with the Fifty-eighth Section of the Doctrine and Covenants?"

"I—I believe so?"

"'Verily I say, men should be anxiously engaged in a good cause, and do many things of their own free will, and bring to pass much righteousness.' The Lord said this to Joseph Smith. Do you recognize this verse?"

"Yes, I do."

"Don't forget it, Elder Shunn. Stay anxiously engaged. Don't give yourself time to brood about your past life." He leaned across the desk, beaming now, an expanding sun moving too close to the earth. "And remember, if you ever feel your priorities getting out of alignment, I'm always available to talk."

He rose, came around the desk, and knelt, gesturing for me to join him in a brief prayer, which he offered. When we stood again he swept me into a bear hug.

"I'm going to have my eye on you, Elder Shunn," he said, as if this were a good thing. "Never doubt it. Would you send in Elder Nash next, please?"

Troubled, I shambled back along the hallway. The scrap of foil in my wallet, folded twice lengthwise, was a twin to the one I'd wrapped around Katrina's ring finger not six hours earlier. However unwittingly, President Tuttle had nailed my biggest preoccupation.

I was anxiously engaged.

CHAPTER 2

TWO YEARS EARLIER, MY FATHER AND I WERE DRIVING BACK ROADS somewhere east of Victorville in the California desert when he sprang a terrifying question on me. "Son," he asked, "do you want to serve a mission?"

I didn't know what to say. I must have fielded that question hundreds of times growing up, from relatives, family friends, or congregants at church, and the expected "Yes" was always my reflexive answer. But the look on my father's face told me this time was different.

He wanted a truthful answer. I didn't know how to give him one.

TWO BASIC, FOUNDATIONAL STORIES RULED MY EARLY CHILDHOOD. I cannot recall a time when I was not aware of them both.

The first, appropriately, was the story of the First Vision. In the year 1820, by his own account, a fourteen-year-old boy in upstate New York named Joseph Smith was confused about which of the many nearby churches to join. Half his family went to one church, half to another, and they all kept trying new ones. Joseph hiked into the woods to pray about what to do. But no sooner had he knelt and opened his mouth than a terrible dark force fell upon him, stopping his tongue so he could not speak.

Afraid for his life, Joseph cried out mightily to God in his heart. The dark force released him as a pillar of light descended from the sky. Two glorious personages stood in the light. The first pointed to the second, saying, "Joseph, this is my beloved Son. Hear him!"

The second personage told him he should join no church on earth, for they all were fallen and corrupt. That was the beginning of Joseph's life as a prophet of God. After this he would go on to bring forth the Book of Mormon and restore the true gospel of Christ to the world.

I was one of the privileged few who knew this story. Most children were not lucky enough to be born into families like mine, which had the truth.

I said there were two stories. The second was about my father. As a younger man he'd been a missionary in Germany. He spent months learning the language just so he could teach the people there about Joseph Smith. This was his duty. Because he knew the truth about Heavenly Father and Jesus, he needed to share it with other people. One day when I was big enough, I would follow in his footsteps and do the same.

Oh, how I looked forward to that day.

When I was small we lived in Los Angeles. My father and I shared a close bond there. I was named after him—my birth certificate reads DONALD WILLIAM SHUNN II—though instead of Don he called me Bill, which was the name of his favorite uncle. As firstborn I occupied a position of privilege in the family hierarchy. My favorite of the German phrases he taught me, in fact, was good only for asserting that position: *Ich bin der Erste* ("I am the first"). I always loved tagging along with him, whether to the school where he taught or the college where he took classes. He seemed to be friends with every colorful character in town, from the Protestant minister next door to the gas station attendant down on Eagle Rock Boulevard. Once, at his favorite barbershop, I insisted on having my hair cut just like his—and he was nearly bald on top.

My parents sometimes invited the local missionaries over for dinner. I adulated those clean-cut, smiling young men, even if my understanding of their day-to-day lives was vague. We called them "Elder" because they were special, while the other men at church were just called "Brother." After dinner the missionaries would set up a flannel board in the living room and practice teaching us the story of Joseph Smith's First Vision. I would watch enraptured as they moved their cutout figures through the familiar contours of the tale. Sometimes they would ask my little sisters or me to fill in what happened next. I never hesitated. I could tell the story almost as well as they could.

It was with some confusion that I began attending Good Shepherd Lutheran School in 1972. An affordable alternative to public school in our largely Latino neighborhood, Good Shepherd was where I first smacked heads with a competing religious philosophy. I was a good student in most respects but drove my poor teacher crazy with my frequent contradictions of her morning gospel lessons. Once for show-and-tell I proudly brought the German edition of the Book of Mormon that my father had carried as a missionary. I couldn't understand the puzzled looks this drew until Miss Schaeffer attempted to make clear to us that not all faiths use the same scriptures. Actually, what she said was "Oh, is that one of your *Mormon* books?"

The realization that I shared a Bible but not much else with my classmates was quite unsettling. I lay awake at night puzzling over what would have happened had my spirit been sent down from heaven to a Lutheran family instead. Would I have been raised believing a false religion?

My childhood was a minefield of mixed messages. I'd been reading since the age of three, and my father, shop teacher by day and doctoral candidate by night, filled our shelves with discarded math and science books from his school library. Trips to Disneyland alternated with visits to the Natural History Museum of Los Angeles County. Yet my father insisted, despite what I read in those books and learned from planetarium shows, that my beloved dinosaurs had never existed, and that Earth was a mere six thousand years old. His firm pronouncement on the subject of cavemen—no such thing!—made me feel profoundly sinful when I sneaked peeks at the scary Neanderthal skulls in my book on early man.

The harshest of these messages were delivered at the end of a leather belt. Inside this same man who called me his beloved son, who gathered his family together every Monday evening for lessons in goodness and grace, raged an unpredictable temper. One day he might settle a spat between my sisters and me with patient calm, the next with whippings to our bare asses. The mere threat of the belt was enough to send us into spasms of sobbing and pleading. When these punishments were over, it was impossible to sit.

Late in 1973, when I was six, we relocated to Grantsville, Utah, a tiny desert town south of the Great Salt Lake, which my parents hoped would prove a better place than Los Angeles to raise their growing Mormon family. I'd been working well ahead of my first-grade class before the move, so my mother enrolled me directly in second grade at my new school. It sometimes bothered me that my classmates were a year older than I was, but what I found truly strange about Grantsville was that the kids I saw at school were the same ones I saw at church. The border between the two domains blurred. It was sometimes hard to know where one ended and the other began.

My father had landed a mid-year job teaching shop at the local high school. It wasn't the kind of position he ultimately wanted, but he had high hopes it would serve as a stepping-stone to bigger and better things—a career as a principal, an administrator, a figure of consequence and cachet here in the Promised Land. I do remember, though, how proud he was of the DR. SHUNN nameplate on his classroom door.

Born in 1936, my father had dragged himself up from his poor California roots through hard work, stubbornness, and a big assist from some mentors in his local Mormon leadership. Though exposed to the church as a child by his mother, he hadn't thrown himself into it until early adulthood, after both his parents were dead. He credited the church with rescuing him from a life of liquor and other louche pursuits. And typical of a faith forged under extreme circumstances, his bordered on zealotry.

If the church became my father's lodestone, then its emphasis on education was his compass north. Between a stint in the Army, missionary service in Germany, and teaching gigs in both L.A. and Salt Lake City, he earned bachelor's and master's degrees at Brigham Young University. His doctorate from UCLA, the culmination of a decade and a half of struggle, was going to be his young family's ticket into security and respectability.

But in Utah that dream began to curdle. My father had taken a fifty-percent pay cut and lost all his seniority to move us to this backwater, where now it became clear that advancement wasn't in the cards. He was, by his own admission, impatient and abrasive with his superiors, especially those he considered incompetent. Trapped, he scoured the back pages of educational journals for an escape route, sending job applications as far away as Guam.

Meanwhile he grew more physically abusive. I earned the belt for walking the wrong route home from school, for repeating novel and interesting words I'd learned from my classmates, for crimes my sisters falsely pinned on me. I remember getting an erection once while trying to pee, and the terror of trying to hide it when my father blundered onto the scene. The situation wasn't what it looked like, but that hardly mattered to the belt.

Most people seem to understand that perfection is not achievable by mortals. My father was not one of them.

We moved a few more times, settling finally in Kaysville, a town of about 10,000 to the north of Salt Lake City, and I pulled further away from my father. The arbitrary and often unearned disciplining, the belittling corrections when I offered an answer or opinion he didn't like, and the constant sense that I was doing something *wrong* taught me to keep my mouth shut around him and drove me to avoid him as much as possible. The physical abuse tailed off as I grew older, but the damage of course did not. I took refuge in science fiction and schoolwork, earning top grades despite the painful awkwardness of the age difference between me and my classmates.

My father had found a stable teaching job, though not the advancement he sought. The family grew to eight children, large even for our Mormon community. The fact that I would one day serve a mission was never questioned, particularly since I was expected to set an example for my two much younger brothers. When I was fourteen, between my sophomore and junior years of high school, my father arranged a cabinetry job for me so I could start saving money for my mission. Missionaries are expected to pay their own way if at all possible, so every paycheck I earned went straight into the bank. My father called this a "consecrated fund," since it was earmarked for service to the Lord. Occasionally I took some cash out to spend on myself, but every withdrawal felt like embezzling from God.

As a child I'd looked forward to the adventure of a mission, dreaming of the exotic lands I might visit, but as I grew older I came to dread and resent the two-year imposition looming at age nineteen. A missionary's time is not his own. He can't watch TV or movies, can't read newspapers or any but a handful of approved books, can't listen to music other than the Mormon Tabernacle Choir, and, most dauntingly, can't undertake personal projects of any kind. By my junior year my love of science fiction had developed to the point that I'd begun submitting my own short stories to magazines. Two years without the chance to work at my craft was as awful a prospect as two years without a novel to read. The only upside might be learning another language, but there was no guarantee I'd be called to a foreign mission. The church would send me where it needed me, not where I might want to go.

I fantasized about skipping out on mission service, but I couldn't see a way to make that happen in real life. I was too afraid of my father's reaction, too reluctant to shame myself before my family, too unwilling to shame my family before the community. And I couldn't overlook the fact that a lack of mission experience would damage my chances of finding a suitable Mormon wife. The church cautioned its young women to avoid serious relationships with men who were not returned missionaries.

My misgivings made me feel wicked, ungrateful, hypocritical. I confided them in no one, not even my closest friends. The only course I could see was to pray to God to change my heart so I could find the joy in doing what I knew was right.

I graduated from high school in 1984, still two months shy of my seventeenth birthday, with a full-tuition scholarship to the University of Utah in hand. My parents would have preferred to see me attend their beloved alma mater, Brigham Young University, but they accepted my choice because I could live at home and commute the 25 miles to the Salt Lake City campus. As my father liked to remind me, I was hardly ready to think about living on my own.

IT WAS NOT UNUSUAL FOR MY FATHER TO DRAG ME OFF ON A ROAD trip to California. He loved long drives, and he'd make the run to Los Angeles, where crash space with relatives was plentiful, on the flimsiest of pretexts. He preferred back roads, maybe because they reminded him of his early student days when he would barrel home from Provo in his storied Corvette convertible. In his company, those desert highways had become as familiar to me as the route from my bed to the bathroom in the middle of the night.

As hard as I'd tried to wriggle out of this latest trip, there I was riding shotgun, lodged deep in the uncomfortable silence that always reigned when my father and I were alone together. When he broke that silence to ask if I wanted to serve a mission, my first instinct was to throw myself out the car door and take my chances in the gray desert.

I never for a moment considered giving an honest answer. Where that might have led, what it might have changed, I do not know.

I groped for a plausible evasion as the dusty landscape churned past my window. The words of the prophet Spencer W. Kimball rang in my head: "*Every young man should serve a mission. It is not an option; it is your obligation.*"

With what I hoped was a casual shrug, I said, "It's what I'm supposed to do."

"No, son," my father snarled. He hunched over the wheel of our old brown station wagon like he was gnawing his tongue off. I cringed, though he hadn't laid a hand on me since I was ten or eleven. His eyes blazed blue as he fixed his gaze on me. "That's not the kind of answer I want to hear. Do you *want* to go on a mission?"

My ears roared. My lungs burned. The reptile in me—firstborn, example, martyr—curled its scaly armor around the underbelly of my hidden self.

"Yes," I said. "That's what I want."

"Why?" he demanded.

Boys go on missions for a lot of different reasons. Some because their parents promise them a car or college tuition when they get home. Some at the insistence of their girlfriends, who would otherwise marry someone more devout—and often do, anyway. Some out of inertia, or boredom, or to put off other, more momentous life decisions. It's the path of least resistance.

I often heard it said at church that there are no wrong reasons to go on a mission, only wrong reasons to stay. But I needed a *right* reason. Though he rarely said much about his own mission, I was sure that my father had gone for the right reason. In his day, missions lasted two and a *half* years—itself down from three or even four in earlier eras. You don't do that for the sake of a car.

"I want to serve God." The words were ashes in my mouth. "I want to spread the gospel, so other people can feel the same joy we know."

"It's a solemn responsibility," my father said, eyes narrowed. "Not to be undertaken lightly."

"I know."

He gazed at me balefully, then returned his attention to the road. "Okay, then."

A green milepost ticked past.

"The church is true, son," my father said, staring down the asphalt into the future or the past, his face painted with that jumble of cynicism, grief, and resolve I'd learned to recognize in him as solemnity. "If it weren't, the missionaries would have destroyed it long ago."

I usually chuckled at this, as if I understood the joke. But this time it didn't sound funny.

CHAPTER 3

ELDER FOWLER TOSSED A GOLF BALL LIGHTLY IN THE AIR AS I trailed him up the shady walk. He bobbled the catch, and the ball clacked off the concrete.

"Aw, shit," he said, lunging for it on the bounce. He snagged it and glanced back at me apologetically. "There I go again. You must think I'm awful."

I waved him off as best I could while balancing a precarious stack of dark blue books. "Don't worry about it."

"You're sure? I warned you, I can't live without my cuss words."

The fact that my first companion, my trainer, couldn't keep from swearing was both a disappointment and a relief. I was reasonably fluent in profanity myself, having studied the language in the company of friends since at least third grade, but that was one of the many practices I expected to put behind me now that I was here in the field, in Canada. What I hoped, what I frequently prayed for, was to find some kind of peace in mission service. I hoped to emerge strong and transformed at the far end, with a confident authority and a testimony like a rock, but still be myself. I wanted to fuse my righteous half and my mischievous half into a functioning whole. I wanted to put the war inside me to rest. My trainer's inability to let go of his cuss words suggested that this might not be as automatic a process as I had hoped. At the same time, though, I was glad he didn't seem to be the drill sergeant I'd been dreading.

"Don't worry about it, really," I said. Confrontation was never my style.

"'Damn,' 'hell,' and 'shit,' that's it, I promise."

"It's fine, it's fine."

Elder Fowler grinned and led the way onto the porch of the brick house. "All right, son, now watch and learn." He rapped the golf ball smartly on the wooden front door.

"Why do you use that?" I asked, wondering where this mysterious sphere fit into missionary lore.

"It gives you a nice, resonant sound when you knock," Fowler said, his rangy body curved like an unstrung bow inside his shiny brown suit. Not even a regulation missionary haircut could obliterate his jet-black curls. "Spares your knuckles too, especially when it's cold out."

Juggling my slick books, I asked, "Why not just ring the doorbell?"

That characteristic grin split his face. "Knocking's classier. Jesus didn't say, 'I stand at the door and press the buzzer.'"

Footsteps sounded from inside. I tensed. This was my first day of door-to-door tracting, an activity that took its name from the religious pamphlets bulging my companion's pockets. It was, to be more precise, my first *minute* of tracting, and, despite all the hours spent role-playing at the Missionary Training Center, I had no clue what to expect. Would we be invited inside? Thrown off the porch? Would I melt with embarrassment?

The door creaked open and a heavyset old woman with dyed hair and owlish glasses poked her head out. "Yes, what can I help you with?" she asked, peering suspiciously back and forth.

"Well, good afternoon, ma'am," Fowler drawled, sounding like a cowboy tipping his hat. "I'm Elder Fowler, and this is my companion, Elder Shunn, and we're representatives from the Church of Jesus Christ of Latter-day Saints, sometimes known as the Mormons.

We're visiting people in your neighborhood today with a very important message from our Father in Heaven, and we wondered if we could
come in for a few minutes and share that with you."

The woman was shaking her head even before Fowler finished his
spiel, clutching shut the neck of her housedress as if we were trying to
peep. "No, thank you, I don't think so. Not today."

Fowler craned forward. "Ma'am, is there a more convenient time we
might come by to share our message with you?"

She had already begun to retreat, but like an indecisive bird she
peeked back around the door. "No, actually I don't think so."

Before she could close us out, Elder Fowler nudged me. From my
stack I thrust forward a copy of the Book of Mormon, a thick paperback with the title stamped in gold on its pebbled blue cover.

"Ma'am," said Fowler, "if you learned that our Heavenly Father had
sent us a second book to stand hand in hand with the Bible in testifying of the divinity of Jesus Christ, wouldn't you think that was a wonderful thing?"

"Thank you, boys, but I'm Lutheran and that's the way I'm going to
stay." Some peevishness was manifesting at last. "At my age I'm not
looking for any big changes."

The needle on my Cringe-O-Meter quivered deep in the red, but
Elder Fowler wasn't nearly ready to give up. "Ma'am, we'd like to offer
you the opportunity to read this other testament of Christ for free. If
you'll promise to read these passages we've outlined for you, we'll leave
this copy—"

"Thank you, *no*," said the woman, pulling her head back in and
slamming the door.

Fowler shook his head and removed an index card from his breast
pocket. "Okay then," he said, jotting a note. "We'll take that as one resounding 'I'd rather burn in hell.' Next."

It was a sunny autumn afternoon in Brooks, Alberta, a booming
oil town two hours east of Calgary on the Trans-Canada Highway.

Wednesday evening, after a sumptuous dinner at the Tuttle home, the apes had passed out sealed envelopes to all us greenies. These contained our first assignments—companion and proselytizing area. Anxiously we ripped them open. The Canada Calgary Mission covered Alberta, the Northwest Territories, and a corner of British Columbia. One of us could potentially be going to Yellowknife, as far north of Calgary as Calgary was north of Salt Lake City. There was even a rumor that missionaries might be sent to Inuvik, a mere hundred kilometers from the Arctic Ocean.

I unfolded and scanned my brief letter. BROOKS, it read. ELDER MARTIN FOWLER.

I felt vaguely let down. No Arctic adventure for me. That privilege went to Elder Vickers, who would make the flight to Yellowknife the next afternoon.

In the morning, the apes took us to open checking accounts at the Royal Bank of Canada and to apply for Social Insurance cards. When we got back to the mission office, the tiny parking lot was buzzing like a beehive with comings and goings. It was a transfer day, the mission-wide shuffle that takes place every four to six weeks when fresh meat arrives from the MTC. A good sixth of the two hundred elders and sisters in the mission were being reassigned that day—elders promoted to leadership positions, feuding companionships broken up, problem missionaries moved from problem areas, good missionaries stuck in one place for too long offered fresh scenery. Everyone being transferred seemed to detour through the mission office, and every missionary in the city seemed to have turned out to greet them.

The elders who most attracted my attention were the two-year vets checking in for their last night before shipping home. Beaming, confident men, looking hale and fit, *ages* more godly and mature than the greenies I'd arrived with. I couldn't imagine ever being one of them, with their easy, solemn camaraderie, couldn't imagine crossing the vast gulf of time that lapped at their backs, landing on that distant shore a new man. Some of them insisted they'd re-up for another two years if they could, a sentiment I did not understand.

It was in that overwhelming chaos of backslapping and taleswapping and homesickness that Elder Fowler found me. He'd been stationed until now in Calgary itself, a district leader in charge of four companionships, but now, near the end of his mission, he was being dispatched to a lonely prairie town for what would likely be his final assignment—training me.

"This is exactly what I wanted," he told me as we settled into our mission-owned Citation and headed east, into the unknown. "I went to Prez and I told him I wanted to die in a nice, quiet town away from the city, where maybe I could raise another son."

Missionaries tended to talk that way, casting their service in terms of life events and familial relationships. This logic made Fowler my "father," and his long-departed trainer my "grandfather." Going home was "dying."

Now, in Brooks, this new father of mine led me all the way back to the sidewalk from the old woman's front porch, though it would have been quicker just to cross her lawn to the next house. Training me not to cut corners.

"That lady really didn't let you get a word in, did she?" I said. I wasn't sure whether to be more dismayed at the woman's lack of interest in our message or at my companion's mortifying tenacity.

Fowler shrugged. "Oh, that was nothing, Elder. Wait'll you meet someone who's *really* not interested. Like the kind who opens the door pointing a gun in your face and says you got five seconds to beat it or he starts shooting."

I boggled. "Did that really happen?"

"More'n once."

Brick bungalows lined this block, snug as nursery rhymes beneath a canopy of interlocking elm branches and changing leaves. We turned up the walk to the next house, and Fowler handed me the golf ball.

"Your door, Elder."

My heart stuttered. "What, me?" I stopped and tried to give him back the ball. "I, I, I don't know how to do this yet. I can't even remember what you said back there at that door, let alone what I do if we get in. Let me watch you a few more times."

He held up his hands. "Naw, it's better this way. You're only gonna learn by doing it, so you may as well start now."

"But—"

"Don't worry—it's not as hard as it looks. And I'll be right there for backup in case you get in trouble."

This was suspiciously similar to my uncle Doug's proclamation the summer I was twelve, right before he threw me out of a tree into a lake. Several humiliating seconds later he had to jump in after me and haul me, thrashing, to shore.

"All right, all right," I said, rolling the warm ball around in my hand and leading the way up the porch. I didn't want my new companion to think I was a wimp. Better to take control of the moment than let the moment take control of me. I stopped in front of the white storm door, golf ball poised to knock.

Fowler pointed to the storm door. "Open that first."

I looked at him. "It's okay to do that?"

"You don't want to dent it, do you?"

I tugged at the collar of my white shirt. My tie felt too tight. I reminded myself that I was doing this for the sake of my soul, and that my reward at the end of it would be Katrina. I squared my shoulders and grabbed the storm door by its handle. Holding it propped open with my shoulder, I rapped the golf ball several times, hard, on the wooden door inside.

"The goal is to produce sound without actually damaging the property, Elder," said Fowler dryly. "And three or four knocks is plenty."

"Sorry, sorry." I waited, my heart hammering in my throat, but after fifteen seconds or so no answer had come. "Okay, no one home." I turned to leave.

"Give them a chance," said Fowler with a palm to my chest. "Maybe they didn't hear you. Of course, they'd have to be deaf not to have heard that, but maybe that's the case. Or maybe it's a cripple who has to hobble up from the basement on crutches. Try again."

Every second we waited on the porch seemed to increase the odds that the door would open, which was the last thing I wanted. But I knocked again and after another minute concluded with relief that there really was no one home.

Elder Fowler selected a tract on eternal families from his pocket, scratched our phone number on the back, and tucked it inside the storm door. When he had finished his notation on the index card and we were back at the sidewalk, I held the golf ball out to him.

"Your door, Elder," I said.

"Oh, no," said Fowler, shaking his head. "No turnovers till someone answers the door."

"Oh, come on."

"That's the way it's done, sorry." He shaded his eyes suddenly, gazing off into the southern sky. "Hey, do you see that plane, Elder?"

I peered in the direction he was pointing. What looked like a silver speck inched across the sky, spinning behind it a gauzy filament. "Yeah."

"How far away do you think it is?"

I had no earthly clue. "Ten miles? Twenty? I don't know."

Fowler shook his head, grinning. "Ten weeks for me, two years for you."

My face burned, and the backs of my eyes stung. For the past few minutes I'd managed not to think about the time still ahead of me, but now my companion had slapped me in the face with it.

Fowler laughed and laughed. "Oh, you should've seen the look on your face!" He tousled my hair. "I've been waiting all day for a chance to use that one."

"Great, yeah," I said, smoothing my hair and fuming.

"Do you know what they call missionaries like me? I'm a double-digit midget! Less than a hundred days to go."

"Let's just get this door over with."

I marched up to the next house while Elder Fowler chortled in tow. Three sharps raps of the golf ball brought an older man in a plaid shirt and thick glasses to the door. He looked like a startled rabbit.

"Yes?"

"Um, sir, yes, hello," I stammered. "We're, um, missionaries from the Church of Jesus Christ of Latter-day Saints? And we're just bringing people a message today about the other testament of Jesus Christ . . ."

I fumbled to get one of the books up into view, but the old man was already waving a peremptory hand and withdrawing. "No, no, no," he said, and the door closed in my face.

"Hmm," said Elder Fowler, inscribing a note on his index card. He tapped his pen against his chin. "Maybe we should role-play this a little as we walk."

I handed him the golf ball. This seemed more appropriate than throwing it at him.

OUR TRACTING HAD GOTTEN OFF TO A VERY LATE START THAT DAY. We had left our modest apartment, inherited from the previous missionaries, at 9:30 that morning, right on time, emerging onto a street of withered lawns, struggling saplings, and squat multi-unit dwellings. The grayish tang of the dark, spongy wood that trimmed our own quadplex set my teeth on edge just to look at. It was my first morning in Brooks, and if that weren't enough in itself to make me homesick, the neighborhood's barrenness under its small northern sun made me feel disoriented and dispossessed, a conscript into unending exile.

We drove to the industrial fringe of town, where the first stop we made was not some potential convert's hovel but a health-and-racquet club Elder Fowler had found in the phone book. We were dressed in civilian clothes.

"Don't feel like you have to join up," he told me, "but I can't get by without my workouts."

A gym membership was definitely against mission rules—whether due to the expense, the time commitment, or the proximity to hot, sweating female bodies, I did not know—but I didn't want to be a stick-in-the-mud. Besides, if I hit the machines regularly maybe I could go home to Katrina all pumped up. Fowler, a slick if homey talker, negotiated us a nice, discounted weekly rate.

Our next stop was Canadian Tire, a superstore chain so powerful that many other retailers across the nation accepted its in-house currency. I bought a heavy parka, thermal underwear, and snow boots in preparation for winter. While we were at it, I picked up a cheap racquetball racquet too.

After that we hit the municipal library. "It's a missionary's best friend in a town like this, partner," Fowler said. "You don't want to be a bucket, but you need *something* to keep you sane."

"What's a bucket?"

"A slacker, a goldbricker, a lazy ass. But I'd rather get called any of those than give up my Louis L'Amours."

This delighted me, as I hadn't taken my new companion for a reader, but the good Mormon son in me worried that I was starting off my mission on the wrong foot. Though Fowler and I weren't wearing our suits or name tags, I spent our time in the library paranoid that some local church member would spot us there and rat us out to President Tuttle. We left with a couple of space operas for me, a stack of westerns for him, and a library card apiece.

We bought groceries next and ran them back home. Our apartment was neat, clean, and in good repair, with charts pinned to the walls and pamphlets stacked on most every horizontal surface. The living room featured stylish faux-brick paneling, while the kitchen was airy and bright. As we devoured peanut butter sandwiches, apples, and approximately a quart of milk, Fowler pored over the maps and notes the previous missionaries had left us.

After lunch we changed into our proselytizing clothes—or "pross" clothes—and drove a few miles south of town. North lay the jumbled desolation of the Alberta Badlands, but the landscape here was a patchwork of farms. Leaving our car on the shoulder of the provincial highway, Fowler marched us into a tangled thicket of poplars that cut the cold wind. We knelt in the dirt while Elder Fowler offered a priesthood blessing dedicating the town of Brooks to missionary work.

Only then did Fowler feel we were ready to pick a neighborhood from the map and begin our day's tracting. According to the records in our apartment, Brooks had been thoroughly canvassed at least four times in the past couple of years, which perhaps accounted for our poor reception. The only person who actually invited us inside was a talkative old woman who told us she'd been a member of the church all her life. We stayed a few minutes to visit and eat the cookies she offered. When the street came alive with kids on their way home from grade school, I found myself longing for the freedom of their unstructured afternoons.

"*Man*, this is hard," I said as the latest door closed in my face. Though my delivery had improved a little, we had so far placed only two copies of the Book of Mormon, despite what felt like hours of tracting. We trudged back to the sidewalk. "No one wants to take even a minute to listen to us. It feels like we've been going all day, and I can still see where we parked the car."

"If it's ground you want to cover, don't worry. You're gonna see a ton of Brooks before you're done here."

"It's already hit me like a ton of Brooks," I said, handing him the golf ball.

"Hey, good one, Elder! You still have your sense of humor, that's important. You realize we've only been going for an hour and a half, right?"

I groaned. "I can't believe we have to do this eighteen hours a week."

"At *least* eighteen."

My stomach clenched as I ran a quick calculation in my head. Over eighteen *hundred* more hours of this before I'd see Katrina again.

"All in all, though, we have it pretty good," Fowler continued. "Under President Farrow we had to do twenty-four. Now, he was a *real* hardass. Turtle's a downright pussycat in comparison."

"Turtle?"

Fowler's grin looked both mischievous and abashed. "You know— President Tuttle." At my blank stare, he said, "Remember that cartoon show, *Touché Turtle*? A swordfighting turtle with a big stupid dog for a sidekick?"

"Oh, yeah. Dum Dum, that was the dog's name. I *loved* that show."

"Don't you think President looks just like Touché? Same baldy head, same beaky nose, same receding chin."

Fowler's impiety thrilled and frightened me, as did the weird way he used "President" like a first name. "Well . . . kind of, I guess. Sure."

"There you go. Turtle."

Feeling reckless, I asked, "Then who's Dum Dum?"

"Depends. It changes every time they bring in a new ape."

We had reached the next door. "You're going to hell, Elder," I said, not without admiration.

"Never said I wasn't."

He knocked. No one answered. We soldiered on.

"I bet you're excited to go home soon," I said.

Elder Fowler's face clouded. "I guess so. I don't know. I miss my family and all."

"You don't sound very sure."

"It's just, things make a lot of sense out here. You know what you're doing, you know it's important. You have a purpose. It's hard work, but it brings you joy. Nothing's that clear back home."

Things back home seemed clear to me—perfectly crystalline. "So, what? You'd stay out longer if you could?"

Fowler frowned. "Let me tell you something, Elder. You know why folks call me Methuselah?"

He was almost 23, he had told me earlier, having waited until 21 to start his mission.

"Because you're older than everyone else?"

"Well, that's part of it. It took me a couple extra years to make sure this was what I really wanted to do. But once I did, I was committed." He nodded to himself. "You remember when missions were eighteen months?"

Did I ever. The announcement had come my junior year of high school. For women, missions had always been eighteen months in duration, but in 1982, to encourage more young men to serve, *all* missions were shortened to eighteen months. This helped me and many of my friends to breathe a little easier. Then, just as I was starting college, the church reversed itself. The new policy hadn't impacted missionary numbers as hoped, and elders were going home just as they reached their peak effectiveness as proselytizers. Missions for young men were reset to two years.

"I remember," I said, feeling the sting all over again.

"That's how it was when I sent in my papers. I got called for eighteen months, but it changed back just before I went into the MTC. When I got there they gave us a choice. We could stand pat at a year and a half, or we could go two years, but we had to decide there. Most of the guys stood pat. Me, I said hit me." He waved a hand. "I mean, good hell. Were we there to serve the Lord or what? Shit or get off the pot, I say."

I said nothing, thinking uncomfortably about which choice I would have made. I was ashamed of judging Fowler for his cussing. I had no business here among the real missionaries.

"Anyways, that's when the guys in my MTC district started calling me Methuselah, on account of how I was gonna outlive them all."

"If you're happy here, can you extend an extra month?" I'd heard that if you were a valuable missionary, the church might let you do that.

Fowler shrugged. "I asked, but I think they're sick of me. And this way I'll be home for Christmas."

We were two blocks from our car, having covered two short side streets as we progressed. Now we turned a corner into another spruce little cul-de-sac. We garnered one flat rejection apiece at the first two houses on the block.

I passed Fowler the golf ball. "How many people have you baptized from tracting?"

He thought a moment. "One lady up in Edmonton," he said.

I gaped. "That's it? In two *years?*"

"Well, there are definitely more effective ways to proselytize. Especially in a town that's been tracted out so thoroughly already."

"Then why do we have to spend so much time doing it?"

"Oh, lots of reasons. First off, obedience. President says tract, so we tract, and that's how you get the Spirit—through obedience. Second, it's a way of getting out in the community and being visible. The members have to see us busy and diligent so they'll set us up with their non-member friends. And last, I guess, it's an exercise in faith, and sometimes faith gets rewarded. That dunk in Edmonton? Wouldn't have happened if we hadn't gone tracting that day."

Perhaps this wasn't the message Fowler meant to send, but an overwhelming realization was dawning on me. The souls in this city were my sacred responsibility. If I failed to find the ones who were ready and waiting for the gospel, their eternal salvation might be lost. I shuddered at the prospect.

But tracting still didn't strike me as the route to success. "You'd think by now there'd be no one new left to meet."

We had reached the next porch, where Fowler's spiel was quickly rebuffed. The burden of one more soul shifted from us back to its owner.

"Elder, there's always someone new left to meet," Fowler said as we plodded away from the porch. "People move out, people move in, and some folks just slip through the cracks, no matter how many times you've been down their street." He passed me the ball. "Your door."

The next house was a cozy brick cottage nestled in shade. Something about the circular window beside the door reminded me of a fairy-tale illustration.

At my knock the door opened wide, and so did my mouth. The woman who stood there couldn't have been far from my age. Her head, capped with a loose bonnet of curls the color of spice cake, came to just under my chin. I could have lifted her with one arm. She blinked her large brown eyes expectantly, but it wasn't that or her heart-shaped face or her tiny sweet mouth or her faint spray of ginger freckles that held my gaze.

It was the low-cut V of her sweater. *Low.*

"Hi, what can I do for you?" she said, her voice the laughter of birds.

The fawn-colored cable-knit's deep, deep neck plunged most of the way to her navel. She wore nothing beneath it, and the inner swells of her breasts beckoned the touch like fresh snow beckons a sled. Thoughts of Katrina fell out of my head.

I don't remember what I said to this woodland sprite, this gamine enchantress, this vision in chestnut, but I must have gotten it right, because she stepped back from the door.

"Come in, please," she trilled.

HALF AN HOUR LATER, ELDER FOWLER AND I STOOD OUTSIDE AGAIN, blinking in the sunlight. In the voice of an earthquake survivor, Fowler said, "Okay, let's, um, go over what you did wrong there."

I turned unseeing eyes toward him, my retinas seared. "Wrong?" Honey thickened my tongue. "I thought that went well."

He patted my shoulder absently, staring off into the sky. "There were some, well, fundamental errors at the outset that sort of undermined the whole proceeding."

"Errors?" The word did not compute. "Heidi"—the very name was a magic incantation—"took a book. I got a commitment from her to read it. We're coming back to teach the first discussion to her and her boyfriend."

Fowler inclined his head. "She said maybe."

"Fine. Maybe. But what could be wrong about that?"

"Walking through that door at *all* was wrong."

I still saw her before me, legs tucked beneath her on the overstuffed sofa, chin propped up on one exquisite fist, eyes rapt and lips parted, thirsty for the knowledge we offered. "How so?"

"It's in the White Bible." Invoking our pocket-sized rulebook, Fowler ran a shaky hand through his hair. "We never teach a woman alone in her home without a female chaperone present."

"But she invited us in."

"Yes, Elder. And when she did, the first thing we should have asked was if her husband or father or some other man was at home. If she said no, we should have tried to arrange a time to come back when one was, or when we could bring a woman from the local ward along with us. Under no circumstances should we have gone in there alone."

"But nothing happened," I protested, weak with distress.

"Doesn't mean it couldn't have. Hell, it doesn't mean she couldn't *say* it did. It'd be our word against hers."

"But Heidi isn't like that."

"You can't know that, Elder." He took me by the shoulders, eyes beseeching. "But look, this wasn't your fault. I could have stepped in at any time. *Should* have." I had handed him the golf ball before we went inside. Now he bounced it off the sidewalk with a hard clack and sighed. "And I'm afraid there's another thing you do really need to learn."

The color drained out of the afternoon. "What?"

"When you're teaching a woman," he said, "you should look her in the eyes at least as much as the chest." He pocketed the ball. "Come on, that's three book placements. I think we're done tracting for today."

CHAPTER 4

MY MISSION BEGAN AROUND THE TIME THE PROPHET EZRA TAFT Benson forcefully reaffirmed Joseph Smith's declaration that the Book of Mormon was "the most correct of any book on earth, and the keystone of our religion." It was the absolute center of our proselytizing efforts, the axis around which all else revolved.

Joseph published the Book of Mormon in 1830, when he was 24 years old, in the wake of a revivalist firestorm that swept through western New York. New religious movements had sprung up left and right, and utopian societies were a dime a dozen. The region was fertile ground for experiments in faith, having already given rise to such charismatic figures as Jemima Wilkinson and Mother Ann Lee. Joseph and his book would go on to eclipse them all.

Joseph Smith, Jr.—named, like I was, after his father—was born into precarious circumstances in Vermont on December 23, 1805. He already had two older brothers and an older sister—another brother had died in childbirth—and his father shuffled the growing brood from one New England town to the next, hounded by bad luck and debt. Joseph's was a childhood steeped in magic and visions from his father, but also, from his mother, in deep love and reverence for the Bible.

In 1816, the Smiths fetched up in the western New York town of Palmyra, where they found some measure of stability. Joseph's father taught school and farmed ginseng root, but he was best-known in the region as a "money-digger"—a mystic for hire who used seer stones and other folksy implements to dowse for buried gold. As Joseph grew older he joined his father in this work, eventually leading his own band of diggers.

Joseph's First Vision came, he later claimed, in 1820, when he was fourteen—though records would appear to suggest he didn't talk about the experience at the time, even with family members. The divine visitation certainly didn't seem to change him much, as he grew into something of a rogue in his mid-teens. Handsome, charming, and tall, he was popular with the girls, adept at street wrestling, and no stranger to wine. "[M]ingling with all kinds of society," he wrote of those years, "I frequently fell into many foolish errors, and displayed the weakness of youth, and the foibles of human nature; which, I am sorry to say, led me into divers temptations, offensive in the sight of God."

More than anything, Joseph had a way with a tale. He was quick to embellish an anecdote for the amusement of his friends, and even his mother took note of his storytelling flair. She wrote that Joseph "would occasionally give us some of the most amusing recitals that could be imagined. He would describe the ancient inhabitants of this continent, their dress, mode of travelling, and the animals upon which they rode ... This he would do with as much ease, seemingly, as if he had spent his whole life with them."

Still, it weighed on Joseph that further celestial visions were not forthcoming. "I often felt condemned for my weakness and imperfections," he wrote, fearing his sins and very character were to blame for the silence of the heavens. On the night of September 21, 1823, when he was seventeen, Joseph harrowed up his soul in bedside prayer, begging God's forgiveness.

In answer an angel appeared before him, standing in the air and radiating light. The angel introduced himself as Moroni and announced that he'd been sent by God to lead Joseph to an ancient book buried in a nearby hill. The angel appeared twice more that night and once again in the morning—each time, like R2-D2 on the fritz, delivering the same message.

Joseph hiked to the hill Moroni had described. There the angel awaited, directing Joseph to pry a large, flat rock up out of the ground. Beneath the rock, in a box of mortised stone, lay a treasure for the ages—a book made from sheets of hammered gold and bound with wire hoops. These "golden plates" were engraved with strange hieroglyphs. He bent eagerly to retrieve the book, but the angel, sensing the greed in Joseph's heart, forbade him.

Moroni explained that this was an ancient and sacred record kept by the former inhabitants of the Americas, a record Joseph would one day be called upon to translate if he remained faithful. Disappointed yet determined, Joseph agreed to meet the angel at that same spot one year later.

Joseph returned the next year, and the next, and still Moroni would not allow him to take the plates. Then in late 1825, Joseph traveled south, nearly to Pennsylvania, to work for an old farmer named Josiah Stowel. Talk of the boy's treasure-finding abilities had spread, and Stowel hoped Joseph could help him locate a fabled Spanish silver mine. They hunted through the winter, unsuccessfully, with Joseph also doing handywork and odd jobs around the farm. His salary was fourteen dollars a month.

But in March 1826, according to court documents, Stowel's nephew Peter Bridgman hauled Joseph before a judge on charges of being "a disorderly person and an imposter"—in essence, a con man. Joseph was found guilty, though his punishment is not listed in the report. This is the first recorded instance of his many encounters with the law.

Though he seems to have stopped his money-digging at this point, Joseph stayed on with Stowel several months longer, as he was secretly courting a beautiful Pennsylvania woman two years his senior named Emma Hale. Joseph somehow kept his annual appointment with Moroni near Palmyra in September—denied the plates again—then eloped with Emma in January 1827, quite against her father's wishes.

The newlyweds moved in with Joseph's parents. Joseph was now 21, with a wife and, perhaps, more incentive than ever to make something of himself. So it was that, on September 22, 1827, flushed with excitement, Joseph brought a heavy sack home to Emma and his parents. Inside, he told them, was a book of gold to which an angel had guided him. He couldn't show it to them, for to look upon it meant certain death, but their help was needed to keep the treasure safe.

Word of Joseph's golden treasure soon got around, and at least one attempt was made by thieves to secure the plates. Luckily, Joseph had foreseen the raid and, as he told his family the next day, whisked the plates away to a new hiding place in advance.

At last, using two seer stones as translating devices, and without even removing the plates from their sack, Joseph began the work, with Emma as his scribe, of rendering the strange engravings into English.

THE PLATES, AS JOSEPH'S DICTATION REVEALED, CONTAINED THE writings of a series of prophets of ancient America and were engraved in a hitherto unknown language called Reformed Egyptian. The record began with an Israelite prophet named Lehi who fled Jerusalem in 600 BCE, ahead of the Babylonian invasion. Lehi and his sons built ships that carried them and their wives to America, where the family multiplied and splintered into two rival clans—the white-skinned Nephites, favored of God, and the dark-skinned Lamanites, savage and wicked. The account lent spectacular credence to a popular theory of Joseph's day, that the American Indians were descendants of the Lost Tribes of Israel.

Joseph wasn't far into his project when a prosperous farmer named Martin Harris visited him. Joseph had done work for Martin in the past, but now Martin was so enchanted by the story of the plates that he offered to underwrite the translation work. Neighbors would later testify to Martin's suggestible and flighty character, but he did pay Joseph's debts and provide enough additional money to let the younger man devote himself to the book.

Martin's wife, Lucy, was less than pleased with this arrangement. She did not share her husband's credulity and had watched him skip from one faith to the next like a stone skimming a pond. Certain Joseph would bleed her husband dry, she tried to no avail to talk Martin out of giving the prophet more money. In April 1828, Martin joined Joseph and Emma at a house Emma's father had provided the couple in Pennsylvania. Emma was by now pregnant, and Martin took over as Joseph's scribe. Lucy had come as well, determined to see these golden plates with her own eyes, but as often as she ransacked the house she never managed to find where Joseph kept them hidden. Why this might be so, I leave as an exercise for the reader.

Martin, like Emma before him, sat writing on one side of a curtained divider while Joseph dictated what he read in his seer stones. As June arrived and the manuscript crept past a hundred handwritten pages, Martin badgered Joseph to let him take it home to show his angry, skeptical wife, who had returned to Palmyra. Joseph resisted at first, but eventually Martin departed with the first 116 pages of the Book of Mormon in his possession.

Every writer worth his salt knows you don't let the only copy of your manuscript out of your sight, but the young prophet had yet to learn this lesson. There were other things for him to worry about, such as Emma's impending delivery. On June 15, Joseph's first son was born but died the same day. Emma herself barely survived the birth. Joseph spent two weeks caring for her before he could think about traveling north to see what had become of the absent Martin Harris.

In Palmyra, Joseph arranged for Martin to meet him at the Smith family home. Martin arrived hours late, despondent, and, to Joseph's horror, confessed that Lucy had stolen the manuscript. As hard as Martin had searched, he couldn't find it anywhere.

This posed Joseph a vexing dilemma. He could go back and re-translate that first section of the book, but if the result did not match the original translation then Lucy and her confederates could demonstrate to the world that Joseph was no prophet. But to abandon the task he claimed was divinely assigned would be to make the same admission.

After much deliberation and prayer, Joseph issued a revelation from God. To frustrate Satan's plan to discredit the book, he must stop translating Lehi's account. Instead, Joseph must switch over to the writings of Lehi's fourth son, Nephi, which covered the same events, then continue with the remainder of the plates.

With the trap neatly sidestepped, the work of God rolled on.

MARTIN HARRIS RESUMED HIS WORK AS SCRIBE FOR A TIME, until Joseph replaced him with the more capable and reliable Oliver Cowdery, a young schoolteacher. Between April and July of 1829, Joseph and Oliver cranked out the vast bulk of the translation.

The record, handed down from one seer to the next, detailed a thousand years of New World history—wars, intrigues, cataclysms, and prophecies. Most of its writers set down important discourses, filled with doctrine of the coming messiah, the Christ. Nephi copied fourteen chapters of Isaiah's writings into the record, "for," as he said, "my soul delighteth in his words." Remarkably—or perhaps not so—they appear in Joseph's translation nearly word for word as in the King James Bible.

Just as remarkably, the text reports that the Nephite civilization flourished over the centuries not just because of wise kings and democratic laws, but also with the aid of such tools as the wheel, refined steel, and domesticated animals like horses and elephants. That there is no credible archaeological or paleontological evidence to support the existence of any of these in the Americas during the period recorded in the plates only makes these claims that much more miraculous.

But most amazing of all, the record claims that Jesus himself appeared to the people of Nephi after his resurrection, performing miracles and delivering sermons that match his words from the Gospel of Matthew with uncanny precision. After this visit, we are told, peace ruled in the land for four generations.

Over the next two hundred or so years, however, the Nephites and Lamanites alike forgot Jesus and descended into wickedness and savagery. The prophet and general Mormon, having abridged the records of his predecessors onto one set of engraved gold plates, led the dwindling Nephites in a bloody war against the Lamanites. The dead of both nations were already heaped upon the land with their swords and shields, to be buried en masse under giant mounds of dirt, when the remnants of the two armies came together for one great final battle. By the time it was over, only Mormon's son, Moroni, of all the Nephite people, still lived. The bloodthirsty Lamanites had triumphed utterly.

The Lamanites harried and pursued Moroni for the remainder of his days. Still, in about 421 CE the fugitive prophet completed the abridgment his father had begun. He added a few final words, then buried the plates in a hill called Cumorah.

It was this same Moroni who returned as a resurrected angel 1400 years later to lead Joseph Smith to their resting place.

WHERE ARE THE GOLDEN PLATES TODAY? NO ONE KNOWS. WHEN Joseph completed his translation, Moroni took them back into his possession. But wherever they are, we can rest assured they remain safe from the clever hands of thieves and opaque to the prying eyes of archaeologists and linguists.

A penitent Martin Harris, having left his wife, mortgaged and eventually sold his farm to finance the first printing of the Book of Mormon. It appeared for sale on March 26, 1830. With that, the grand work of Joseph Smith's life—the restoration of the lost keys of Christ's gospel, and the reestablishment of God's kingdom on earth— was underway.

CHAPTER 5

IT WAS SOMEWHAT RARE FOR TWO ELDERS TO BE SENT COLD INTO A new proselytizing area together. Usually only one companion at a time was replaced, so the one remaining always had a good working knowledge of the town and its people.

This was not the case for us in Brooks. The city had traditionally been a post for sisters, who made up only about ten percent of the missionary force. Women, unlike men, weren't allowed to serve missions until the age of 21, giving them every opportunity to get married first instead. Even the spinsters who made it still single to that age faced nothing like the pressure to serve that men did. And while men over thirty were discouraged from serving missions, the same did not hold for women. If they weren't having babies or serving their husbands, Mormon women needed *something* to make them feel useful.

"The sisters have been in Brooks a long time," President Tuttle had explained to me, taking me aside after dinner Wednesday night at the mission home. "They've always done a marvelous job for us, but lately the work hasn't been as fruitful there as it used to be. We think that sisters may have exhausted their usefulness there for the time being. Oh, not that they haven't been working hard, not at all.

But sometimes a particular strategy's played out and it's time to try something new. So we're taking out the sisters and sending in elders."

He gripped me by the upper arm and lowered his voice. "I'm sure I don't have to tell you what a big responsibility this is, Elder Shunn. One of the greatest challenges you and Elder Fowler will face will be winning over the hearts of the good members in Brooks. Members get used to the way 'their' missionaries do things. They feel comfortable referring their non-member friends when they know the missionaries and what to expect from them.

"Now here *we* come, not just switching out both their missionaries at the same time, but changing sisters to elders as well. Sisters carry with them a very special and different spirit. The members may not feel they can trust you at first. You'll have to earn that trust. You'll do that by teaching practice discussions in their homes, by bearing your strong testimony to them whenever you have the opportunity, and most of all by keeping the rules and working hard. Because make no mistake, Elder—the members *will* be watching you, and they *will* know whether you're working hard or slacking off."

Elder Fowler's assessment of the task ahead was far more succinct: "I don't care if you're Jesus himself. Blisters are a hard act to follow."

"Blisters?" I asked.

"Sisters."

It was Sunday morning and we were on our way to church for sacrament meeting, Fowler behind the wheel. I would not be certified as a driver on mission vehicles until I had memorized a certain number of scriptures, demonstrated mastery of all six discussions, and passed other arcane competency requirements.

Everything out my passenger window looked gray. Green-gray leaves on the trees, aqua-gray corrugated siding on trucking offices, once-modern schools of yellow-gray brick, ancient boxy houses of reddish-gray brick, teal-gray paint jobs on the pickups in the driveways. Even the denim jackets and cowboy hats on the infrequent pedestrians seemed shadowed with menace or despair.

I rubbed my eyes. "Do sisters really make better missionaries?"

"I don't want to be a chauvinist here, but basically yes. I never met a sister who wasn't worth a whole district in elders. I don't know if they're naturally closer to God or what, I just wish you could bottle whatever they have. Nylund and Youtz in my Calgary district? Amazing. They're the ones who consistently kept our numbers up. Then there was this little gal I knew in Lethbridge, name of Herzog. Dynamo, just a dynamo. Man, did she haul them into church. Only four-foot-ten, tiny, but *hell* was she feisty! We used to call her Mad Dog on account of how fierce she got when we cheesed her off."

"What did you do to . . . cheese her off?"

Fowler laughed. "Mostly called her Mad Dog. There's also Sister Roper. I don't know her well, but I hear tell she's a real bobcat. Hardcore diligent, bucking for promotion to elder. She's practically a legend in the mission. Did you meet her at the office on transfer day?"

"I don't think so." The name rang a bell, but I'd met a lot of people that day. "I'm not really sure."

"Trust me, you'd remember if you had. Now, ready to start quaking in your boots?"

"Why?" I asked apprehensively.

"That's who we just took over from."

I groaned.

"No shit," said Fowler, grinning in that infectious way of his. "We got us some *big* ol' pumps to fill, Elder."

THE BROOKS WARD MET FOR SUNDAY SERVICES IN A RESPECTABLE residential neighborhood. The tan brick church was devoid, in the Mormon fashion, of any iconography beyond an unadorned spire pointing heavenward. The building followed the standard architectural plan for an LDS meetinghouse of its size, which meant that the moment Elder Fowler and I walked through the doors, we knew right where to find the chapel, the bishop's office, the baptismal font, the cultural hall/basketball court, the coat racks, the restrooms, and the bulletin board with its world map showing the locations of the ward's missionary sons and daughters. Everything was familiar. It was the most at home I'd felt since arriving in Canada.

And we were mobbed like rock stars the minute we entered the foyer.

"Hello, Elders!"

"Very nice to see you, Elders."

"Where are you from, Elders?"

"How long have you been out, Elders?"

"What do you think of Brooks so far, Elders?"

"Glad to see elders here again, Elders!"

"I served in Rhodesia myself, Elders." (Bastard.)

"We're sure going to miss those sisters around here, Elders."

Couples with two or three toddlers in tow, teenage girls giggling in clumps, grave-looking older men with beaming wives, elderly singletons smiling and nodding in patient loneliness, all wanted to shake our hands and exchange a word. One eager fellow, thirtyish and wiry with shaggy hair, told us he'd have a rent check for us later that week.

For all I'd been told about the power of the black name tag, this was the first I'd experienced it for myself. I liked it.

Before the service started, the ward's bishop, a quiet little man named Neuwirth, introduced himself. With his fussily trimmed mustache, I pegged him as an accountant in real life. He invited us to sit on the dais behind the pulpit with him and the other ward leaders during sacrament meeting. It was a good call on his part. Not only could the congregation get a good look at us, but also, I realized as the service dragged on, we were forced to stay awake. During the program of inspirational talks by ward members, my head began to nod, and I caught more than one elbow in the ribs from Elder Fowler.

After sacrament meeting, as the congregation drained away into Sunday school classrooms, Bishop Neuwirth introduced us to a cadaverous man in his forties. "This is Brother Whitaker, our ward mission leader. He'll take you now to your weekly planning meeting."

The man looked us up and down as he shook our hands, watery blue eyes drowning behind Coke-bottle lenses. "You elders both from the States?"

"That's right," Fowler said.

Whitaker turned to the bishop. "Sure grow 'em ugly down there, eh?"

Bishop Neuwirth gave us a pained little smile and excused himself.

WE MET WITH BROTHER WHITAKER IN AN UNUSED CLASSROOM. The ward mission leader's job was to coordinate proselytizing efforts with the missionaries, so he filled us in on which part-member families might be worth visiting.

"How about this Van Ricky guy?" Elder Fowler asked. "The sisters left us a pretty strong note about him."

"Van *Rijk*," said Whitaker. "Ib Van Rijk, but he likes to be called Buddy. Nice fella. Wife's a member. Three kids, all under baptismal age. Sisters tried him more'n one time. That Sister Roper just wouldn't give up, but not everyone wants women teachers, eh? I could see about settin' up an appointment with him for you boys, though."

"That'd be great. In the meantime, I'd love to get the members excited about missionary work again. How about if we schedule some dinner appointments? We could teach the families practice discussions afterward so they can see what we're made of."

"Don't look like much from where I'm sittin'," said Whitaker, raising a dubious eyebrow.

Fowler grinned. "How about we start with *your* family?"

Whitaker mushed his lips together and sighed. "Oh, that'd be all right, I s'pose. Day we can't spare a can of beans for the missionaries, we may's well lay down and die."

As the crowd in the foyer thinned out after classes, I touched Elder Fowler's elbow.

"I'll be in the chapel for a minute." Before he could tell me otherwise, I slipped away.

The chapel loomed dim and silent, seeming somehow smaller when empty. At one end of the dais was a locked organ console, at the other a black-lacquered Kawai baby grand piano.

In the prickly hush, I seated myself at the piano and lifted the fall-board. The keys gleamed. A missionary was never supposed to leave his companion's side except for bathroom activities, but surely it wasn't so urgent that we stick together inside the safety of church walls.

Quietly I started to play.

I led with the reverent chords of "Psalm 121," a choral piece I'd transcribed for Andy Kilmer. Andy was the first friend I made when I moved to Kaysville in the middle of sixth grade. Those first awkward years we both wore targets painted on our backs, but somehow in high school Andy managed to transform himself from nerd to hipster to junior anarchist. He introduced me to jazz fusion, experimental rock, and new wave music, often supplying me with cassettes I could smuggle home, where any records I found interesting were frowned upon. Much to my father's annoyance, I cribbed from Andy's fashion templates of cargo pants and army boots, or pegged jeans and deck shoes. It was Andy who would eventually give me my first Gabriel García Márquez novel, a gift as mind-altering as any drug.

Andy was far more adventurous in his rebellion than I was, more willing and able to stand up to his parents. By the time we graduated from high school he had drunk beer, smoked pot, and gone to second base with girls, none of which I'd managed or even dared to attempt. I was too aware from church sermons that "petting" led directly to fornication, and that fornication ranked just behind murder in the great Mormon hierarchy of sins. I wasn't taking any chances on hell, but I did spend an inordinate amount of time devising fantasy scenarios in which I had sex against my will, thus remaining blameless. *My worst sins, in fact, were mostly thought-crimes of this sort*—at least when you factored out the coarse language I used, the art films I knew would contain nudity but watched anyway, and the jerking off.

But worldly as he was, even Andy could not withstand the pressure to serve a mission. We carpooled to classes at the University of Utah during our first year of college, but as my second year was getting underway, Andy was putting in his mission papers. In October he received his call, to Brazil. He was instructed to report to the MTC in January for eight weeks of Portuguese immersion.

It was Mormon tradition that the family of a departing missionary would arrange the program for his last sacrament meeting at home—choosing the hymns, assigning the speakers, and supplying special musical numbers. After receiving his call, Andy asked me a favor. "You know that opening tune from the *Falcon and the Snowman* soundtrack?"

"Sure," I said. Our musical heroes, Pat Metheny and Lyle Mays, had composed the score. The first track was a choral setting of a psalm from the Bible. "What about it?"

A sly grin creased his face. "Do you think you could transcribe it? I want my family to sing it at my farewell."

His intent could not have been more clear to me. "I'm on it."

Crouched over the piano at home, running a cassette tape forward and back, I picked out the four-part harmonies as best I could. The movie told the true story of childhood friends who sold American secrets to the Soviet Union, and I was never for a moment unaware that Andy and I, too, were trying to pull a fast one under the noses of a community whose values we couldn't entirely embrace.

On a cold Sunday in January, Andy and a chorus of his relatives stood before the Kaysville 10th Ward and lifted their voices in song.

While most of those listening heard a haunting plea for God's companionship, only Andy and I knew the performance for what it was—a big middle finger to the church that demanded such sacrifice of us. *When you look at us, you may think you see something holy,* we were saying. *But you will never know what truly lies in our hearts.*

Of course, it was an empty, adolescent gesture. And it didn't keep the black name tag from claiming Andy three days later.

PLAYING "PSALM 121" IN THAT EERILY FAMILIAR CHAPEL UNLOCKED deeper, more heartsick chambers inside me. As I shifted into my classical repertoire, all my reluctance and resistance and confusion and helplessness came flooding out. I missed the friends who'd left on missions before me. I missed my typewriter, my classes at school, my daily piano regimen, my clandestine music collection. I missed the friends I'd made at my summer science fiction workshop in Michigan a year earlier (though I probably would have been missing them no matter where I was). I missed Katrina—everything I'd ever hoped for in a girlfriend, dangled before me like candy and then cruelly snatched away.

I missed my life before the black name tag.

What was I *doing* here? I trembled on the precipice of the fathomless gulf of my mission, a gulf so wide I couldn't see the other side, pushed inexorably from behind by forces I couldn't withstand but unwilling even now to commit to the crossing...

"That's lovely, Elder," said an echoing voice. "Debussy?"

My hands sprang back from the keys. A man in his mid-thirties was resting his elbows on the railing of the dais, watching me. I recognized him from earlier as the first counselor to the bishop, but I couldn't remember his name.

"Right," I said. "The First Arabesque."

"I thought so." He spoke with a slight Latin accent. His bristly black hair swallowed the light but for a trace of silver at the temples. "You play it well. How long did you study?"

"Seven years." Self-consciously, I added, "Just lessons in the neighborhood. My dad made all of us learn the piano so when we went on missions we'd always be able to fill in for the accompanist at church. I guess in his mission they didn't have many elders who could play."

"It sounds as if you learned much more than hymns."

I shrugged.

"Please, keep going," he said. "Do you mind if I listen?"

"Uh, not at all."

He took a seat in the fourth or fifth pew, straightening the crease in the trousers of his expensive black suit. Alvarez, that was his name. Brother Alvarez.

It took me a couple of tries to find my place again, but when I did, the music came more easily. It usually did when someone was listening.

CHAPTER 6

BISHOP NEUWIRTH HAD INVITED US OVER THAT AFTERNOON FOR
Sunday dinner with his wife and two teenage children. It was a delicious meal, but formal, with the family still dressed in their Sunday clothes. If I weren't a missionary, my tie would have been off and my jeans on within about a minute of getting home from church. I felt sorry for the kids—especially the son.

Sensing the bishop's reserve, we left soon after dessert, trying not to overstay our welcome. After that, we dropped in on a few of the part-member homes on our list to introduce ourselves and ask when we might start teaching the missionary discussions. We struck out at every door.

Fowler drove us home through the dusk. "It's so sad seeing families like that—one parent in, one parent out. How can you raise a family that way? No hope of eternal life together. It makes me want to work my ass off, get those families repaired."

"Then shouldn't we get some tracting in before we go home? Gather those blessings?"

I wanted to take the words back as soon as they left my mouth. Impulsiveness was not always my friend.

"What? Nah, tracting never goes over well on the sabbath. You think people hate us on a Saturday, try bugging 'em today." Fowler looked at me and grinned. "Anyways, P-day starts at sundown."

Monday was our "preparation day," our one day a week for cleaning, laundry, shopping, and—as a last priority—recreation. Technically, P-day would not begin until 9:30 the next morning, after companionship study, but I was learning that the letter of the law did not always trump the reality of the mission field.

We parked in front of our quadplex. "Hey!" called a rough voice as Elder Fowler was unlocking the front door to our apartment. "What happened to your dresses?"

We turned in the entryway. Four or five young men in workshirts and ball caps were hanging out across the street, leaning against a beat-up brown Impala, beer cans in hand.

Fowler raised his voice. "I think you got us confused," he said, offering them a cheery wave.

"No, you cut your hair," another called out. "I'm not sure I like it that way." His comrades brayed.

"Okay, then, gentlemen," Fowler said. "God be with you!"

The back of my neck prickled and didn't stop until well after we were inside with the door bolted. "What a bunch of jerks," I said. "Does stuff like that happen a lot?"

Fowler's smile was a rictus. "Sometimes. Not that often, really." He sounded casual but looked like a twanging banjo string as he took off his jacket and loosened his tie. "It's not something we really worry about that much."

I didn't need two days of tracting to tell me there were people in the world who harbored a deep dislike or even hatred for the church. I knew the stories about the persecution that drove the Mormon pioneers west to the shores of the Great Salt Lake, and I'd seen the fanatics peddling their evil, lying, inflammatory pamphlets outside Temple Square. What I couldn't understand was why people didn't leave us alone. Why not live and let live?

I trailed Fowler through the apartment, chest constricted. It could have been the hoodlums outside that made me feel that way, or the orderly towers of pamphlets and books defining the borders of this new life of mine. Elder Fowler attributed the unusual cleanliness of our apartment to its long occupancy by sisters, but still the place depressed me.

The back room featured twin beds with a cheap nightstand between them, reminiscent of Bert and Ernie's setup on *Sesame Street*. The arrangement complied with one of the most important rules in the White Bible, one that had provoked much uncomfortable joking at the MTC—that companions must sleep in the same bedroom but never in the same bed. I think we realized such rules did not arise in a vacuum.

Elder Fowler and I hung our suit coats up in the bedroom closet. He dug civilian clothes out of his dresser and tapped a framed photograph of his parents. "I notice you haven't put out any pictures, Elder. Don't you have any? You must've brought some of your family, or a girlfriend or something."

I was taking off my tie, but I reached for my wallet, flooded with pride. I didn't have a picture of Katrina big enough to frame and display, but I did have two small school photos her mother had mailed to me while I was at the MTC. *These are the last extras I have,* the accompanying letter had read, *so please send them back to me if you ever break up with her.*

"Here's a couple of my girlfriend," I said, passing my open wallet across the bed. "I'll have more when I can get my film developed."

Fowler examined the pictures. "Hey, she's really pretty."

"We're engaged." This came out sounding to my ears like bluster.

"Well, congratulations!" Fowler passed the wallet back to me and started taking his pants off. "A lot of elders'll give you shit for having a girlfriend, you know. Even more for a fiancée. They'll tell you it won't last. They're just jealous, though, because they probably got their Dear

Johns already. Me, I think a girl back home's a great thing to have. Gives you a reason to work hard and study and grow. Learn yourself some responsibility, get in touch with those spiritual skills you'll need to be a good husband and father."

I studied Katrina's photos before putting my wallet away again. I wished I had more recent shots. These showed her as a brunette, when it was a blonde I'd fallen in love with.

"Do you have a girlfriend at home?" I asked.

Fowler was pulling on a pair of blue jeans. "Nah. My Dear John came about a year out."

That was not reassuring. "I'm sorry, Elder."

He waved away my sympathy. "Don't be. She wasn't the right one anyways. Obviously."

"Yeah, I guess not." I tried to keep my insecurities to myself, but my mouth had its own ideas. "It *does* work out sometimes, though. Right?"

"Oh, sure, definitely. Sometimes." Fowler looked solemn for a moment, but then his face lit up again. "But I'll tell you another good reason to have a girlfriend back home. It'll keep your eye from wandering, and that's important. Ever heard that saying? 'If you don't look once, you're not a man, but if you look twice you're not a missionary.'"

"Yeah." I'd heard it a lot from my cousin Jared while he was preparing for his mission.

"Well, sometimes even once is too much. The last thing you want out here's a g.c."

I kept my back to Fowler as I changed into my civvies. "What's a g.c.?"

"'Girl challenge.' That's what it's called when you fall in love out here. You don't want to do it. Nothing kills the Spirit faster. Matter of fact, it could kill your whole damn mission."

My eyebrows rose. "That doesn't happen much, does it?"

Fowler sighed, crossing behind me to hang his shiny suit pants in the closet. "More than you wanna know. Believe you me, Elder, you've never *seen* girls go crazy like they do for that black name tag. To a horny young member girl, you're prime husband material. You're what she's been taught all her life to set her sights on, and if you end up in her crosshairs, brother, you better duck and cover." He shook his head. "Hell, you gotta look out for *non*-member girls too. The fact that you're off-limits? That can be a major turn-on."

"Gosh," I said with an involuntary grin.

"Tell you a trick. You ever hate your area or your comp so bad you can't stand it one minute more, just call Prez and tell him you have a g.c. You'll get transferred like *that*, I guarantee you."

He spoke so knowingly it made me curious. "Did *you* ever have a g.c.?"

A wistful look crossed Fowler's face. "Sooner or later, Elder, everyone has a g.c."

LATER THAT EVENING, AFTER A DINNER OF GENERIC CORN FLAKES and milk, I sat on the living room couch deliberating between my two choices of reading material. What would it be—*Jesus the Christ*, by James E. Talmage, or *Rogue Moon*, by Algis Budrys?

With a sigh I cracked open the Talmage, an antique gifted to me by my maternal grandfather. As I was debating whether I should mark up the pristine pages in colored pencil, the jangle of the telephone shattered the silence.

"Will you get that, Elder Shunn?" Fowler called from the bathroom.

I found the clangorous thing on the dining room floor, its long cord snaking from behind the old couch. "Hello?"

An enthusiastic female voice responded. "Is this the LDS missionaries?"

"Um, yes. That's us."

"Elder Shunn? Hi, this is Sister Nylund in Calgary! How are you doing?"

This was an odd surprise. "Pretty good, I guess."

I'd met Bonnie Nylund at the mission office on Wednesday, where she'd sought me out as a fellow Kaysvillian. I'd graduated high school with her younger brother, Taylor. He was a spiteful bully, but his sister had seemed all right.

"How's your pit?" she asked.

"My ... uh ... ?"

"Your apartment."

I was still trying to work out why she might have called. Missionaries in different districts weren't supposed to talk to each other on the phone. "Oh, right. It's okay. It's not bad."

"Elder Fowler treating you all right?"

"Yeah, he's fine."

"Good. When I found out he'd be your trainer, I told him to take extra good care of you. He was my district leader here the last few months."

"Right, I think he mentioned that."

"He's a great missionary, Elder Shunn. You're lucky to have him for a companion. You're going to learn a lot from him. Is he around? There's some stuff here we need to ask him about."

"Sure, hang on." I covered the receiver to yell, but Fowler was emerging from the bathroom. "Sister Nylund's on the phone for you."

"Oh, thanks." He plucked the receiver from my hand, still fastening his jeans. "Hello? Oh, hi! Yes, ma'am, we made it here just fine. Thank you, thank you, you too."

With a shooing motion Fowler gave me to understand I should retire to the bedroom. Trying not to show my annoyance, I gathered my books.

FOWLER HAD JUST REENTERED THE BEDROOM, TUGGING OFF HIS tan polo shirt, when the phone rang again. "Elder Shunn, will you get that?"

"It's probably for you," I said, sighing hard but swinging my legs off my bed. I had already changed into my flannel pajamas, but Fowler was my superior in the great mission hierarchy. I'd be blessed for my obedience, even in a matter this small.

I followed a mile of cord to the dining room table, where I caught the phone on the fifth ring. "LDS missionaries, Elder Shunn speaking."

"Elder Shunn, hello," said a voice plummy enough for easy-listening radio. "This is Elder Garrett, your district leader. I've been trying to get through for an hour. Is everything okay?"

I glanced toward the bedroom door, where Fowler was standing with eyebrows raised. "Yes, Elder Garrett, I'm so sorry." I shot my companion an eyebrow of my own. "I only just noticed it was off the hook."

"Hmm." Garrett was stationed in Medicine Hat, seventy or so miles southeast on the highway to Saskatchewan. "You know it's time to report your weekly numbers, right?"

Widening my eyes, I mouthed *Numbers!* at Fowler. He ambled toward the table while I scanned the mounds of tracts.

"Sure, just hang on a second." I clamped my hand over the receiver and thrust it toward my trainer, who shook his head. I shoved a pleading look his way, but he only plucked a pen from a cup and a fresh blue planner from the pile on the table and motioned that I should keep talking.

I rolled my eyes and huffed. The blue planner was a grid for keeping track of all our appointments and proselytizing hours, printed on heavy paper and scored so it could easily be folded into thirds and carried in your shirt or jacket pocket. Elder Fowler began scrawling numbers into the TOTALS column. As far as I could tell, he was making them up.

"Just another sec. I think Elder Fowler left it in his coat."

"Mm-hmm." The long-distance hiss crackled in my ear, pregnant. "So. Elder. Enjoying Brooks so far?"

"Oh, for sure. This is a great town."

"You've got a lot to live up to. Those sisters really tore it up."

"So I've heard. And they apparently didn't leave a lot of leftovers."

My attempt at levity thudded like a bag of wet cement. "With that kind of attitude," Garrett said icily, "you won't *find* many leftovers."

Fowler capped his pen and slid the stiff sheet across the table.

"Um, yeah," I said. "Well, hey, here we go, got 'em!"

"Good, I'm ready. We'll just go down the totals on the far right one by one." Garrett spoke like you might to a bright three-year-old. "Hours tracting?"

I peered at Fowler's handwriting. "Eleven?" I said, looking up at him with my brow furrowed. We hadn't done anything like eleven hours of tracting.

Fowler nodded, gesturing at the planner.

"Eleven?" Garrett said. "These aren't combined with the sisters' numbers, are they? Just your own since Thursday?"

Only the cells in that last column had been filled in. Everything else was empty. I covered Monday through Wednesday with my hand and glared inquisitively at Fowler. He gestured at the planner with both palms, nodding fiercely.

"Yep, just ours."

Garrett sighed. "I need the full week's numbers."

I circled the left half of the grid with my finger, looking at Fowler, but he only shrugged.

"We couldn't find the sisters' numbers." My stomach was starting to hurt. "We looked."

Garrett sighed more loudly. "All right, I suppose I'll have to track down Sister Roper. Or guess. Let's keep going, then."

I reported book placements (6), first discussions (1), total discussions (1), dinner appointments (1), member discussions (1), and total proselytizing hours (35).

"*Thirty-five?* Really? You must not have stopped moving since the moment you hit town."

I could feel my face flush. Our numbers were not *all* exaggerations, but this one certainly was. "Fowler's pretty much running me ragged. I know he wants to finish his mission up strong."

"Hmm, well," Garrett said with somewhat less pomposity, "don't let him run you into the ground, okay? Now, active investigators?"

That was our term for people "investigating" the possibility of joining the church. "One."

I could practically hear Elder Garrett putting down his pen as his voice reinflated with pedantry. "Wait, Elder Shunn. You have one active investigator, but your only discussion this week was a first? Do you have a followup appointment for the second discussion?"

"Not a specific appointment, no, but she did say we could come back."

He let out a long breath. "I'm afraid we can't count it without a specific commitment to take the second discussion. So that's zero active investigators. And I'm going to take a stab in the dark and say baptisms are zero too."

"But it won't stay that way," I said.

"That's the spirit. Now, how about your mileage on the car?"

"Oh, sorry, that one I don't have handy."

"Well, I suppose I can get that one next week. All right, Elder Shunn, I wish I could stay on with you longer, but I have to get these numbers totaled up for Elder Severin in Lethbridge." That would be Garrett's superior, our zone leader. "Would you put your companion on for a minute first, though?"

I handed the phone to Fowler and slunk straight back to the bedroom. I burned with shame, and I didn't want to hear even one side of the conversation that was starting.

LATER, AFTER WE'D HAD OUR COMPANIONSHIP PRAYER AND THE lights were out, Elder Fowler's voice jerked me back from the edge of unconsciousness.

"Shunn, you did a good job tonight," he said. "I'm so flippin' glad to have you for a companion. Good night."

I rolled onto my side, toward the wall, clutching the little plush penguin that smelled of Katrina's perfume. I might have smiled a tiny bit as I fell asleep.

CHAPTER 7

ON MONDAY MORNING, I WOKE UP AROUND SEVEN, SHOWERED, AND dressed in my suit and tie. I was sitting on the couch reading my scriptures half an hour later when a bleary-eyed Fowler shuffled past en route to the bathroom.

He stopped. "Elder, what are you doing?"

"What you mean?" I asked, confused. "Studying."

Fowler was dressed only in his temple garments, the sacred white underwear we wore beneath our clothes to remind us of the covenants we'd made with God in the endowment ceremony. While I'd brought eight sets of cotton garments with me into the field, Fowler's were made from a silky polyester mesh. Like mine, the scoop-necked top of his was stitched with a backward L at the right nipple and a small V at left. The boxer-like bottoms went all the way to the knees. Fowler's mesh fabric was a touch transparent for my comfort, but he seemed to feel no self-consciousness. My father sometimes lounged around in his garments too, which I'm not sure quite honored the spirit in which they were meant to be worn.

Fowler pointed at me. "Your whites. Why do you have them on?"

I blinked. *My* clothing was the problem? "Well, the White Bible says—"

"I know what the White Bible says, but I don't know a single elder who goes shopping in his whites on a P-day. I won't let you break the tradition."

I grinned. "Twist my arm."

"And remember, P-day doesn't end tonight at six-thirty. It ends when we go to bed. Hey, don't blame me. Them's the rules."

After using the bathroom, Fowler went back to bed. I tried to pick up with my studies, but an uneasy feeling was stealing over me. Working from 9:30 AM to 9:30 PM Tuesday through Saturday, with an hour out for lunch, would only give us 55 proselytizing hours. If by some miracle we managed twelve hours on Sunday, then we'd still need those three hours tonight, from 6:30 to 9:30, to hit our weekly requisite of 70. This seemed impossible under the best circumstances, let alone if we let P-day overrun its banks.

We were never going to hit 70 hours a week, I realized. But every Sunday night we would lie to Elder Garrett and say that we had.

A load of stones pressed down on me. I closed my Book of Mormon, marking my page with the sewn-in black ribbon. I'd bought a deluxe, oversized set of scriptures for my mission, with my name stamped in gold on the faux-leather covers, but now my purchase seemed ostentatious, pharisaical. And heavy.

I'd started a journal at the MTC, something every missionary was commanded to do so his faith-promoting experiences could be reread and passed along to his descendants. I retrieved it from the makeshift desk in the corner of the living room and cracked it open. I'd written six or seven entries over my first ten days at the MTC, then nothing more. Scanning through, I saw that it was about one third spiritual insights from my classes, one third anecdotes about my new buddies, and one third heartache at missing Katrina. Already, every sentence read like a dispatch from a younger and more distant self, vapid and naive. My chest swelled. I tried not to cry.

I knew I should start writing in my journal again, but I couldn't muster the will. Instead I turned to the back page, where in an obsessive hour at the MTC I had written out all the integers from 731 to 0 in reverse order. This was the number of days in my mission, including 1988's leap day. I'd drawn lines through the first 25 numbers in the list. Now I crossed out the next.

Only 705 days until I'd see Katrina again. Another 705 stones to shrug from my shoulders, one by one by one.

AROUND ELEVEN, ELDER FOWLER AND I LOADED OUR DIRTY CLOTHES into the car and drove to the nearest self-service laundry, all of three grimy blocks away. We shared the place with a couple of sullen housewives who kept their distance from us and from each other. Though we both wore civilian camouflage—Fowler even sporting well-worn cowboy boots—I still felt dangerously conspicuous.

As I dumped out my clothes and started sorting, Fowler leaned close. "Something to remember, Shunn," he said in a low voice. "Never, and I mean *never*, do we leave our wash unattended. If one of us wants to step outside for a Coke, that's fine, but the other has to stay inside."

"Got it, no leaving the wash. But why?"

Fowler looked around. "This happened in another mission a few years back. I heard about it from one of my companions who had a friend there. Kansas City, I think." He shook his head.

I was hooked. "What was it?"

"Okay, so these two elders were doing their wash on a P-day. When their clothes went into the dryer, they headed down the street to grab a sandwich. What they didn't know was that this really nasty anti-Mormon couple owned the laundromat. When they came back from lunch, they found . . ." He glanced around again and spoke even more quietly. I leaned in so close I could smell his breath. "They found their G's in the front window with a big sign saying 'Check out the magic Mormon underwear!'"

"Criminy!" I whispered, my stomach in knots. I pictured the garments duct-taped to the glass, obscenely spread-eagled, their sacred symbols on naked display. "What the flip did they do?"

"What *could* they do? They called their prez and told him what happened. *He* called Salt Lake, and pretty soon their instructions came back down the chain."

I couldn't stand the tension. "What instructions?"

Fowler allowed himself a grim smile. "President gets these elders back on the phone and tells 'em—" He took a deep breath. "He tells 'em to stand out in front of the laundromat late that night and 'shake off the dust of their feet.'"

This rang a vague, disturbing bell. "What, like in the New Testament?"

"Exactly. Like the disciples used to do when the people in some city tossed them out on their ears. It's an actual priesthood ordinance, though you don't hear about it much."

"What does it do?"

Fowler shrugged. "It's a testimony against the wicked. Don't ask me how it works. But this is a fact. Within a week, that laundromat had burned to the ground."

"Holy smokes!" I exclaimed, jerking upright. This was actually possible? Kids like us were granted the power to *do* that kind of thing? Our enemies must truly be evil—and very real.

"You said it, pard." Fowler pulled two crumpled suits—jackets and trousers—out of his laundry bag. "Now here's a *real* miracle for you." Before my horrified eyes he tossed the items into a washing machine. "Steel-belted polyester. Couldn't hurt these with a blowtorch."

THE REST OF OUR P-DAY PASSED INNOCUOUSLY, IF NOT ALWAYS QUI-etly, with some grocery shopping, some lunch, some bowling, some time at the library, and whole lot of reading and letter-writing. True to Fowler's promise, we didn't put our whites on at all, and we didn't do a lick of proselytizing.

But Tuesday it was back to work—after morning racquetball, at any rate. Over the grinding hours that followed, I became acquainted with the manifold ways there were for people to tell us no.

In fact, that's the way most of the week went, and if I learned one thing, it was to loathe tracting. Like in baseball, the long stretches of drudgery were separated by the rare brief explosion of action, as when some daysleeper frothing with rage would fling open his door to scream imprecations in our faces. Between those fleeting moments of drama came encounters with children and the elderly, with the feebleminded and the infirm, with "No, not today" and "No hablo inglés," and even with the twitching curtain that meant our quarry was home but not answering the door. More often the houses we approached remained as still as tombs. Occasionally, very occasionally, some kind-hearted or easily swayed soul would accept a copy of the Book of Mormon and would promise to read the sections we'd painstakingly marked in colored pencil.

To help those interminable hours pass, we sometimes made bets: which of us would place the next book, how many houses it would take before someone yelled at us, how many words we'd get out before the next door slammed shut on us. But mostly we talked. Movies, music, girls, books, school, family, *girls*, his job on the construction site, mine in the cabinetry shop—all the subjects that as missionaries we were discouraged from dwelling on. What I ate up most, though, was when Fowler doled out juicy nuggets of mission wisdom, gossip, and lore.

On Friday of that week, we were talking heavy metal when I mentioned my love of Rush.

"Ah, you're one of *those*," said Fowler. "Same as every other missionary in Canada, eh? You know last May they had a concert scheduled up in Edmonton?"

"That was the *Power Windows* tour. What a great show! I saw it in Salt Lake."

"Well, I was serving in Edmonton back then. I swear half the elders in town must've had tickets."

I gaped. In my civilian life, I had the right to choose to see a rock concert if I wanted, whether or not the church or my father approved. But for a missionary, ordained and set apart as a representative of Jesus Christ, the rules were different. No popular music, especially not rock, and *especially* not *live* rock. That was like handing Satan the keys to your soul's front door.

"Including you?" I asked.

"Naw, Rush ain't my thing. But anyways, the day of the show this massive blizzard hits. No joke, in *May*. Shuts everything down. No planes in or out. Concert canceled."

"Whoa."

"You're telling me. You think God wanted all those missionaries rocking out in clouds of dope smoke? No way. It would have killed the Spirit dead in Edmonton for a month."

This particular afternoon we were doing callbacks, dropping in on homes where we'd placed books and trying to commit the recipients to taking the six missionary discussions. I paused on the porch with golf ball in hand. This house looked familiar.

"Hey," I said, "isn't this, um . . . ?"

Fowler consulted his index card. "Heidi Sherman."

My pulse quickened. "Right, *Heidi*." If any contact in this town was golden, it surely was Heidi.

I knocked and stood waiting, like a flower on a cloudy day awaits the sun.

The door opened a crack and I exhaled, ready to breathe in Heidi's heady bouquet once she recognized us and invited us inside. But all that appeared was a downcast eye and a cinnamon curlicue of hair. Heidi remained hidden behind the door, no welcoming décolletage in evidence. "Can I help you?"

"Um, hello," I said, glancing back at Fowler in confusion. "We're, uh,

Elder Shunn and Elder Fowler, if you remember? From the Church of Jesus Christ of Latter-day Saints?"

"I'm sorry." Her white fingers clung to the edge of the door. "My boyfriend says I'm not supposed to talk to you."

"Did you read the verses we marked for you?"

But the door was already closing. "I'm sorry," she said. Gently she sealed herself inside.

I don't know if it was for her sake or mine, but with the click of that door my heart broke a little.

CHAPTER 8

In January 1994, when I was 26 years old, I sat down in my bare, cold room to write my first novel.

In many ways, yes, the conditions were ideal. I had no commitments, nothing else to do, nowhere to be, and no worries for the moment about money. I'd been honing my craft for years with short fiction, and my third story for a major magazine had just appeared in print. I'd taken a stab already at the story I wanted to tell, in the form of a 30,000-word novella, and I'd thought long and hard about how best to expand that piece to novel length. I knew my invented world forward and backward. Like a monk in his cell, there was nothing to distract me from the task I felt called to complete.

The hard part was starting, but once I did, the words gushed out of me like I'd slashed a swollen artery. I wrote for eight hours a day almost from the start, often taking meals at my little desk. I had the general shape of the book in my head, but at first I let my characters, who seemed so real to me, lead me where they wanted to go. My writing days edged up to ten hours, and my speed increased. A week passed like time in a dream, two weeks, three. Weekends were a quaint societal construct, no longer relevant to my existence.

As I approached the story's midpoint, index cards in a riot of colors blossomed on my wall. It was time to start nudging my volatile characters into each other's paths, to erect the obstacles that would force them toward conflict and climax. My sessions continued to lengthen. On my peak day I worked steadily for fourteen hours, spraying out 10,000 words in one long burst. I could scarcely tear myself away from the page.

In March, with disbelief, I typed THE END. I stood up blinking from my chair, exhausted and empty. I couldn't think what to do next. I had wakened from my vivid dream into a bleak, disappointing reality. But I could still point to what I'd created—a complete novel, something I hadn't been certain was in me—and feel pride. *The Revivalist* weighed in at 707 manuscript pages, nearly 170,000 words. I'd written it in eight weeks.

In all the time since, I've never come close to producing so much fiction so quickly.

A first novel is an interesting beast. When I look back now at mine, I can see so many of the forces that were at work, forces I could never have identified at the time. The novel is set in a small religious town cut off from the rest of the world by a technological plague. The protagonist, a rational scientist, is only there because he was attending his father's funeral when the disaster struck. He's trapped in a town where he doesn't fit in and where no one likes him, and it's all because of his father.

It's not hard to pick out the metaphor beating at the heart of this deservedly unpublished novel. In fact, if it weren't clear enough already, the text underlines it time and again by giving nearly every other major character a difficult or abusive father. Furthermore, the novel examines the role of religion in mob behavior and scientific illiteracy, portrays its prophets as either evil or deluded, and delivers its sex with an unhealthy infusion of terror.

A first novel tends to be a dumping ground for the issues its author has been dragging around since childhood. It tends to draw heavily on its author's own experiences. It tends to transmute real-life weaknesses and failures into fictional strengths and triumphs. It tends to be more about its author's world than its own.

The Book of Mormon is a classic first novel. When Joseph Smith sat down to write, or rather dictate, his most well-known work, he was a fourth child creating a protagonist, Nephi, who is also a fourth child. He was a young man whose family moved relentlessly from town to town, sending his protagonist's family on a decade-long pilgrimage through the wilderness. He was the son of a man who had dreamed a complicated dream about a fruit tree, recounting his protagonist's father's complicated dream about a fruit tree. He was a frontier magician putting glow-in-the-dark stones into the hands of his characters— not to mention giving them an enchanted compass that receives text messages from God.

Much of the language of the Book of Mormon, moreover, reflects the hot-button issues of Joseph's day. The book's prophets rail against "that great and abominable church, which is the mother of abominations," which is how Joseph's anti-immigrant contemporaries would have talked about the Catholic faith of the Irish arriving to work on the Erie Canal. The book denounces "secret oaths and combinations" as forcefully as New York's most virulent opponents of Freemasonry. Its characters hold forth on topics ranging from infant baptism to the nature of the Trinity, about which Joseph would have witnessed much acrimonious debate.

In short, the Book of Mormon is as much a product of its time and place as Joseph himself.

IF JOSEPH'S AUTHORSHIP OF THE BOOK OF MORMON SEEMS SELF-EV-ident to me now, when I was younger I found the question of its origin far murkier. This was something I struggled with throughout my adolescence and my time as a missionary.

As a connoisseur of swordplay and derring-do, I found parts of the

Book of Mormon exciting as hell. But long stretches of it were so boring, especially the stuff lifted from Isaiah, that it wasn't hard to see why Mark Twain would label it "chloroform in print." More damning, though, were the inconsistencies and anachronisms that jumped out each time I read the Book of Mormon. Over and over I twisted myself into pretzels of logic to reconcile apparent contradictions. Over and over I prayed for the faith to make them make sense.

Take King Lamoni's horses and chariots, for instance, from the 20th chapter of Alma. If we start from the assumption that the Book of Mormon is a genuine ancient artifact, more correct in its translation than even the Bible, then we must assume that the horse and the wheel were known somewhere in the Western Hemisphere at around 100 BCE. These become two of the many pillars propping up the text's authenticity. If archaeologists have failed to turn up any supporting evidence, then it only means that evidence is still waiting to be found, buried underground or perhaps swathed in jungle vines. Otherwise the structure of the Book of Mormon begins to creak and groan ...

Of course, maybe Joseph did not *literally* mean horses. Maybe the original text referred to some New World beast unknown to him, and he chose the word "horse" as the closest equivalent in translation. But if that was true—another pillar cracking, plaster raining down—then why were animals called "cureloms" and "cumoms" mentioned later in the Book of Mormon? Why use made-up names for those and not for the thing that's not really a horse?

And what about the steel, the wheat, the elephants, and more? Through sheer dint of will, I would shore up my shaky edifice by telling myself that better minds than mine, whole departments at Brigham Young University, were working on these problems, and that belief in any sacred text required a generous application of faith.

For my entire life, no one else around me seemed to have any trouble summoning up this faith. What was wrong with me that I found it so hard?

It would have been so much easier for me if I could simply have admitted to myself that Joseph Smith made the Book of Mormon up. But then again, that would have made so many other things so much harder for me that I couldn't let myself entertain the thought.

If Joseph was no prophet, then my life was built on a foundation of sand.

EVERY MORMON CHILD LEARNS AT A YOUNG AGE TO LOVE AND RE-vere Joseph Smith. To us, he is both a larger-than-life figure, renowned for his physical prowess and irrepressibility, and a paragon of humility, faith, integrity, and sacrifice. We believe, as later Mormon scripture declared, that he "has done more, save Jesus only, for the salvation of men in this world, than any other man that ever lived in it." We feel so close to him that we know him by his first name, like we know our friends.

Joseph's life gave us *so* many examples of how to live our lives with goodness, strength, and bravery. Take for example the story of his leg surgery, which was one we heard often in Sunday school. The self-possession and grit he showed as a child was just incredible, and so inspiring.

Joseph was at most seven when his brother Hyrum brought typhoid fever home from boarding school. The disease raged through the family, sparing no one. Both parents and all seven children survived, though for Joseph's older sister, Sophronia, it was a close thing. Joseph himself developed a painful abscess, what he referred to as a "fever sore," in one shoulder.

A local doctor lanced the abscess, which temporarily relieved Joseph's discomfort but also let the bacteria into his bloodstream. The infection soon lodged in his left leg, where his tibia became inflamed with typhoid osteomyelitis. For weeks Joseph suffered unrelenting agony. His only respites came when the doctor returned, twice, to drain the resulting abscess, laying open the flesh all the way to the bone.

But the bone itself was infected and dying. A council of surgeons examined Joseph at home and agreed that he would die unless the leg was amputated. Joseph's mother, Lucy, demanded they make one more attempt to root out the infection. It happened that the chief consultant, Nathan Smith (no relation), had pioneered a grueling technique for removing necrotic bone. He must have been reluctant to try the procedure on a child so young, but Lucy was adamant and the surgeons at last assented. Dr. Smith's fee was a precious eleven dollars.

When the surgeons explained the operation they were about to attempt, Joseph's overwrought father burst out sobbing at the side of the bed. Joseph himself remained relatively calm, agreeing to the procedure but refusing to allow the surgeons to tie him to the mattress. By Lucy's account, Joseph told them, "I can bear the process better unconfined."

The surgeons then insisted that he drink some brandy or wine to dull the pain, but Joseph refused that too. "I will not," he said, "touch one particle of liquor; neither will I be tied down: but I will tell you what I will do, I will have my Father sit on the bed close by me; and then I will do whatever is necessary to be done, in order to have the bone taken out."

Knowing his suffering would be too much for her to witness, Joseph sent his mother not just out of the room but out of the house entirely. The surgeons opened his leg with a crude scalpel that was probably a full foot long. They bored holes above and below the infected area of the tibia, then used forceps to break off pieces of the dead bone. Twice Joseph's screams drew his frantic mother back into the room. The first time Joseph cried out that he could "tough it" if only she would leave. The second time, confronted by Joseph's pale, sweaty face and the buckets of blood drenching the sheets and the surgeons too, Lucy had to be, in her own words, "forced from the room and detained."

In all, the surgeons broke fourteen chunks of bone from Joseph's tibia. He not only survived the harrowing operation but made an ex-traordinary recovery, though he walked with a slight limp for the rest of his life.

What Mormon child could hear this story and doubt for a moment that young Joseph was destined to become the greatest of all God's prophets? What child could fail to be uplifted by his courage and pu-rity, and his protectiveness toward his mother?

What, in other words, was not to love?

IF THIS STORY STRIKES YOU AS MORE HORRIFYING THAN INSPIR-ing, you're not alone. In his book *Inside the Mind of Joseph Smith: Psychobiography and the Book of Mormon*, psychiatrist Robert D. An-derson puts the incident under an analytical microscope, though the part he finds most horrifying may not be what you'd expect:

> Mormon writers have used this story to suggest how good this future prophet was even as a child, and how much his parents cared. In therapeutic terms, this incident is not a commend-able one. Joseph was a young child, possibly five, no more than seven, desperately protecting the emotional state of his par-ents even while he was undergoing a life-threatening crisis and extreme physical pain. The implication is that they were un-stable and that, even at this early age, he has learned that his security depends on providing security for them.

Anderson calls this family dysfunction a "reversal of generations." Viewed in this light, Joseph's story becomes far more heartbreaking than heroic. In fact, the surgeon's bloody scalpel, in Anderson's read-ing, becomes the controlling image in Joseph's emotional development. It appears time and again in the Book of Mormon in the guise of a great sword. We first see it when Nephi stumbles across a distant rel-ative, drunk and passed out, who has tried to kill him and steal his family's treasure. Nephi needs the scriptural records in this man's possession, so the Lord commands him to take the man's sword and cut off his head. A distant relative such as young Joseph may have taken Nathan Smith to be.

Thus is Joseph's great childhood trauma transformed into triumph, turning the tables on his cruel tormentor.

MORMON APOLOGISTS LOVE TO ASK HOW AN UNEDUCATED FARM-boy could possibly have written the Book of Mormon himself, especially given that the bulk of its 275,000 words were dictated in a span of two and half months. It *must* be genuine, they argue. How else can you explain it?

This thinking diminishes Joseph's achievement, his genius at synthesizing Biblical language and thought with American preoccupations and ethics, his gift for improvisation on a theme. The more appropriate question would be how the Book of Mormon could have been written by anyone *but* this uneducated farmboy, this charming con man, this intuitive theologian—this Joseph Smith.

CHAPTER 9

DESPITE THE FACT THAT I WAS ONLY SUPPOSED TO WRITE LETTERS on P-days, Katrina and I corresponded two or three times a week, a chain of juggled conversational threads braiding their way back and forth through the post. My every letter was a roadmap of love, longing, and carefully euphemized lust, her every response a promise, a lure, a revelation.

Not that every event she related sat well with me. Her account of an R.E.M. concert at the State Fairgrounds Coliseum pained me like an infidelity. Her disquieting report of the movie *Blue Velvet,* which her hellion friend Michelle had dragged her to see, made me fear for the fate of her precious, corruptible soul. I knew my feelings weren't rational, that the asceticism my mission service exacted in no way obligated her to keep herself on ice, but I still found it unnerving that her life was free to roll along in its usual course while the church held mine in abeyance.

At moments like these it seemed impossible that the conveyor belt of daily living wouldn't carry her off into a story of her own while I stood frozen, helpless to hold her back.

BUT KATRINA WASN'T THE ONLY ONE OUT AND ABOUT. AS October dragged by, Fowler and I managed to squeeze in a few small adventures between the dull days and weeks of tracting. One P-day we drove north to the Badlands, where we hiked and shot photos of the rock formations and dinosaur fossils. On Canadian Thanksgiving we went birdwatching—well, we fed some ducks, anyway—then enjoyed a holiday feast with one of the local member families. The next week, careful that no members spotted us, we sneaked into a pool hall for burgers and video games. We were really living it up.

We had frequent dinner appointments with the local members too. I particularly enjoyed our meal with the Alvarez family. Sister Alvarez was a gorgeous Argentine who served us a beef and pumpkin stew we couldn't get enough of. I couldn't help but admire Brother Alvarez, not just for the air of culture and spirituality about him but for the way he carried himself. He wore his Mormonism like a bespoke suit, elegant and perfectly fitted. Mine felt more like clean but ill-fitting hand-me-downs. It might look fine from the outside, but it chafed.

Elder Fowler and I sometimes crossed sight lines with the shitkicker crew across the street as we arrived home at night. Abandoning all pretense of wit, they would jeer and hurl epithets like "Mormon faggot motherfuckers." Fowler smiled and waved and called "God bless you!" back, but his trembling anger was obvious when we made it inside. On one of these occasions he said to me, clenching and unclenching his fists, "I think we're starting to see why Prez pulled the sisters out of this place."

The encounters made *me* want to hide in a closet and pull down all the clothes on top of myself. I enjoyed attention, but not the kind we tended to draw from gentiles. I felt all too conspicuous and vulnerable behind my suit and black name tag. I wasn't sure protecting us from getting our asses kicked was high on God's priority list.

Meanwhile, I studied morning and night, determined to pass all the requirements for full missionary accreditation by the earliest possible date. I was on the couch one evening trying to memorize my fiftieth or sixtieth Book of Mormon verse when the telephone rang. Elder

Fowler sat laboring over a letter at the kitchen table, with headphones on. (He swore he was listening to "Mo-Tab"—the Mormon Tabernacle Choir.) Near his right hand steamed a cup of Postum, a barley-based coffee substitute. He gestured at the phone.

I grunted in exasperation and tossed down my scriptures. Fowler had made it known that, as junior companion, answering the phone was my responsibility. I figured this was in case Elder Garrett or anyone else he didn't want to talk to was calling. But usually it wasn't Garrett. I rose from the couch.

"LDS missionaries, Elder Shunn speaking," I said, pretty sure what was coming.

"Hi, Elder Shunn," said a salacious voice. "It's Sister Youtz. What's goin' down?"

Youtz was Sister Nylund's companion. I'd met her briefly that first day at the mission office in Calgary, and remembered her as a blonde with complicated hair and blotchy skin. Her voice scraped my nerves like teeth on concrete, and for some reason she always wanted to talk to me when Nylund was calling for Fowler.

I tapped my foot. "Not much. Just, you know, studying the Book of Mormon and all that."

"Cool, cool." She made that sound like *hot, hot.* "I guess you both survived transfer day."

I had four weeks now in the field. The latest batch of greenies had arrived the day before, which meant my MTC comrades and I were no longer the newest in the field. A transfer for either Fowler or me had been unlikely, and in fact Elder Garrett had called that morning with the news that we were both staying put.

"Yup, still here," I said.

"Us too. Anyway, Sister Nylund wanted to chat with Elder Fowler for a bit. Just thought I'd say hi first. Hey, stop it, I am! Okay, here she is."

I took the phone on its ridiculously long cord to the kitchen table.

Fowler thanked me and hustled the phone into the bedroom. He shut the door behind him.

I returned seething to the couch. It was more than just the insinuating tone in Sister Youtz's voice. It was the fact that I only had one other human being around to talk to. It was the grinding work. It was the boredom. It was the fact that a month in the mission field had not magically transformed me into the kind of servant who could lose himself in the joy of laboring for souls. (I was the kind of servant with a countdown calendar, which now stood at 681 days.)

It was the fact that I was homesick, horny, and had more urgent things to do with my life.

You need to pray for a better attitude, Elder Shunn, I berated myself. *And then you need to start working for it.*

But I am working *for it!* I argued back.

Then you need to stop being such a child, carried about by every wind of doctrine.

That was an easy sentiment to berate myself with, but it didn't make my situation any easier to bear. All I could do for the moment was to pick up *A Hidden Place,* by Robert Charles Wilson, my latest science fiction purchase, and try to lose myself in it.

An hour later Elder Fowler emerged from the bedroom in his garments and set the phone back on the floor. "Shunn, I'm about to hit the hay. Companionship prayer?"

I'd only managed to fight my way through fifteen pages of the novel. "Yeah, sure, I'll be right there."

But instead of heading into the bedroom, I sat staring over my shoulder at the telephone. I wished I had another friend to talk to, like Elder Fowler obviously did. I must have stared for a good ten minutes, fighting myself.

Finally, when I heard the sound of snores from the bedroom, I stood up and eased the door shut. I carried the telephone back to the couch and sat with it in my lap for another five minutes. I shivered, though the room was warm.

"Screw it," I said.

I picked up the receiver and with shaking fingers dialed a phone number I could not imagine ever forgetting.

One ring. Two. Then a click.

"Hello?" said a sweet, sleepy voice, staticky with distance. She might have been on the moon, she sounded so insubstantial and ghostly.

Goosebumps pebbled my skin. Thank goodness I hadn't reached one of her parents. "Hi, there. Have I by chance reached my fiancée?"

"Bill? *Bill!*" Katrina squealed. I had to hold the receiver away from my ear.

We talked for an hour about how much we missed each other. It was the shortest hour of my life.

CHAPTER 10

ON THE MORNING OF THE LAST MONDAY IN OCTOBER, FOWLER
and I dressed in jeans and sweaters, packed our overnight bags, and set
out east on the Trans-Canada Highway. Our destination was Medicine Hat, a prairie city that thrived on the natural gas lurking below it.
Mission rules usually forbade us from traveling outside our proselytizing area, but in this case we had special dispensation. Elder Garrett
had invited us out for a joint P-day, after which we would stay over and
attend the weekly district meeting the next morning.

It was a bright, cold day. Convoys of cloud turned the wheat stub-
ble to either side of the highway from brilliant gold to ash and back
again as they plied the winds overhead. The road ahead ran mostly flat
and straight, and in places the speed limit rose from 110 to 120. Kilometers per hour, of course.

I was driving. On Friday morning I'd passed the last of my certifi-
cation requirements, which meant I could now operate church-owned
vehicles.

Elder Fowler craned his neck to sneak a glance at the odometer.
"How we doing on mileage?" He had helped me pass so he could score
a chauffeur, but he seemed to be having a hard time staying in the passenger seat.

"It's fine, we're fine."

"How far have we come?"

"About sixty klicks."

"How much farther?"

I sighed. "Forty, forty-five. Another half hour."

"Not good." Fowler shook his head. "We're going to use almost a quarter of our mileage on this trip, and it's not like we cover a small area. Damn Garrett."

Because our proselytizing area covered several tiny towns in the region, the mission office allowed us a thousand kilometers per month on the car. For every klick over that limit, we were fined a dollar. So close to dying—going home from his mission—Fowler was squeezing every penny.

"I guess we shouldn't have gone clear to Dinosaur Park for that P-day," I said.

Fowler glared at me.

"Don't *worry*. We'll be fine."

He exhaled dramatically, sliding down in his seat and staring out the window. "I guess this means no road-tripping in November."

"Road-tripping?"

"Yeah, like if we wanted to sneak off to Calgary or someplace and bucket out. Visit old companions, see a concert, whatever. Not that we *would*," he hastened to add. "I was just talking out my neck."

I had developed a morbid fascination with tales of blatant rule-breaking. More to the point, I had begun to wonder about what an elder would have to do to actually get sent home from his mission. "But some elders do?"

Fowler sat up straighter. "It's been known to happen. These elders in Edmonton, for instance, snuck off to Banff to go skiing once."

I boggled. Skiing was one of the biggest no-no's in the White Bible, almost as bad as swimming or riding in a boat. Satan was said to hold dominion over the waters, which made swimming pools and the open sea perilous places for missionaries to be. I wasn't sure quite how snow factored into the equation, but elders on skis would no doubt have sent the mission's insurance coverage climbing.

"And they didn't get caught?"

"Nah. They unhooked the odometer cable, so no one ever knew they'd driven that far. Not a course of action I particularly condone, you understand, it being a felony."

"I can't even change my own oil, let alone unhook an odometer."

"Keep it that way." Fowler looked out at the stubbly fields, or to somewhere beyond. "I heard about these elders in another mission—Spokane, probably, since that's where all the screwups get sent—and they road-tripped all the way to Disneyland. Outside mission boundaries for three days and they never got caught." He turned to me. "But if they had, they'd have been put on the next plane home, I guarantee you that."

Damned if there wasn't admiration in his voice.

Medicine Hat dwarfed Brooks, the wide streets home to more than 40,000 people. Its low buildings glowed in the sunlight with the warmth of freshly sawn maple wood. Everything had a new-toy finish. It was an oasis in the middle of nowhere.

Referring to a sheet of scrawled directions, Fowler navigated us through residential neighborhoods to the LDS meetinghouse. It was larger than the one in Brooks, shared by more than one ward, built from bricks the same maple color as the rest of the city. I parked our Citation beside the only other car in the lot, a shiny red Chevy Cavalier.

"That's a d.l. car for sure," said Fowler. "Probably still smells like the factory."

The central space in every meetinghouse is not the chapel but the "cultural hall," a huge room usually with a proscenium stage. Events like plays, talent shows, and ward dinners are held in the cultural hall, but with a backboard at either end of the room and court markings on the flat carpet, the most frequent use is for basketball. That's where we found the four Medicine Hat elders, playing a rough game of two-on-two. Spying us, an elder in a gray T-shirt and knee-length cut-off sweatpants broke off from the action.

"Elder Garrett," he said, shaking my hand, though I could have identified him by voice alone. "Glad to have you here, Elder Shunn. I'm sorry it took us so long to get you two out to one of our district meetings. You can start to feel a little isolated with no other missionaries around."

"Good to be here," I said, though I was already eyeing the basketball court with some trepidation.

Garrett didn't look a thing like he sounded. He was my height, with one of those boyish faces that looks wrong on an adult body. His hand was soft, and I resisted the urge to wipe off the residue of his touch on my jeans.

He gestured at the carpeted court where the tallest of the other elders was giving Fowler a sweaty, back-thumping hug. "Do you play hoop?"

"Um, a little."

"Come on." Garrett turned and raised his voice. "All right, guys, three on three. Hamilton and I get Shunn, Ramsey and Torres, take Fowler. That way we've each got a six-footer. Let's play ball!"

If the LDS Church were to declare an official sport, it could only be basketball. With organized leagues for men and boys of every age, you could find a casual game or a tournament matchup at your local meetinghouse most any night of the week. But church ball had such a reputation for ugly play and violence that I remember hearing letters from Salt Lake City read in priesthood meeting demanding greater civility on the courts—or any civility at all.

Athletic I was not, and I avoided church ball whenever possible. I could shoot a free throw reasonably well, but, though racquetball had emboldened me, I still tended to shy away from any move inside the key that might mean catching one of the elbows thrown so liberally by my nice fellow Mormons. After half an hour on the court with the Medicine Hat elders, it was painfully obvious that I wasn't making friends of my teammates. We ended the game twenty points down, and I knew the others blamed it on me.

For lunch we relocated to a grungy nearby burger joint. Fowler and Hamilton, who had served in the same district in Wetaskiwin, reminisced boisterously at one end of our table, while Garrett and Torres made greenie jokes at the expense of Elder Ramsey and me. Ramsey, a jug-eared kid with a permanent hangdog expression, had been out a month longer than I had. I thought he was good at dishing back, even if his dry ripostes fell dead at the feet of our tormentors.

During a lull in the general pandemonium, Fowler said, "So y'all are coming to Brooks for district meeting next month, right?"

"I guess that's fair," said Elder Garrett.

"We'll try to make it worth your while," said Fowler. "Maybe we'll have a baptismal candidate for you to interview by then."

One of a district leader's jobs was to interview any investigator recommended for baptism, to assess his or her readiness and worthiness. Garrett's brow furrowed. "I didn't think you had anyone that close."

"Not yet, but we do have faith and determination," Fowler said. "Ain't no way I'm going home without a dunk in my last area."

"Are you ready to extend to April?" asked Garrett. The other elders broke up laughing.

Fowler grinned with good humor. "If that's what it takes. They don't call me Methuselah for nothing."

"They don't call you Methuselah at all," said Hamilton.

Chewing and chuckling, Fowler wiped his mouth with the back of his hand. "Damn, these burgers are good." He took a long pull of his root beer. "But you know what'd go best with 'em? A nice, cold Bud."

"Here we go," Hamilton said, rolling his eyes as the table exploded in raucous debate.

"No way, Miller High Life!" said Torres.

"Ew," said Ramsey. "Coors all the way."

"Flippin' snobs," Garrett said, shaking his head. "Old Milwaukee, man. Case or two, hit the beach in La Jolla, nice driftwood fire, you could stretch that crap out all night."

"Colt Forty-five," said Elder Hamilton, patting his belly. "Nothin' better after football practice."

The conversation rapidly devolved into a competition to see who could tell the best drinking story. I sat on the fringe of it all, silent, cheeseburger and Coke curdling in my belly.

"Hey, Shunn," said Torres as the laughter ebbed, "how about it? You got a story too, right?"

The blood roared in my ears like the grinding of giant rocks. A Mormon commandment called the Word of Wisdom strictly forbids the use of alcohol—no ifs, ands, or buts. Had I so much as looked sideways at a bottle of beer, my father would have knocked me into the next century.

I shrugged. "Not really."

Hamilton gestured with his straw. "Come on, man. Everyone's got a story."

"Really, I don't." I coughed. "I never drank."

The others fell silent, staring.

"What, *never?*" Fowler eyed me with bewilderment. "You must have tried it sometime."

"I never did," I said, squirming in my seat. "Honest."

"I know you're the new guy, Shunn, and you want to look good," said Torres, "but you can drop the act. We're not gonna *tell* anyone."

My head swam and my fingertips tingled. "I'm telling the truth. I've never had alcohol, not ever. Why's that so hard to believe?"

Torres shook his head. "Have it your way."

"Judas Proust!" I said. "Am I the only one here who actually grew up in the church?"

"Hey, Shunn, come on, settle down," Garrett said. "We believe you. It's just—you know, *weird*."

I hunkered over the cold remains of my burger. "I don't see what's so weird about it." I took a deep pull of my soda.

Garrett rose up in his seat and peered into my cup. "What's that you're drinking, anyway? Coke?"

"Yes," I said suspiciously.

"You shouldn't, you know. It's against the Word of Wisdom."

"Is not," I said, vacuuming up the last few swallows as noisily as I could. The Word of Wisdom *does* forbid coffee, which many Mormons take to mean anything with caffeine.

"Hey," said Garrett, raising his palms, "it's your eternal salvation."

I belched as the other elders laughed.

FOWLER AND I STAYED OVER THAT NIGHT AT THE TWO-BEDROOM apartment the other four elders shared. After our district meeting the next morning, Elder Garrett led us all out on tracting splits.

Split-offs are when missionaries swap companions. Sometimes splits last an hour or two, sometimes a day or longer, depending on the circumstances. In this case, the purpose was to pound the pavement on the north side of Medicine Hat to help Hamilton and Torres get their numbers up.

The six of us started at the same intersection but headed off in three different directions. Fowler went with Hamilton, Ramsey with Torres. Garrett took me, which I think had been his plan all along.

"Those are some big sticks, Elder Shunn," he said as we started toward our first porch.

I looked down at my scriptures, dangling from my hand in their zippered vinyl carrying case. Their jumbo size felt more than ever like an affectation. "The better to teach you with, my dear."

Thank goodness he laughed.

It was a cold day; the thin layer of snow that had fallen overnight made the streets a slushy mess. We mounted the steps and knocked. I was nervous at demonstrating my door approach in front of Garrett, but the pointers he offered afterward on my performance were gentle and constructive.

"Let me ask you something, Elder Shunn," he said a few minutes later when we were out of sight of the others. "And please be honest with me."

My heart seized up. *Here it comes. He knows I called Katrina. I'm not sure how he could have known that, but I was sure he did.*

But that wasn't the question Garrett asked. "What do you think of Elder Fowler? What kind of missionary is he?"

I slogged through the muck with my head down, thinking, as the cold seeped into my bones. Discomfort tempered any relief I felt. Telling stories on Elder Fowler seemed inappropriate, even if there'd been anything more substantial to report than racquetball matches and library books. Well, and telephone calls.

"I think he's a great missionary. I'm learning a lot from him."

Elder Garrett stopped, hands in his pockets. "Do you think he's enduring to the end?"

"He could have gone home in June if he wanted," I said, turning to face him.

"Maybe going home scares him. That's not the same as staying diligent."

"Look, I may not have anything to compare him to, but it seems to me like he's working hard. He's working *me* hard, anyway."

"But still you have no investigators. You don't teach very many D's. As your district leader, I have to be concerned about that."

I shrugged. "Brooks is pretty dead. But I have faith that if anyone can resurrect it, Elder Fowler can."

"And you, Elder Shunn. Don't forget *your* importance. You're the one who'll have to carry on after he's gone."

Oh, great, yes. Thanks for reminding me, Elder.

We resumed tracting in uneasy silence.

AT NOON WE ALL MET BACK AT OUR STARTING POINT, WHERE GAR-rett had parked the red Cavalier.

"Well, Elders," he said to Fowler and me, "thanks for all your help here today. I guess it's time to take you back to your car and send you home to Brooks." He lifted one eyebrow. "Though it'd be a shame for you to leave without paying homage to the Saskatoon Mission ..."

Before you know it, the six of us had piled into the car and were heading east on the Trans-Canada Highway. Hamilton drove, Ramsey and Fowler crammed next to him up front, while I rode wedged between Torres and Garrett in the back.

"So, Fowler," said Torres over the roar of the engine, "you die in like a month, right?"

"Guess so."

"Got any plans? A woman or anything? Any wedding bells back home?"

"I got plans."

"Yeah, to join a dating service," said Hamilton. "Ol' Methuselah's lady dumped his butt *way* back."

I could see Fowler's narrow smile, but he said nothing in response.

"My woman Johned me too," said Torres, "but you don't see me crying about it. I'm glad she's gone. She's not the kind I'd want to spend eternity with. She didn't even like to kiss with tongue."

"That's a must," said Hamilton. "If she won't even French, imagine what she'll be like in the sack."

Ramsey shook his head. "That won't matter in the Celestial Kingdom, when we're all gods. They *have* to have sex with you then, lots of it. How else you gonna have all your billions of spirit children?"

"Well, duh, they have to do it *then*," said Garrett. "It's a *rule*. It's part of the Plan."

Hamilton nodded. "And even if they won't, there's always another wife where that one came from. But I'm talking about *this* life—the next fifty years, man. If your wife hates doing the nasty, I don't care if you're the prophet himself, you're living in a world of hurt."

"Doesn't matter if she hates it," said Torres. "I'm not getting married so I can be a monk. We're gonna do it every night, whether she likes it or not."

Fowler barked a laugh. "Every night? Get real, Torres."

"Okay, five nights a week. At least. And she better not flippin' get fat on me. I expect her to look as good at forty as the day I picked her up from cheerleading practice."

"From wrestling practice, you mean," said Hamilton.

"Yeah, hoser, like *you're* gonna marry Brooke Shields."

"Maybe not," said Hamilton, "but *I* have a plan. You know what I'm getting my wife for a wedding present?"

"A dildo?"

"Hey!" said Garrett, reaching around me to thump Torres on the back of the head. "Remember who you are, you bucket."

Torres rubbed his head. "*Sor*-ry."

"What are you getting her?" asked Ramsey.

"A health club membership. She's gonna work out every day, no chocolate or any of that crap. And if she doesn't, then it's D-I-V-O-R-C-E."

Garrett snorted, trying not to laugh. "Is that how you spell 'relief'?"

"You got it, boss."

Outside the car the barren wheat fields clocked past, gray with the night's snowfall. I looked at Fowler. He still wore his inscrutable smile, but he wasn't laughing with the others.

OUR TRIP TO THE EDGE OF ALBERTA TOOK A LITTLE OVER HALF AN hour. A mile past a tiny town called Walsh we pulled over to the side of the highway. We clambered out of the car and onto the shoulder of the road. The land stretched flat to the horizon in every direction. Just ahead a huge sign bid us a hearty WELCOME TO SASKATCHEWAN.

"There it is, Elders," said Garrett to Fowler and me. "That's the boundary of the mission right there. Cross to the other side and you're in serious trouble." He glanced around at the others, then shouted, "Last one there's a blister!"

The Medicine Hat elders broke for the border in a wild pack. Fowler and I brought up the rear, though I felt a chill of dread when I passed the sign. Leaving Alberta meant leaving the protection of the Holy Spirit.

We stood there for few minutes in a group, breathing clouds of steam, just *being* in Saskatchewan. Thumbing our noses at mission rules.

Then we turned around and tramped back to the car.

CHAPTER 11

ONE SECRET I NEVER TOLD ELDER FOWLER, OR ANYONE ELSE IN the mission, is that before I entered the MTC, Katrina and I had only known each other for three weeks.

I mean, we'd gone to high school together. We had some of the same classes, but we'd never exchanged more than a few words. I'd had a crush on her since at least our junior year, when my friend Glen Cary pointed out, as we leered around our locker doors, that Katrina had the best legs of anyone on the drill team. She was brassy, svelte, and beautiful. Even after we graduated, I could replay in my head every interaction we'd ever had.

I vividly remembered the moment during our senior year when I was crossing the school parking lot on my way to meet friends at an afternoon football game. It was a gray day. I had on the black trench coat, aviator sunglasses, and fedora I'd affected since becoming editor of the school paper. Several drill team members were trotting parallel to me across the asphalt in their short skirts and white high-heeled boots, pert as a line of ponies in dressage. Katrina, whose long legs I was covertly checking out, spotted me and called out, "Way to go incognito, Bill!"

Burning with embarrassment, I looked at the ground and pretended I hadn't heard. But I floated through the rest of the afternoon. Katrina McCormick knew my name!

But I didn't even consider asking her out. A nerd like me could never date a girl as popular as she was. Not in high school.

In my sophomore year of college, Katrina began working as a teller at my bank branch in Salt Lake City, near the university. I looked forward to my visits to the drive-up window, hoping for a glimpse of her through the glass or, grail of grails, the exchange of a few friendly words over the intercom. When we spoke, she always sounded happy to see me.

In mid-August, at the height of too short a summer, I finally resolved to go inside and see her face-to-face. I had nothing to lose. In three weeks I was due to report for duty at the Missionary Training Center.

Katrina and two other tellers were working in the small branch. I dawdled over my transaction slip, assessing the speed of the line, until I judged the moment was right to join the queue.

I thought I noticed Katrina notice me in line. I thought I noticed her smile to herself.

A few sweaty minutes later, whether due to my timing or hers, I approached her window, my stomach in knots.

"Bill, hi," she said with a smile.

"Uh, hi, Katrina." I passed her my transaction slip. "I've got this, uh, little withdrawal to make, that's all."

"Okey-doke." She keyed my information into her console. "So how's your summer?"

"Pretty busy."

"Yeah? You working?"

"Not for a while. Since school got out—just, you know, doing stuff. I went to California. I tried out for *Jeopardy!*"

"Hey, you'd be good at that." She somehow kept her eyes on mine while she typed, her sly smile never faltering. "Did you get on?"

"I qualified, but I won't get on the show."

"How do you know that?"

I took a deep breath. "I got my mission call not long ago."

I didn't know much about Katrina. I didn't know if she was a straight arrow or a party girl. In fact, with thirty or forty wards in Kaysville, Fruit Heights, and Farmington, I didn't even know whether or not she was Mormon. If she'd thought about me at all since I'd started showing my face at the bank, she'd probably assumed I *wasn't* going on a mission. With most guys, if more than two years had passed since high school and they hadn't gone yet, they weren't going at all.

Shit. If Katrina had any interest in me, then breaking the news to her this way, at this time, was cruel. Once it was out of my mouth, I wished I hadn't told her. I wished I hadn't come.

But Katrina didn't bat an eye, and her smile didn't fade. Making arcane notations on my transaction slip, she said, "That's great. Where are you going?"

"Calgary. You know, Canada."

"It's supposed to be really beautiful up there." She counted out my cash. "You'll be there for the Olympics, I guess."

"That's right." In fact, the prospect of the '88 Winter Olympics was one of the few attractive aspects of my call to Calgary.

"Very cool." Katrina handed me my money, which nearly wiped out a checking account I'd be closing soon anyway. "So, when do you leave?"

I dug out my wallet. "Three weeks."

"Wow. When's your farewell?"

"The, uh, thirty-first. That's a Sunday." I grimaced. *Of course it's a Sunday, you idiot.*

"Which church? I'd like to stop by."

I almost dropped my wallet but managed to fumble the bills inside and jam the whole mess into my pocket. "You know the chapel on Crestwood?"

"I do. I'll definitely be there." She smiled. "It's good to see you, Bill."

"Good to see you too."

I waved awkwardly as I backed away from the counter. When she waved back, I almost tripped.

"You gotta ask her out," said Kevin Kilmer.

We were sitting on the edge of the brick planter in my front yard after dark, drinking Big Gulps of Coke. Kevin was my friend Andy's younger brother and had just graduated high school. We'd always been friendly, but I'd started hanging out with him more after Andy left on his mission earlier that year.

"There's no point," I said. "I'm leaving in three weeks."

"She *likes* you."

"You don't know that."

"Dude, she was on the flipping *drill team!* If you don't ask her out, I'm gonna kick your ass."

I exhaled sharply. "There are, like, eleven McCormicks in the phone book."

"Call them all. If you don't, I will."

I was about to protest when a car cruised slowly past us, a dark shape with only its parking lights on. It pulled to a stop one house down. I could make out two shadowy figures through the rear window. They appeared to be having an animated discussion.

I pointed. "What's up with that car? Whoever's in it keeps looking back here."

"Let's find out." Kevin cupped his hands around his mouth and bellowed, "Hey! Who is that?"

I flinched. "Quiet!"

"Dude, shut up."

A head of dark, tousled hair insinuated itself out the driver's window. "It's Katrina McCormick!" shouted the shadow, a girl, while the passenger tried to pull her back inside.

Kevin saluted me and started ambling down the street toward his car. "That's my cue to skidoo, stud," he said with a grin.

"What are you talking about?" My heart thumped like a pile driver. "Please, I can't do this by myself."

"You'll be fine," he called back.

Abandoned, I turned to the idling car. Like a gunslinger in an old western, I moved cautiously down the sidewalk, hands at my sides. The passenger window slid down as I approached. Inside, looking mortified, was Katrina.

"Hi." She didn't quite look at me.

"Hi."

"You, um, you know Michelle Bannister?"

Michelle, a striking girl with long dark hair, waved happily from the driver's seat.

"Yeah. Hi, Michelle."

"We were, um—" Katrina looked at Michelle, and they both started to giggle. "We looked up your last name in the phone book and were, um, just planning to drive by and look."

"Yeah," said Michelle, "but there you were, right out front. We thought we were busted."

I went for broke. "We were, uh . . . were just talking about you."

A dog barked somewhere in the silence.

"Well, listen," said Katrina, "Michelle has to get home soon." She bit her lower lip. "What if she drives me home to my car . . . and then I come back?"

"Yeah," I squeaked. "Great."

Half an hour later, I was sitting in the living room watching the ten o'clock news with my parents—something I rarely did. I'm sure they both thought it odd, but neither one commented. When the doorbell rang, I sprang up to answer it. My parents both raised their eyebrows when I let the gorgeous blonde into the house and introduced her as a friend from high school. My father in particular looked like he was biting his tongue. More calmly than I felt, I led Katrina to the dining room, where we sat down to chat.

After Johnny Carson's monologue, my mother made a big bowl of hot popcorn and brought it to us, probably so she could get a better look at my guest, but otherwise my parents left us alone. Among the stunning things I learned as we talked that night were that Katrina read science fiction almost exclusively, that her favorite writer was Frank Herbert, and that *she'd* had crush on *me* since at least our senior English class.

When I walked her out to her Hyundai sometime after midnight, I asked her if she'd like to see a Tom Stoppard play with me that weekend. She said yes.

I came inside walking on air, but my mother was waiting for me. "I can see why you like her, Bill. She's very beautiful. But you do understand that you're about to leave on a mission, right?"

She made it sound like I'd just had sex on the dining room table. "Yes, Mom, I understand."

"I'm just making sure."

I gritted my teeth. *And what,* I wanted to ask, *is so wrong with a cool drink of water before a journey through the desert?*

THREE NIGHTS LATER, WE SAW A PERFORMANCE OF "THE REAL INspector Hound" in Salt Lake City, and for the next two and a half weeks after that we were inseparable. She was everything I'd ever dreamed of in a girlfriend—smart, sexy, irreverent, and tuned in to my weird aesthetic sensibilities. She loved that I was a writer, and she completely grokked my pride at having studied under giants like Damon Knight and Joe Haldeman the previous summer.

Katrina's commitment to the church was not the greatest, but she was trying, she told me, she was trying. Of course, in my heart of hearts I wasn't actually looking for a woman whose faith was the defining factor in her life. The last thing I wanted was the kind of unthinking über-Mormon girlfriend who'd want to start squeezing out little squalling miracles the instant I returned from my mission.

The icing on the cake, though, was that Katrina loved to make out. I'd never dated a girl who loved to kiss so much, or who was so good at it. Though we could barely keep our hands off each other, I was careful never to take things below the neck, as was she. In fact, fifteen or twenty minutes into making out in the dark on her parents' front porch after a date, Katrina would inevitably push me away and say, "Okay, I'm hot now. Which means I need to go inside and you need to go home."

I couldn't have offered a specific definition of the word "hot," but I had more sense than to argue with her.

My father was always waiting in the living room as I arrived home, glaring at me over the top of a spy novel. Sometimes I managed to slink past him without an argument, sometimes not. It was time, he might say, for me to start practicing the ascetic discipline life in the mission field would require, not to be swinging hard in the other direction—and especially not with a spiritual gold digger who obviously wanted to use me to bootstrap herself out of a life gone awry.

Right. Because I was such a powerhouse of righteousness myself.

The night before I left for the Missionary Training Center in Provo, Katrina and I sat on her front porch together, holding hands and kissing. During a brief time-out, I summoned all my courage. "Katrina, I love you," I told her. It was the first time I'd ever said it to a girl.

She didn't quite meet my eyes. "I love you too," she said in a tremulous voice.

Despite the ecstatic warmth spreading through me, I could not at that moment have resented God more.

"Families," according to an aphorism inescapable in the Mormon world, "are forever." This is the church's biggest selling point, and the one around which its entire conception of the afterlife revolves.

Integral to this is the idea of eternal marriage. Civil marriages may end at death, but a marriage solemnized and sealed in a Mormon temple is one with the promise of lasting for all time. And not only are husbands sealed to wives, but children of temple marriages are sealed to their parents, part of an everlasting chain that stretches forward and backward as far as faithfulness and virtue will allow.

Only couples sealed in a temple can achieve the highest level of the Celestial Kingdom, where they will continue to learn and progress without end, creating, populating, and ruling worlds of their own. Mormon children are taught from a young age to remain pure and faithful so that, at the appropriate time, they can find that eternal mate and get married in the temple. The appropriate time for a young man is generally considered to be soon after he returns from his mission. For a young woman, the appropriate time could be as early as the end of high school.

I had always feared that my One Eternal Mate would be someone I didn't find attractive, or whose greatest priority in life would be the gospel, to the exclusion of any lasting interest in sex. As soon as I got to know Katrina, I could see how different she was from most Mormon girls of my acquaintance, and I became desperate for our brief time together to stretch into something not just lasting but infinite. She was so much what I'd always dreamed of, so vanishingly rare, that I feared she might be my one shot at happiness on this earth. I felt like an astronaut who'd come untethered from his vessel and was shooting off into deep space on an inexorable vector. Katrina by some miracle had drifted into my path, and if I didn't latch onto her while she was still within reach then I was doomed to fly forever into darkness, on a trajectory of loneliness and celibacy.

There would be no second chance, no second miracle. Or so my callow heart told me.

During my three weeks at the MTC, Katrina and I wrote each other nearly every day—desperate, tortured letters filled with protestations of longing and devotion. Before bed every night, kneeling on the cold tile of my dorm room, I pled fervently with God to give her the strength to wait faithfully for me through the next two years. I squeezed my eyes tight and tried to will my desires into being. From time to time I sensed a comforting presence at my back, a manifestation I hoped was the Holy Ghost and not merely a product of wishful thinking.

On the morning of my departure for Canada, my family came to see me off at the airport in Salt Lake, as did Katrina. My father was clearly unhappy to see her there on what he considered a family occasion, but Katrina hovered quietly in the background. When her turn came for goodbyes, she gave me only a quick, chaste hug and a kiss on the cheek.

The other missionaries from my MTC group, many of whom did not have family near Salt Lake, had gathered not far away in a nervous, murmuring clump. My father chatted with a few of them in the avuncular way he had with other people's children. While he was occupied, I handed my Canon AE-1 to my sister Seletha and asked her to take a couple of pictures of Katrina and me together.

My father was giving me another reminder to follow every mission rule to the letter when I looked at my watch. My family had been visiting with me for nearly forty-five minutes.

"Speaking of which, I guess it's time to say goodbye." I patted the breast pocket of my jacket, where my White Bible was tucked away. "The rulebook says families seeing missionaries off at the airport are required to leave at least thirty minutes before the flight's scheduled boarding time."

My father frowned, but he couldn't argue with me. He was the one who always said that strict obedience was the only recipe for success in the mission field. My family offered me their tearful last goodbyes and left. Katrina trailed along behind them with a wave and a lingering look.

When my family was well out of sight, I slipped away from the other missionaries. Halfway back along the concourse I spotted her, waiting for me in an otherwise unoccupied departure lounge. Katrina.

"I ducked into a ladies' room," she said as I joined her. "I think I got away clean."

We grabbed each other.

"Oh, my gosh," she said, breathing hard, when we came up for air. "I've missed you so much I can't stand it."

"Oh, I know. I've been out of my mind."

We kissed some more, tumbling interlocked into two uncomfortable plastic seats. After another couple of minutes, she disengaged. Glancing at the gate attendants who were very pointedly not looking our way, she wiped the smeared lip gloss from her face and reached into her purse.

"This is for you." She held out a plush penguin.

"Opus!" We were both big fans of *Bloom County.* "This is terrific! Thank you."

"Smell it."

I put the toy to my nose and sniffed. "That's your perfume."

"I know." She rummaged in her purse again and drew out a small flowered box. "And when it starts to fade, just give it another shot."

I cradled the box in my hands: ANAÏS ANAÏS.

"Now you'll always think of me when you're falling asleep at night," she murmured.

"This is—I can't believe this." I shook my head, throat swelling. "This is wonderful."

"*You're* wonderful."

We kissed again.

A boarding call for Occidental Airlines interrupted us. The flight! My heart flooded with panic. Was this the first announcement, or had I missed earlier calls in the heat of our passion?

"Katrina, we don't have much time. I don't know how to tell you everything I want to say." I felt the awful gulf of two impossible years widening at our feet, bearing us apart. I took her hands in mine. "I just—I don't know what I'm going to do if I come home from my mission and you're not still here."

"I can't stay at the airport for two years," Katrina said, eyes sparkling. "I do have to go to work."

"*Très drôle*, McCormick. You know what I mean."

Katrina looked down at our linked hands. The shadow of a smile trembled at the corner of her mouth.

"Well, Bill, there *is* one thing you could ask me that would make sure of it." Her eyes met mine for a brief, shining moment. "One question."

I couldn't breathe. I'd been praying to God every morning and night for a sign, and this was it. I scooted out of my chair and dropped to one knee before her.

"Katrina Joan McCormick," I said, "would you do me the honor of being my wife for time and all eternity?"

Grinning, Katrina bobbed her head up and down so hard I thought it would fly off. "Yes. Yes, I will. Yes."

Giddy, I kissed her again, then reached into my pockets with trembling fingers. "Okay, I've got to do this quickly."

I took out two sticks of gum and removed the foil wrappers. I gave one stick to Katrina and popped the other into my mouth, then folded the first wrapper lengthwise a couple of times, shiny side out. I asked a puzzled Katrina to extend her left hand. I wrapped the foil strip around her ring finger to measure it, then tore off the overlap.

From my wallet I removed my temple recommend—the laminated card signed by my bishop and my stake president that granted me entrance to those holiest of all LDS sanctuaries. Two strips of Scotch tape were stuck to it.

"I went to the Provo temple a few days ago. I'd been praying about this for a while and I thought I had an answer, so I took this tape with me." I peeled one strip off the card and taped the ends of the foil together in the shape of a ring. "I guess I wanted to sanctify the tape, so our rings would get some sympathetic sealing power from the temple."

I slipped the makeshift ring onto Katrina's finger. She gasped.

"Kind of silly, I know."

"No," she said, shaking her head, staring at her hand. "It's not silly at all. It's the most amazingly romantic thing ever." She smiled wryly. "Does this mean I can use the F-word now when I talk about you?"

"The F-word?"

"Fiancé."

Now it was my turn to gasp. "Oh, yes. You certainly may."

I was about to kiss her again when I heard the sound of a throat clearing. Elder Vickers, district leader for the duration of our stint at the MTC, was frowning about fifteen feet away, arms folded across his chest. He looked at his watch, red-faced, then turned and walked away.

"Shit," I said, stuffing the leftover materials into my pocket, "I have to go. I'll have to put my ring together later."

Katrina took my face in both her hands and kissed me. "I love you, Bill."

"I love you too." I hugged her close. "See you in two years."

I turned and sprinted to my gate, where Elder Vickers and Elder Munoz were waiting for me.

"Stud," said Munoz, grinning.

Though I could tell he was seething, Elder Vickers clapped me on the shoulder like a brother. "You're a good man, Elder Shunn," he said tightly. "A good man."

We headed down the boarding ramp. The gate sealed itself behind us.

CHAPTER 12

"Have you told your parents yet that we're engaged?"

I sighed, hunched on my bed in the semi-gloom, the telephone receiver cradled between my ear and shoulder. It was Wednesday night, and this was the second time I'd broken mission rules to talk with Katrina. I eyed the line of yellow light beneath the closed door and hoped Elder Fowler would keep reading out there for a while longer.

"No, I haven't told them yet," I said.

"It's probably time. My mom knows. I've sworn her to secrecy, but she's way too excited to keep her mouth shut for long. Your parents need to hear it from you before they hear it somewhere else."

"I know, I know. It's just . . ."

"The last thing they need is even *more* reason to hate me."

"My parents don't hate you."

"Your father hates me."

The silence crackled.

"But *I* love you," I said at last. "Look, okay, I'll tell them. I'll write them."

"Tonight?"

I tugged at my hair. What Katrina was saying made sense, but I still had a bad feeling about it. "All right, tonight. I'll do it tonight."

"It's the right thing to do, Bill. Maybe I can help by bringing your father some kind of peace offering. A snack or something."

"Buy him off with treats?"

"If he can be bought. What does he like?"

"*If* he can be bought, it's with burnt almond fudge ice cream. And Oreo cookies."

"Burnt almond fudge, Oreos. Check."

"Katrina, I love you," I said in a rush, like an incantation against evil. "You think of everything."

"I love you too, Bill. Write that letter."

I hung up and carried the phone back out into the living room. Elder Fowler's eyes flicked up briefly from his book. I knew he must know I'd been talking to Katrina, but he said nothing.

I grabbed a pad of paper and a pen, and sat down in the armchair. *Dear Mom & Dad* came easily enough, but for the life of me I couldn't figure out what to write next.

OUR PROSELYTIZING SLUMP CAME TO AN END THE NEXT EVENING. Brother Whitaker, the ward mission leader, had set us on the trail of a new investigator named Pam Laduke.

Pam was eighteen, pregnant, and newly married. Her husband Teddy, the father-to-be, was twenty, a local ward member who favored hockey jerseys and had decided not to serve a mission. Pam was not a member of the church, but her new family situation, together with pressure from Teddy's parents and Bishop Neuwirth, had her thinking serious thoughts about Mormonism.

We taught Pam Laduke the first discussion at their tiny rented house, and it went so well that she readily agreed to have us back for the second discussion two nights later. Teddy, with his sparse mustache, was effusive in his thanks as he saw us to the door. After all, we were helping him turn an unfortunate situation into a shot at the eternal marriage every good Mormon longs for.

We taught Pam every second or third evening for the next week. She was sharp, receptive to everything we taught her, a true golden investigator. We had only been home a few minutes from our fourth discussion—the one about eternal life and chastity—when the telephone rang. Elder Fowler grabbed the receiver from his seat on the couch.

"LDS missionaries. Oh, hello. Uh, yes, okay. Sure, I'll put him on." He covered the mouthpiece, looking concerned. "Hey, Shunn, it's your mom and dad."

I stood to take the receiver, and I turned my back to Fowler as he went to put the kettle on. My mouth was dry. Fowler must have assumed something bad had happened. I was pretty sure I knew what it was. "Uh, hi?"

"Hello, Bill," said my mother in her never-ruffled telephone voice. The house could have been burning down around her and she would have sounded just as calm. "Or rather, I mean, Elder Shunn."

"Hello, son," said my father, so forcefully that I winced.

"Hi." I did my best to keep my voice even, but my hands were already shaking. "Is everything all right? You know this number's only for emergencies."

"We know we shouldn't be calling," said my mother. "But we've been talking here, and we—"

"Listen, son," interrupted my father, "we read your *letter*, and I have to say that we're concerned, your mother and I."

I knew it. I knew the letter had been a bad idea. I tried to pace, constrained by the furniture in the tiny room. They had no right to break mission rules and call *me*. I wanted to yell at them to write me a damn letter.

"Concerned about what?"

"About this girl, son. This . . . *engagement*." His distaste for the word was audible.

"She seems like a perfectly nice girl, Bill," my mother said. "Smart and pretty. Don't get us wrong."

"But, son, you two hardly know each other. Three weeks is not enough time to know someone, to make an eternal decision like this."

"It's hardly any time at all."

"And any relationship where you have to *deceive* your family and *sneak* behind their backs at an *airport?* There's just something not right about it."

"Don, that's not what—"

"It's true, Ann."

I was shrinking, shriveling, regressing. "I knew I shouldn't have told you that part," I muttered.

"Son, I wish you hadn't told us *any* of it."

"Donald!"

"Mom, Dad, listen. I don't know how better to put this across, but I know it's the right thing. I prayed about it in the temple in Provo. I got my confirmation."

My father sighed, a sound like stones rattling down a well. "As a missionary, you're not *entitled* to a revelation like that. This time of your life belongs to the Lord, exclusively."

"Maybe he gave me my answer precisely *so* I could relax and focus on my mission."

"It doesn't work like that," my father said.

"How do you know?"

"Bill," my mother said, "try to see it from our point of view. You meet a pretty girl you had a crush on in high school, you go out on a few dates, and you decide just like that to get married. It just—there doesn't seem to be a lot of *thought* to it."

"I've given it a *lot* of thought, and prayer too. I understand the formula as well as anyone. I teach it here every day." I clutched my forehead. "I don't see why you can't treat me like an adult and be more supportive. Katrina's mother is *incredibly* supportive. She even sends me cookies."

"Of course she does!" my father said. "What mother wouldn't want you for a son-in-law? You're foreordained for great things, son, and you shouldn't give yourself away so easily. Especially to people who aren't good enough for you."

His words sucked the air out of my lungs. I couldn't speak.

"Nice going, Don," said my mother. She had to be very upset to call him out in front of me. "I'm glad we discussed how we were going to approach this. Aren't you?"

"Well, it had to be said. I don't know why he doesn't want to go out with nice girls, like that Amy Ross."

Dizzy, I sat down hard on the couch. He meant girls with family money and church connections.

"I—I really have to be going to bed soon," I said. "Mission rules."

"We love you, Bill," my mother said plaintively. "That's all we're trying to say. We want what's best for you. Why don't you just, just think about putting off any commitments until you get home, until there's a chance to really make up your mind. Just see what happens."

"I guess that's how it'll go no matter what," I said, quietly and bitterly. "It's not like I can speed the process along."

"Young *man*," said my father, his voice trailing off from a tone of warning into the ultraviolet of despair.

"Good night," I said. "Thanks for calling."

I hung up the phone. Elder Fowler, saying not a word, brought me a cup of Postum. How he'd gotten me hooked on the stuff when I'd never even drunk coffee was a mystery to me, but at that moment it was exactly what I needed.

I rubbed my temples. I'd never thought of myself as willful or stubborn, but the idea of Katrina was wedged in my head like a spike, and my parents were only driving it deeper. A red-hot, jagged spike, pressing on the back of my eye.

CHAPTER 13

BY THIS POINT ELDER FOWLER AND I HAD FOUND OURSELVES A
new living situation. It started the night in late October when we
emerged from our car after a dinner appointment to a volley of abuse
and an empty beer can that fell short of us. I had to hold Fowler back
from charging across the street to confront the drunken hooligans.

"I could've taken three of them scumbags," he raged when we were
safely inside, the hoots and jeers no longer audible.

My nerves were thrumming. "Sure, I know, but the other two
would've beat the crap out of me."

"I wouldn't have let that happen." Fowler was stalking around the
living room, smacking a fist into his open palm. His upper lip twitched.
"Shit, shit, shit! I know you're right, we can't go around fighting everybody. But *damn*, I want to knock someone's teeth down their throat."

"I'll make some Postum," I said, to have something to do.

By the time I brought him a steaming mug, Fowler had settled
down on the couch, elbows on knees and head in hands. He accepted
the drink with a nod and took a careful sip. Then he set it down on the
coffee table. "I think it's time for us to move."

I was on my way back to the stove for my cup, but I stopped. "What?"

He was shaking his head, not looking at me. "I know we're close to the end of the month, but there's got to be something else we can find in this town."

I spooned Postum crystals into my mug and filled it with hot water. "Can we even do that? Move, I mean?"

"We have to get permission, but yeah. And anyway, this place is a little extravagant, and I hate taking money from the ward. I'm not sure they're too happy giving it to us, either, now that we're elders and not sisters."

The local ward was contributing fifty dollars a month toward our rent, which totaled $350. Fowler and I split the balance, but even so, my budget was stretched to the breaking point. Early church missionaries like Samuel Smith, David Patten, and Brigham Young were commanded to go forth and preach "without purse or scrip," relying on charity and good will, but in our day and age we were expected to live without outside assistance if at all possible, on our own three hundred dollars a month. (Well, four hundred in Canadian dollars.)

"Okay, I guess we should start looking," I said, though I wasn't exactly eager to move to a smaller place, or a worse part of town.

"I hate to feel like we're running away," said Fowler. "But I'll look at it like we're saving someone's life. Even if they don't deserve it."

WE WERE HARDLY THE FIRST MORMONS TO HAVE TROUBLE GET-ting along with their neighbors. This was a tradition going back to the earliest years of the church.

As the creation of the Book of Mormon proceeded, Joseph accrued an expanding cloud of acolytes. Besides Martin Harris and Oliver Cowdery, there was David Whitmer and his brothers, not to mention Joseph's own parents and siblings. To the most useful of his new followers, Joseph would offer personalized revelations from God, often commanding their obedience to this task or that.

Revelations and visions quickly proliferated among the group.

Martin Harris walked and talked with Jesus in the shape of a deer. Oliver Cowdery prayed in the woods with Joseph so long and hard that he saw an angel, whom Joseph identified as John the Baptist. Eleven men in all, after sessions of strenuous prayer under Joseph's direction, were sufficiently convinced that they had seen and handled the Golden Plates to add their names to witness statements printed in the front matter to the Book of Mormon. (I picture an "Emperor's New Clothes" scenario, with no man daring to admit the box that holds the plates is empty.)

On April 6, 1830, shortly after the book's debut, Joseph organized his flock into an official new religion, which he called the Church of Christ. It purported to restore the original Christian faith, which had become corrupted and lost as the Twelve Apostles died off. It also restored the "priesthood," which Joseph defined as a literal power which could be spread from one man to another by the laying on of hands, like fire, or a virus.

It's hard to say how seriously Joseph took his Book of Mormon project when he first lugged home that heavy sack. A neighbor of the Smith family, Peter Ingersoll, claimed in a sworn affidavit in 1833 that Joseph had told him the plates were a fabrication. But it seems clear that something changed in the interim. It could be that the belief he instilled in others, reflected back at him, altered him in some fundamental way. It's certainly possible, even likely, that he began to be convinced of his own stories.

The new church grew rapidly, as convert after convert fell under the sway of Joseph's persuasive charisma. His followers clustered in enclaves near the Finger Lakes in the north and the Pennsylvania state line in the south, which meant frequent travel to visit them all. But for all the friends he could number, his enemies had not forgotten his days as a money-digger. After the baptisms of more than a dozen converts near Colesville, New York, Joseph narrowly escaped a mob of fifty men. His opponents no doubt assumed the church was some new scam and wanted to run the prophet out of town before he could defraud more of their friends and relatives.

That same day, Joseph was arrested on a charge of disorderliness and remanded to South Bainbridge to face trial. He might have fallen into the hands of the mob that very night if not for the alertness of the constable set to guard him. Joseph was acquitted at trial, then acquitted again of similar charges in a neighboring county. He eluded another mob after the second trial, sneaking home to Pennsylvania with Oliver Cowdery under cover of darkness, but his hosts in Colesville were not so lucky. The family cowered in their house while their property was vandalized by the angry mob, and their wagons tipped over.

To Joseph, who took the Constitution's promise of religious liberty as divinely inspired, there could be only one explanation for such violent opposition from his fellow countrymen. It was the hand of Satan, trying to hold him back from an urgent work of righteousness.

ELDER GARRETT AND ELDER RAMSEY CAME TO SEE US IN BROOKS on the last Thursday of October. We were waiting to sign a lease on a tiny, dank basement apartment in an old three-story house, the only affordable place we'd been able to find on such short notice. It was half the size of our current pit—cramped, gloomy, and cold. Fowler could barely stand up straight inside it. Even so, nothing could dissuade him from his determination to move there.

We needed our district leader's approval before we could rent any new apartment. Elder Garrett conferred with us in the snowy gravel driveway, away from the landlady, after his inspection tour. "Look, there's no technical reason for me not to sign off on this. The place meets mission requirements. But Fowler, I'm telling you, it's a *dump*. I really hope you'll reconsider."

"No can do, boss," Fowler said.

"At least wait one more month. Take the time to do a more thorough search."

"We can't do one more month. It's got to be now."

Garrett's heavy sigh steamed out in a cloud. "All right. But remember I told you this was a bad idea."

After the lease was signed, the four of us spent the rest of the afternoon on tracting splits. It had been snowing on and off. Elder Ramsey and I trudged along under a sky of dirty gauze, without success.

When we all met up again, Fowler looked unhappy. Elder Garrett took me aside.

"Elder Shunn," he asked me quietly, "are you sure you haven't noticed anything wrong with your companion?"

"You mean besides the razor cuts on his arms?"

Garrett's eyes widened. "The *what?*"

I smiled without humor. "Just kidding." Something was definitely up with Fowler, but I was taking a dislike to Garrett and his probing insinuations. "No, I haven't noticed anything wrong. Like what? What do you mean?"

"I don't know. Evasiveness, not looking you in the eyes. Shunn, is it really that bad at the old place? He's got one month left. He couldn't tough it out?"

Now that we were locked into moving, the taunting didn't seem like such a big thing, but still I rallied to Fowler's defense. "He's not thinking about himself. He's trying to make sure missionaries are safe here after he leaves."

"It's going to get a lot colder after he leaves. You'll stop seeing people like that out on the street." Garrett frowned. "Well, how do *you* feel about the new place?"

I felt like the new place was a depressing hole. I felt like I wanted the spotlight off me. "Spending less on rent will be good."

Garrett waited for me to say more, then shook his head. "Just . . . please call me if you need to, okay?"

"Sure."

A short time later, Fowler and I stood in front of our old apartment as the Medicine Hat elders got into their car. Garrett rolled down his window as he started the engine. "If you need help moving on Saturday, just call. And good luck with that new gator tonight!" That was the evening we were teaching Pam Laduke her first discussion. "I knew you elders would find someone golden."

As their taillights vanished into the twilight, Fowler said, "That guy's a dick."

DISRESPECT AND INSUBORDINATION WERE ANOTHER HEADACHE Joseph had to deal with in the early months of the church. Everyone in his inner circle felt empowered to issue revelations from God. Hiram Page, one of the Book of Mormon witnesses, was churning them out by the dozen with the aid of a seer stone, while Oliver Cowdery, Second Elder of the Church, tried to put his own revelations on an equal footing with Joseph's.

This chaos could have splintered the church, but Joseph stamped it out at a priesthood conference in September 1830. He put himself forward as the only one authorized "to receive and write Revelations & Commandments for this Church." After debate and investigation, the conferees voted to adopt the resolution. This pretense to democracy continues in the church today, where the members periodically vote to "sustain" their leaders by a show of hands. The approach to revelation continues as well, with each individual free to receive revelation on his own behalf, or for whatever body he is appointed to lead, with ultimate authority over the church itself resting in the prophet alone.

Missionaries armed only with the Book of Mormon were being dispatched in every direction. After the conference, Joseph sent Oliver on an expedition to convert the "Lamanites"—the Indian tribes being pushed relentlessly west of the Missouri frontier. Oliver's other task on this trek was to locate a suitable place for building a New Jerusalem, where Joseph prophesied his people must gather for protection against the great natural disasters that would presage the Second Coming of Christ.

Meanwhile, a copy of the Book of Mormon had fallen into the hands of a prominent Campbellite preacher named Sidney Rigdon, who was trying to reestablish the primitive Christian church in Kirtland, Ohio. Within three weeks, he and his small congregation had all converted to Mormonism. Sidney left immediately for New York, intent on meeting Joseph Smith for himself. Accompanying him was a well-to-do hatter named Edward Partridge—who also happens to be my fourth great-grandfather on my mother's side.

Joseph received Sidney and Edward warmly, delighted to have made such respectable converts. He was particularly taken with Sidney, who had founded a communistic society amongst his congregation in Ohio. By the end of 1830, Sidney was firmly entrenched as Joseph's right-hand man. In January 1831, Joseph ordered his followers in New York to pull up stakes and relocate to Kirtland. It took cajoling, arm-twisting, and finally a pointed revelation, but soon the migration was underway—the first of many for the Mormon people.

In Kirtland, Joseph and Sidney set up a social system called the United Order, under which all members would pool their property and hold their goods in common. Edward Partridge was ordained the church's first bishop and tasked with administering the program. This experiment did not begin well. A local convert named Leman Copley contributed a thousand acres to the United Order for the New York émigrés to live on, then took it back again and evicted them after they'd made significant improvements to the land.

Oliver Cowdery had in the meantime settled on a location for the New Jerusalem—the town of Independence in Jackson County, Missouri, on what would one day be the outskirts of Kansas City. Oliver had established a tiny congregation in Independence, to which Joseph and a retinue of hand-picked men paid a visit in July 1831. The town was small, rough, and unprepossessing, but after inspecting the area

Joseph nonetheless issued a revelation declaring it Zion. This was to be the center of the *world* in his grand conception of the Last Days, the place from which the gathering of Israel would be accomplished. Though he instructed the church to buy up all the land to the state line, Joseph singled out one specific lot as the future site of a magnificent temple.

Among the men who accompanied the prophet to Independence was, of course, the competent and reliable Edward Partridge, who was charged now with running the United Order in Missouri *and* with managing the lands the church would need to acquire. Edward for his part was dubious about the town's prospects and did not hide his disillusionment from Joseph. A revelation chastising him for his lack of faith soon followed. (From my interactions with the family, the Partridges would seem to have toed the line ever since.)

The displaced New Yorkers began arriving to claim their lots in August, while Joseph made the 800-mile journey in reverse, back to Kirtland. But all was not rosy in Ohio. Even as the church continued to grow, defectors were breaking away, disgruntled with their treatment under the United Order or unhappy at some perceived slight by the prophet. One disaffected apostate, Ezra Booth, stirred up a mess of hatred with a series of letters in the *Ohio Star* that called out Joseph's intent as "the establishment of a society in Missouri, over which the contrivers of this delusive system, are to possess unlimited and despotic sway."

The rising anger came to a head one Saturday night in March 1832, when Sidney Rigdon was beaten senseless by a mob that included at least a few disgruntled former Mormons. Joseph, too, was attacked and dragged struggling from the house where his family was staying. The mob stripped him, scratched him, strangled him, tarred and feathered him, and tried to jam a glass vial of poison into his mouth.

Joseph's family and friends spent the night scraping tar from his bleeding body. Some of the mobbers were at church the next morning to gloat when the prophet, battered and bruised but unbroken, took the pulpit to preach. But his triumph came with a bitter price. Joseph and Emma had adopted twin infants, one of whom died later that week from exposure to the cold during the attack. The child was eleven months old.

Sadly, this was only a foretaste of persecutions to come. In Missouri, the original settlers of Jackson County had begun to fear that the continuing influx of Mormon converts would soon tip the balance of local political power. (It probably didn't help that the Mormons bragged openly about their intention to possess all the land around Zion.) In July 1833, civic leaders gave the Mormons six months to settle their affairs and leave the county. Mobs underscored the ultimatum by razing the Mormon press and tarring and feathering poor Edward Partridge. Acid mixed into the pine tar left him with chemical burns on top of the expected discomfort and humiliation.

Joseph found himself helpless to offer much aid or comfort from Ohio. When the Missouri Mormons hired lawyers and appealed to the state government for help, the mob harassment worsened. Houses and other property were destroyed. Finally, after one Mormon and two mobbers were killed in a clash, the local militia disarmed the Mormons and ran them out of the county.

Days shy of his twenty-eighth birthday, Joseph issued a harsh revelation on the topic of these persecutions. "They were slow to hearken unto the voice of the Lord their God," he wrote of the Saints in Missouri, "therefore, the Lord their God is slow to hearken unto their prayers, to answer them in the day of their trouble."

The promised inheritors of Zion had been made refugees—and, according to their beloved, demanding prophet, it was nobody's fault but their own.

ON THE FIRST OF NOVEMBER, A SATURDAY, WE MOVED OUR MEAGER furnishings into the new pit with the help of some brethren from the ward. It wasn't quite like being run out of Jackson County on a rail, but to me it still felt like a defeat.

We didn't discover until later that day how difficult it was to sit on the toilet in the closet-sized bathroom without the door open. We didn't discover until the next morning how inadequate the hot water tank was. The lack of sunlight through the grimy casement windows and the general lack of heat were immediately obvious, of course, but despite all this Elder Fowler remained obstinately upbeat.

I, on the other hand, felt claustrophobic. I've asked Marty Fowler in the years since why he was so dead set on moving. He insists it was the money and the harassment, but I'm still not convinced I know the whole story. Maybe Elder Garrett sensed what I could not at the time—that Fowler was punishing himself for something, and I was just along for the ride.

CHAPTER 14

THE WEATHER WAS COLD AND GROWING STEADILY COLDER. AS WE soldiered miserably through our long tracting hours, every person we met warned us about the brutal coming storm and how we ought to stay indoors. But the morning the storm arrived, Elder Fowler opened our door, climbed the stairwell into the howling Arctic wind, and declared the day business as usual. My protests fell on deaf ears.

We stuck to our own neighborhood, leaning into the wind as we staggered along the sidewalk. The air was more ice than oxygen, a storm of tiny crystalline razors slashing at our exposed faces. Streamers of powdery snow slithered down the streets as if alive. Even my parka and a special set of thermal temple garments couldn't keep out the insidious wind. I had never been colder in my life.

The first old woman to answer her door berated us for idiots. "It's thirty below!" she scolded, shivering inside a thick robe. "The good Lord doesn't want you boys freezing to death! Go home!"

Thirty minutes of similar reactions finally got through to Fowler— or maybe it was the specter of the Reaper at our elbows. With visibility rapidly diminishing, he called off our tracting for the day. We lurched back to our basement apartment like two drunks.

With the door sealed shut behind us, I went straight to the stove and cranked up all the burners. I know that's dangerous, but I didn't feel like I had much choice. When I turned around, Fowler was slouched on the couch, head in his hands. "Hey, Elder. Elder Fowler? Are you okay?"

He looked up at me, eyes hooded, his parka still zipped up. "Shunn, can you keep a secret?"

His bleak expression scared me. "Of course."

"I mean it, man. You can't flippin' tell *anybody* about this, ever." I'd never heard desperation like this from him. "I gotta tell someone, though. It's driving me batshit."

"Of course. I promise." I put the kettle on one of the burners and pulled out a kitchen chair. The apartment was so small that this put us within arm's reach. "What's up?"

He took a deep breath. "You know I was a district leader in Calgary, right? Before I got transferred here?"

I nodded.

"Well, it was a small district. Breitmeyer and me, Nylund and Youtz, just the four of us. We used to hang out a lot. We'd meet up on P-day, go bowling or play some Frisbee. We'd get together for lunch, drop by to play cards in the evening. We started to like each other—a lot. I mean, me and Nylund did. Then Breitmeyer and Youtz too."

"Wait—*like?*" I wasn't happy with where this was going. "You mean *like* like?"

Fowler ran a hand through his curly black hair. "Like like," he said with a sigh. "We started meeting at Prince's Island Park at night, the four of us. We kinda tended to pair off, just walking around and talking, but then pretty soon . . ." His pained eyes bore into mine. "Pretty soon Nylund and I were off in the trees, making out. Then so were our companions." He barked a sharp laugh. "We called it 'going on splits.'"

The kettle whistled. "Judas Proust, Fowler," I said, heading to the stove. I felt sick at heart. Having a g.c. was bad enough, but a g.c. that was also a sister missionary? That was disaster squared, dancing on the rim of a volcano. Double Satan's money's worth if he could get two missionaries sent home at once, and possibly excommunicated. Because if they slipped up and had sex, or maybe just came close, that's exactly what would happen. "This is really serious."

"You have no idea how serious."

I was rinsing a pair of mugs and almost didn't hear him. I shut off the water and turned around.

"It took me a while to realize I'd fallen in love," Fowler said.

I almost dropped the mugs. Fowler looked so radiant I could practically see the bones shining through his skin.

"Are you kidding me?"

"Not a bit, Shunn. And Sister Nylund feels the same way."

"Good grief." I was such an idiot. I always assumed that no one could have secrets worse than mine, even when the evidence was right under my nose—ringing our number almost every night. "That's why you asked to be transferred out of Calgary."

"Shunn, I *had* to leave Calgary. Otherwise we'd have done something we regretted."

I spooned out brown crystals and stirred in the water. "You didn't tell President all this, did you?"

"'Course not. I wouldn't still be here if I had." He took a mug from me as I sat down. "But I knew you'd understand this part, Elder Shunn. Nylund and I are talking about getting hitched after we both get home."

The Postum scalded my tongue. "Yeah, that's great," I said tiredly. "Congratulations."

He perked up. "Really?"

"Really." I forced a smile for his benefit. This surely wasn't what God had intended, but, like with Teddy and Pam Laduke, maybe he could take a situation that sprang from sin and turn it into something worthy. "I'm really happy for you."

"You're a great friend, Elder. I mean it."

Maybe that was just the way the world worked. Maybe that was the only way it could.

THE WEATHER KEPT US COOPED UP ALL DAY. I FOUND IT HARD TO read, hard to write letters, hard to look at my companion. Despite my words of support, I had to ask myself if Fowler's sins were holding us back from doing our best work here in Brooks. If so, then I—with my phone calls to Katrina, my illicit science fiction novels, my failure to wear a name tag on P-days—had blame to shoulder too.

Fowler spent two hours on the phone that night, holed up in the bedroom with the door closed. I sometimes heard his murmuring voice or his laughter.

In the morning we trekked through the bitter cold to sacrament meeting but spent the rest of the day inside again. I was entirely stir-crazy by the time the telephone rang that evening.

"LDS missionaries, Elder Shunn speaking."

"Oh, my *gosh.*" The words oozed into my ear. "Do you know how *gorgeous* your voice is?"

I grimaced. "Youtz, hi. That's just how I answer the phone. Don't get too excited."

"Do you ever think about doing radio?"

"No. I don't know. Maybe." That was, in fact, a secret dream of mine.

"You should. That voice of yours really *does* something to me."

I shuddered. Youtz had been getting bolder, but this took it to a new level.

"So, anyway," she said, "I heard Marty spilled the beans."

Her use of Fowler's first name grated on me. "That's right."

"You're not going to say anything to President, are you? Between you and me, I'm done with Elder Breitmeyer. He's really not my type."

"No, Sister Youtz," I said with exaggerated patience, "I'm not going to say anything to President."

"Good." She inhaled sharply. "Well, Bonnie wants to talk to Marty. But first . . . hey, do you remember that day we met at the mission office? You'd just arrived from the airport."

"Ummm, vaguely?" I said, trying to *sound* vague.

"*I* remember. You were awfully cute. Maybe you and Marty want to road-trip back to Calgary sometime. We could hang out."

I stared at the receiver as if it had just bared its teeth. I set it down, gently but firmly, in its cradle.

THE WEATHER WARMED UP AFTER A FEW DAYS MORE, BUT THAT didn't improve things much, bringing as it did a freezing sleet. After two miserable hours of tracting, we stopped off downtown and scurried into the Brooks One-Hour Photo, hoods pulled tight over our heads.

Brother Whitaker looked up from the magazine he was leafing through at the counter, exposing his crooked teeth in a demonic grin. "Well, look what the cat drug in!"

Shivering, we stamped and shook over the welcome mat. "How's business?" asked Elder Fowler.

"Oh, you know." The little shop was as yellow and dim as a faded photograph. With his cadaverous frame and thick glasses, Brother Whitaker presided over it like an animated corpse, wrapped in the embalming-fluid stink of darkroom chemicals. "I was just thinkin' about Shunn there, though, readin' up on *this* ugly freak."

He held up the magazine. An old *Teen Beat*, Kevin Bacon on the cover.

I groaned. We sometimes dropped by the trailer park where the Whitaker family lived if we couldn't find anything more productive to do at night. The surprisingly pretty Sister Whitaker enjoyed feeding and fussing over missionaries, and we enjoyed being fussed over. On the downside, their thirteen-year-old daughter, Aimee, seemed to have a crush on me. At least, she was always trying to convince me how much I looked like Kevin Bacon, her celebrity boyfriend.

"No, no, that's not me," I said. "Timothy Hutton's my lookalike." I liked *Footloose* as much as the next person, but I couldn't stand Kevin Bacon's stubby nose.

Whitaker looked at the cover. "Huh. *I* can't tell any of you freaks apart." He brightened. "Hey, though, I *was* mighty sorry to hear about that president of yours down there."

Fowler and I looked at each other. "President Tuttle?" Fowler asked, peeling back his hood.

"Not your mission president, dummy. That what's-his-name of yours—Reagan."

Fowler and I exchanged another look. "What happened to him?" I asked.

"Oh, that's right, you boys don't get the news. He's gettin' hisself impeached or somethin' like that. At least, that's what they're sayin' might happen."

My heart raced. I was still ingenuous enough to have a lofty opinion of Reagan. "What are you talking about?"

Whitaker rubbed his hands together and practically cackled with glee. "I guess he was tradin' weapons for hostages with Iran? Nicaragua's in on it too. Looks like a real big mess."

I was itching for more details, but Fowler steered us away from the topic. "I guess we'll have to buy a paper," he said through a tight smile. "Let's talk missionary work instead. Things are going well with Pam Laduke, *very* well, but otherwise we're spinning our wheels. We wanted to drop in and see if there's any other leads you can think of for us. Anything at all."

Brother Whitaker scrunched up his forehead and stroked his chin. "No, sorry, nothin' comes to mind."

"Are you sure? No other part-member families we can drop in on?"

He shook his head. "Sorry, boys, but I call around and talk to the bishop every week. I ain't managed to rustle anyone else up for you."

"Not even Buddy Van Rijk? Did you try him?"

"Sure did, like I do every couple of weeks. Tol' me he didn't feel ready."

Elder Fowler smiled at Brother Whitaker and thanked him, and we made a polite departure. But when we got in the car, Fowler slammed his door shut hard enough to rattle the whole chassis. He pounded his hands on the dashboard.

"Shit!" he barked. "Not ready? Give me a flippin' break. The only thing not ready is *us* if we're not ready to take matters into our own hands."

I started the car. "Okay. Like how?"

"Like tonight we swing by the Van Rijks' house." Steel glinted in his eyes. "Not *ready*. Shit. How 'bout we leave that judgment to the professionals?"

ELDER FOWLER WAS ITCHING FOR ONE LAST BAPTISM BEFORE HE went home. Pam Laduke was coming along, true, but her husband Teddy would probably be the one to dunk her. No, Fowler wanted a convert he could take down into the water himself. Only then would he be able to die in peace.

We found Nancy Van Rijk in the ward directory and showed up at the door unannounced late that evening. Nancy—a normally pragmatic woman, or so we'd been told—bounced like a giddy schoolgirl as she showed us into the living room. The house was new enough that the paint seemed to sparkle on the walls, but the mustiness of young children already hung thick in the air.

"The kids are in bed, but Buddy's just down in the family room. Let me show you there." Her practical bob bounced as she clapped her hands together. "Oh, I'm so happy you're here!"

Buddy Van Rijk, lounging on a gray vinyl couch, barely glanced away from the giant television as his wife introduced us. We sat across from him in wooden chairs Nancy dragged into the room.

"Brother Van Rijk," said Elder Fowler, "we were hoping you might be interested in learning more about the church your wife belongs to."

Buddy turned his square face our direction, then back to the hockey game. "I don't have time," he said in a Dutch accent. "I got to coach."

Nancy stood up in the long pause to turn off the television. "The sisters were here a lot," Nancy said to us, "saying the same thing."

Buddy's mouth tightened, and he exhaled loudly through his nose.

"But Buddy works long hours, and what little free time he has he's coaching Theo's hockey team."

"Oh, really? We'd love to see Theo play." Fowler was leaning forward, hands clasped together, and he never once looked away from Buddy. "We'd also love to share the missionary discussions with you. There's only six, and we can schedule the first one any time that works. We're very flexible."

Buddy spread his hands and looked at the ceiling as Nancy joined him on the couch. I noticed how grimy his fingernails were from the oil fields. "I don't know if I even believe in the Mormon Church."

Fowler chuckled. "Well, Brother Van Rijk, we'd hardly want to waste your time telling you about it if you already believed in it. That's all we want to do, is help you find out about it so you can make up your mind for yourself." He took out the infamous blue planner and a pen. "How would Saturday night work for you?"

"Hockey's on," Buddy said to his knees.

"What about Monday? Family home evening."

Buddy looked at the television, as if for help. "Football."

One of the children, a boy of about four, appeared from the hallway, sleepy and sucking his thumb. His parents couldn't see him from where they sat, but he hung back staring at Fowler and me with wide, frank eyes.

"Boy, I do love football," Fowler said. "Always loved to watch it with my dad. I do miss him, being out here. How about you? You love your kids, I bet."

"Sure."

Fowler nodded toward the hall. "You *would* like to be with them forever, wouldn't you?"

Heads turned, and the boy padded swiftly over to take his father's hand, still staring at us.

Buddy shrugged. "Sure I would."

"Well, Brother Van Rijk, we're going to show you how it's possible. And at the end of our sixth discussion you'll have the chance to decide whether or not you're willing to take the next step toward making it happen. So we'll see you here on Monday night?"

The room was very quiet as Buddy's forehead furrowed. None of us breathed until he inhaled deeply and nodded.

Fowler made a note in the planner. "Wonderful, Brother Van Rijk." He stood up and extended a hand. "It never hurts to talk a little. We'll be looking forward to Monday."

Buddy stood too. He frowned. "Call me Buddy."

"Then we'll see you Monday, Buddy."

Nancy showed us to the door. "Thank you, Elders," she said in a trembling whisper. "Thank you."

After the door was closed, Fowler and I high-fived. "That was amazing!" I exclaimed. "Like, textbook!"

Fowler almost permitted himself a smile. "All due respect to Sister Roper and them, but sometimes the right man for the job is a man."

I HAD JUST CHANGED INTO MY PAJAMAS THAT EVENING AND SET-tled down on the couch with a book when the phone rang. Elder Fowler, in his garments, was making Postum at the stove, so I answered it, still high on our triumph.

"LDS missionaries, Elder Shunn speaking."

"Hi, Elder Shunn." Youtz's voice was pure goo. I squirmed like snakes were slithering over my skin. "What are you wearing?"

My jaw clenched as all my good feelings evaporated. "Nothing! I mean, it's none of—I mean—I'm not—"

"Mmmmm, nothing. I can just picture it now."

I clutched my hair. "That's not what I meant! I meant it's none of your business."

"Oh, I'm going to make it my business, Elder Shunn. You better watch it because I'm. Going. To. Get. You."

I suspect, now, that my obvious squeamishness was like catnip to Sister Youtz, and she wanted to see how uncomfortable she could make me. But all I understood at the time was that I was not attracted to her, and that I could not stomach her aggressive suggestiveness.

"I have a fiancée!" I protested. "I'm not interested!"

"She's a lot farther away than I am."

"Look, Elder Fowler's right here. He wants to talk to Nylund."

"You can't run from me, *Bill*."

The sound of my name in her mouth made me gag. "Just put Nylund on." I held the receiver away from my mouth. "He's grabbing the phone. Hey!"

Muffled voices argued briefly. Sister Nylund came on the line. "Marty?" she said eagerly.

"No, this is Elder Shunn."

"Oh. Is Marty there?"

"Yeah, I'll give you to him in just a minute." I mustered all my sternness. "Sister Nylund, you've *got* to keep your companion from calling me."

"How can I do that? She likes you."

"*I don't like her.* Have you heard what she *says* to me?"

"Elder, she's just having fun."

"I can't stand it! I want to jump out of my skin!"

"All right, I'll see what I can do. But I can't make any promises."

"Take care of it. I don't want to have to call President."

Her tone iced over. "No, you most certainly do not, Elder Shunn. Can I talk to Marty now?"

A grim Elder Fowler was standing over me now, arms folded. I handed him the receiver, grabbed my book, and shut the bedroom door hard behind me.

NEARLY AN HOUR LATER, ELDER FOWLER PUSHED OPEN THE DOOR to the darkened bedroom. "Hey, Shunn, are you awake?" he whispered as his bed creaked.

I groaned. "I am now." I tried to sound groggy so he'd feel guilty, but I hadn't slept a bit. I'd been lying on my face for an hour, Opus and his perfume near my head, fighting the urge to deal with my infuriating erection. I'd tried to hold a picture of Katrina in a wedding dress in my head, but she kept wanting to take it off. Sometimes the image looked like Heidi, sometimes even Sister Youtz. It had been a long hour, but at least I wouldn't be waking up the next morning to the shame, yet again, of a garment top glued to my stomach.

"Oh, sorry. But man, I gotta tell you, that was some conversation I just had with Bonnie. Dang."

"I'm happy for you, Elder." I turned onto my side, toward the wall, and pulled my blankets tight. At least my erection was going away.

"I mean, I was *this* close to finding out what color her nipples are."

Despite myself, I turned my head in the dark and said, incredulously, "What?"

"I been driving myself nuts trying to guess." He sounded enraptured. "I mean, they could be red, or brown, or that really pale flesh color where you almost can't see 'em."

I was used to oversharing from Elder Fowler—whatever the gene for shame was, he didn't seem to have it. But this was something else again. I covered my face with one hand. "Gee, Elder, I can't believe she won't just tell you straight out."

"Give it time." He chuckled. "*She* says I'm gonna have to wait 'til our wedding night, but give it time."

I didn't want to hear this. I didn't think Fowler and Nylund were going as far as having phone sex—for one thing, there was too much innocent delight in the way he related this information—but even this much of a glimpse into their private moments made my stomach hurt. Missionaries weren't supposed to *have* private moments. "Yeah, be sure to keep me posted."

My eyes had just fluttered shut when Fowler said, "You know what I'm gonna do that night? My wedding night? Something I've been looking forward to for a long time. I'm gonna give that girl a pearl necklace."

I ground my face into my pillow. "She'll probably like that," I said with false patience. "Girls like jewelry."

"What?" Fowler barked a laugh. When I turned my head I could see a spectral smudge propped up on its elbow. "You don't know what I'm talking about?"

"If you're not talking about a necklace, then I guess I don't," I said, feeling stupid.

"It's not a necklace, but *man*, does it sound cool. You know about titty-screwing?"

"Um, no."

Fowler proceeded to describe, in detail, a process that culminated with ejaculate adorning a woman's throat. "Cool, huh?"

Katrina was so modestly endowed I couldn't picture this really working for us. Appalled with myself, I clapped my hands to my head and shook it. "Criminy, Fowler, are you sure that's really what you want to do on your *wedding* night?"

He thought about that. "Well, no, you're right. Not the first thing, anyways."

I resumed fetal position and closed my eyes.

I had almost drifted off again when Fowler said, reverently, "I'm hoping they're brown. Nice and brown."

CHAPTER 15

ELDER FOWLER OFFERED A PRAYER AS WE KNELT ON THE CARPET OF
the Van Rijks' family room. When we had resumed our seats, he said,
"Elder Shunn, would you begin the discussion for us, please?"

Toys in primary colors littered the corners of the room. Buddy
and Nancy and their two younger children faced us on the gray vinyl
couch. The eldest, all of six years old, lay on the carpet pushing a Ton-
ka truck in desultory circles.

I cleared my throat, conscious of the eyes on me. The good thing
about teaching a discussion was that we only had to know the main lesson points. As long as we hit those, we could explain everything in our
own words and tailor our approach as we saw fit. This was a big change
from my father's day, when, as he liked to remind me, there had been 31
discussions, each of which had to be memorized word for word.

The church poured a lot of research dollars into developing its curriculum, which it constantly refined and streamlined, and in training
us missionaries to deliver it. At the MTC we role-played the discussions constantly, learning to hit whatever odd curveballs our investigators might throw us. We were also drilled in such teaching techniques
as "Build Relationships of Trust," "Personalize the Message," and "Resolve Concerns." The discussions were, of course, an elaborate sales

pitch, everything geared toward the ultimate goal of closing the deal with baptism, though we were never taught to look at it that way.

"People in all lands and in all ages have believed in a Supreme Being," I began, "though they've called him by many different names. You and I know him simply as God. Brother Van Rijk, do you believe in God?"

He nodded, the barest of motions. "Yes."

"And what is he like? What are some of his attributes?"

His mouth compressed. "Powerful."

"All-powerful, yes. Omnipotent. Anything else?"

Nancy raised her hand. "All-knowing."

"That's right too. Anyone else? Kids? What is God like?"

Scott, the four-year-old from the other night, shot his hand high into the air and grinned. "Jesus loves me."

"Yes, he does. God is good and merciful and just, and he knows you and me and everything about us and loves us anyway." This was one of many precepts from the discussions that I believed only intermittently, but the point had to be underscored and amplified so we could build on it. "Now, because he loves us so much, we should find it easy to love him back. And how do we show God that we love him? Anyone?"

When no one else spoke up, Nancy ventured, "By obeying what he tells us?"

"Exactly. By keeping the commandments. Not only is that how we show our love for God, but it's also how we come to know him. By emulating him, or following his precepts, we become more like him and understand him better."

Little Scott, quivering with pride, thrust his hand into the air again. Without waiting to be called on, he said, "I know how to say my prayer at night!"

"Scotty, quiet," said Buddy.

"Well, prayer *is* an important thing. It's how we talk to God, and that's something we'll get to in a while. What I want to talk about now is *why* God loves us. Does anyone know?"

Blank stares, though maybe Nancy was keeping quiet to give some-one else a chance to answer.

"Brother Van Rijk," I asked, "do you love your children?"

"Of course."

"Why?"

"Because . . . they're my children."

Bingo. This was exactly what I wanted him to say. "There you go. That's why God loves us—because we're his children. Sometimes we even call him our Heavenly Father, because he *is* our Father. You kids probably know a song about how you're each a child of God."

Nancy brought her children with her to church every Sunday, and the younger two did not disappoint me. Scott launched lustily into the lyrics to "I Am a Child of God," and his little sister followed his lead even though she couldn't pronounce many of the words.

"We *are* children of God," I said when the kids trailed off after two or three lines. "And since God is the Father of all of us, that makes everyone on earth brothers and sisters. Theo, how are we supposed to treat our brothers and sisters?"

Without looking up from his truck, the boy on the floor muttered, "Don't hit 'em and take things from 'em."

"Right. We're supposed to be *nice* to them and treat them well. And that's also how we're supposed to treat everyone at school, or work, or wherever, because they're all our brothers and sisters."

"Did you hear that, Theo?" asked Nancy.

"Ye-e-e-es," Theo droned.

Beside me, Fowler stifled a laugh.

"Now, because God is our Father, he wants us to be happy. He wants us to learn and grow and become more like him, just like any fa-ther would. For that reason, he created the Plan of Salvation." I leaned forward, clasping my hands. "Brother Van Rijk, do you believe that you're literally a child of your Father in Heaven?"

"Yes," he said with a nod.

"How does it make you feel to know that?"

He shrugged. "Good."

Of course, the best salesmen are the ones who believe in the product they're selling. "It makes me feel good too. In fact, knowing that I'm a child of God and that he wants us to return and live with him is what made me want to become a missionary and help share that same joy with others." And the ones who don't quite believe need to fake it with sincerity. "Now Elder Fowler would like to tell you a little about the Plan of Salvation."

Elder Fowler and I traded off principles for the remainder of the discussion, involving the children as much as we could. At the end of the hour, Fowler extracted a promise from Buddy that he would start reading the Book of Mormon and praying about it before our next visit.

Now it was time to "Identify the Spirit." "Do you feel that good feeling that's been with us here tonight as we talked about these things?" Fowler asked.

Buddy nodded.

Fowler tapped himself on the chest with a fingertip. "That's the Holy Ghost that we've been telling you about, speaking quietly to our hearts to testify as to the truth of all our words. Now, after we leave tonight, you might sense that good feeling leaving as well. That's because the constant companionship of the Holy Ghost is a gift that is only granted unto us after baptism into the one true church of God. I, also, want to testify to you that I *know* the things we've talked about are true, because I've read and studied and prayed about them sincerely, and I know that if you do the same the Holy Ghost will whisper their truth to you too, and I say these things in the name of Jesus Christ, amen."

After a closing prayer we departed. As I wrestled with sleep that night, I realized we'd probably left the good feeling behind us.

THAT SATURDAY, AT OUR INVITATION, THE VAN RIJKS CAME TO church to see Pam Laduke's baptism. Two dozen people attended in all, watching from folding chairs in the font room. Elder Fowler sat next to Buddy, a few rows back. Brother Alvarez and I stood up front as the official witnesses.

The white-tiled font was filled with four feet of warm water. Pam and Teddy descended the stairs into the water dressed in heavy white jumpsuits. Brother Alvarez's job was to make sure Teddy recited the baptismal prayer correctly, while mine was to watch that he managed to get Pam, including her buoyant, pregnant belly, entirely under the water.

The ordinance went fine, and it gave me the perfect excuse to pay close attention to Pam's swollen breasts as Teddy brought her up out of the water. As she wiped her streaming face, though, and I realized I was speculating on the color of her nipples, I looked away to where Fowler sat quietly explaining the proceedings to Buddy.

Buddy seemed to have taken a real liking to Elder Fowler, and now that he'd started the discussions, he couldn't seem to stop. Maybe he'd been infected by the Spirit, or maybe he'd simply realized how much this meant to his wife. Either way, the ball was finally rolling.

THE NEXT MONDAY NIGHT, WE TAUGHT BUDDY VAN RIJK HIS fourth discussion, the one that contains such sticky principles as the Law of Tithing. Buddy didn't bat an eye when we told him that, if he joined, he'd be required to contribute ten percent of his income to the church. At the end of the evening, Elder Fowler invited him to be baptized that coming Saturday night.

Our taciturn investigator surprised me by saying yes, with no hesitation.

"I knew it would happen," Fowler told me on our way back to the pit. "I had faith he'd be ready."

On Thursday, a family named the Montgomerys treated us to a lavish American Thanksgiving at their home, and by Friday night, with all six of Buddy's discussions behind us, Elder Fowler was walking on air. He was a single-digit midget, with only a week left in the field, and his golden investigator would go under the water the next day. Everything was coming together for him. His six-month extension was justified.

When Fowler climbed into bed that night after his phone call with Sister Nylund, his voice was thick with dreamy, drowsy wonder. "Pink," he said into the darkness. "Elder Shunn, they're pink."

I swallowed the plug of nausea in my throat. I'd grown steadily more agitated over the past week, obsessing over my lack of righteousness and dreading the greater work ethic I felt sure my next companion would demand. I was a festering blob of resentment and anxiety. "Hey, Elder, I've been wondering about something."

"Hmm? What's that?"

I tried to sound only mildly curious. "Let's say I was supposed to, I don't know, perform a confirmation." Which I had, in fact, done the previous Saturday for Pam Laduke. Confirmation is an ordinance that follows shortly after baptism, wherein a priesthood holder lays his hands on the new member's head and gives her the "gift of the Holy Ghost," which is the right to receive continual guidance and inspiration from God. "But let's say I didn't exactly feel worthy to do it."

"Worthy how?" Fowler asked. "In that you're not as good a person as the one in the chair, or in that you've been doing something wrong?"

"B."

His sheets rustled. "Hmm. Well."

"I mean, would the ordinance be any good? I'd be exercising the priesthood unworthily, right? Am I jeopardizing this person's salvation?"

"No, no, God doesn't work that way." I could hear Fowler sitting up. "This person's not gonna be denied any blessings because of you. You have the priesthood. The ordinance is good."

I nodded in the dark. This was the same thing I'd been telling myself, but it was easier to believe coming from someone else. "Okay, that's cool."

"Yeah, the person on the receiving end will be fine." Fowler's voice had lost its carefree bliss. Suddenly I knew he was thinking of the following day's baptism. "But you, as a priesthood holder, exercising your power unworthily? You'd be held accountable for that."

"Okay, yeah, that's good to hear, that makes sense." I felt sorry now for bringing it up, but I didn't know how to say so.

For quite some time I listened to Fowler toss and turn.

AT LEAST FORTY PEOPLE SHOWED UP FOR BUDDY VAN RIJK'S baptismal service, which went off without a hitch—not that I felt at particular peace throughout. Fowler performed the baptism and I performed the confirmation. I could feel the grime clump onto my soul as I invoked the holy Melchizedek Priesthood and administered the ordinance. Afterward, everyone told me what a lovely blessing it had been. No one seemed to notice my filthy state but me.

That evening I answered the telephone in our cold, dark cave. "LDS missionaries. This is Elder Shunn."

"Hi, Elder Shunn. How was your baptism?"

I clenched my fist so my nails dug into my palm. "It was just fine, Sister Youtz." My voice shook. "Very spiritual."

"That's great, I'm so happy for you." The way she said it made happiness sound like a wallow in sin. "Too bad I'm not there to help you celebrate."

"Judas Proust!" I exclaimed, my skin electric with revulsion. "Do you not get it? I don't *like* you. Why would I want your help celebrating?"

She made a little hurt noise. "How do you know you don't like me when you've never even tried me?"

Teeth clenched, exhausted, I clamped a hand to my face. "Sister

Youtz," I said with all the patience I could muster, "if I were the last man on earth and you were the last woman, I swear to *God* I'd cut my dick off and eat it."

A cry of shock rattled my ear, and with a sharp clatter the connection broke.

I felt no better than I had before.

ELDER FOWLER AND I SPENT THE NEXT FEW DAYS MAKING THE rounds—dropping in on our new converts and our favorite ward members. As I drove us home one evening, Fowler broke a contemplative silence. "Shunn, what do you think would be a good job for me?"

"Huh?" I tapped the steering wheel. The thin quilt of snow on the lawns of the houses we passed cast back a pearly light from the streetlamps. "I really don't know. What are you interested in?"

"Not starving."

I swallowed. I realized I didn't know Elder Fowler well enough to give a helpful answer. "Teaching, maybe?"

"Maybe." He didn't sound enthusiastic. He stared out the side window. "Friday I'm home. January I start school, at least in theory, and I don't know *what* the hell I want to do."

"You don't have to figure it out right away," I said, but it was a lame response and I knew it.

Wednesday morning we had one last match at the racquet club before Fowler canceled his membership. Around noon, Lucas Olander knocked at our door in a suit and tie. Brother Olander was a bachelor from the ward who'd been back from his mission for ten years. He had agreed to take the afternoon and the next morning off from work to serve as my temporary companion. The White Bible forbade me from spending any time alone, even during the brief interregnum of transfers.

One round of Postum later, we lugged Fowler's two suitcases up the stairs from the pit. Everything he'd carried with him for two years was in those brittle blue boxes. Brother Olander drove us to the tiny Greyhound depot on the edge of town, just south of the Trans-Canada Highway. Fowler was going to visit some of his converts in Calgary and crash that night with Elder Breitmeyer, his old companion. Thursday would be his exit interview with President Tuttle, after which he'd enjoy a Last Supper at the mission home with the other old-timers. Friday morning he would board his plane for Utah.

We sat in plastic chairs in front of the depot, looking out at the gray, snow-dusted landscape, until the 1:05 bus materialized. Fowler stood up.

"You were a good son, Shunn," he said. "I know you'll take good care of this town."

I stood up too, in a suffocating panic. This moment had come too soon, far too soon. "I'm going to miss you, man."

Fowler scoffed. "You'll be too busy. I just have one request."

"What's that?"

He drew the battered golf ball from his pocket and passed it to me as delicately as an egg. "Carry on the line. Give me grandsons."

We hugged, thumping each other's backs. "Good luck with—you know," I said as the bus juddered to a halt. I meant Sister Nylund.

Stepping away, he touched a finger to his brow like a cowboy tipping his Stetson.

BACK AT THE PIT, I STOOD IN THE EMPTY SPACES ELDER FOWLER had occupied. I understood now why going home was called dying.

BOOK II

ELDER SKELTER

12/4/1986 - 12/31/1986

And now it came to pass when the Lamanites had found that the people of Limhi had departed out of the land by night, that they sent an army into the wilderness to pursue them.

—Mosiah 22:15, *The Book of Mormon*

CHAPTER 16

By the time the bus rolled in, the sunlight had long since died. There was no mistaking the young man who swaggered down the steps and into the light of the one streetlamp. Besides the dorky missionary haircut, he was the only one disembarking. I left the car and its heater running and hurried across the parking lot to him.

I'd been waiting for Elder Dedman on and off all day. He should have arrived at 11:30 that morning, but increasingly frustrated and apologetic phone calls from Fearing and Hardy at the mission office had informed me that Dedman missed the early bus from Canmore, then the next bus, then the bus after that. If he hadn't arrived on this one, I'd have gone back to the pit and hit the sack. Lucas Olander had regretfully returned to work after lunch that day, and I was exhausted from all the trips back and forth from the apartment to the depot, all the sitting around and waiting, all the paranoia at being alone.

"Hey, there," I said to my new senior companion, extending a hand and trying to act cheerful. "I'm Elder Shunn. Welcome to Brooks."

He looked me over without moving, hands in the pockets of his parka, as still as a statue. His eyes regarded me with no emotion.

At last he took my hand, pumping it once, firmly. "Drew Dedman," he said, his breath rising like a plume of exhaust. "So you're Elder Shunn, eh? Do a lot of people *shun* you?"

"Yeah, good one." My patience and composure were already strained. "Never heard that one before."

I helped him retrieve his luggage, which the driver had just freed from the belly of the bus. As we carried the bags to the car, Dedman asked, "Is there anywhere to get some food in this town? I'm starving."

"Sure, whatever you want."

"A cheeseburger would be good."

"I think we can dig up one of those."

As we pulled out of the parking lot, I reminded myself that my library copy of *A Planet Called Treason* was stashed under the front seat. "So, I guess you had a little trouble making the bus today."

Dedman turned his head and arched an eyebrow. "I didn't have any trouble. I caught the right bus."

"Elder, it's ten o'clock. I thought you were supposed to be here before noon."

"Right, sure. That would have meant catching a bus this morning at *five*." His voice was tight with restrained fury. "If flippin' Prez wants me to leave my best area three weeks before Christmas, he can dang well give me time to make the rounds and say goodbye. Anyway, it's transfer day. It's not like we were going to get any work done."

The chill of his anger made me flinch.

Over burgers at a late-night diner, Dedman rhapsodized in dry, flat tones about the town of Canmore, nestled near Banff in the Canadian Rockies. To hear him tell it, Canmore was a magical hamlet where the skies were always blue, the font was always full, and the members were always cool, a town whose every daughter had a pure, unrequitable crush on the missionaries.

"Also," he said, "cross-country season is just getting started."

I listened without interrupting as I sucked down a big chocolate shake. I knew that Brooks must seem like a wretched hive of scum and villainy by comparison, but I hoped a few days here would bring him around.

At the apartment, I dragged one of Dedman's heavy bags down the concrete stairwell while he followed with the other.

"Welcome to the pit," I said, snapping on the living room light.

He entered and glanced around the room with distaste. "I always thought that was just a figure of speech."

Carrying his suitcase into the bedroom, I said, "We've got all the amenities—gas, electricity, hot and cold running mice . . ."

Dedman hadn't followed me into the bedroom, so I went back into the living room only to find him missing. His other suitcase sat in the middle of the floor and the outside door was closed.

"Elder?" I said, absurdly convinced I was looking at the room the wrong way and that if I tilted my head he'd appear. "Elder Dedman?"

Nothing. I opened the front door and poked my head out. "El—?"

"Yaaah!" cried the batlike marauder who leapt down the stairwell. I shrieked like a little girl and stumbled backward into the living room.

Elder Dedman landed at the bottom of the stairs already doubled over with laughter. "Holy heck, Shunn, you should see yourself!" he cackled. "You almost wet your panties!"

"Yeah, very funny. What a scream." In a fruitless attempt to shame him, I hauled his second suitcase into the bedroom.

Dedman closed the front door and joined me. "This is my bed?" he asked, pointing to the one nearer the door.

"Yep," I said, sitting down on my new bed, which until yesterday had been Elder Fowler's. "It's got fresh sheets on it and everything."

Dedman prodded the mattress. "It's probably the sucky bed, right?"

"They're both pretty good," I huffed.

He put his hands in his back pockets and strolled around the room on a short inspection tour that ended at my dresser. I'd recently had Brother Whitaker enlarge one of the photographs of Katrina and me at the airport. Dedman picked it up in its new chrome frame.

"Is this your sister? She's cute."

"That's my fiancée," I said, my voice squeaking.

"Tell me again how long you've been out?"

"Three months."

"That explains it then."

"Explains what?"

He waved the picture. "Why you still *have* this."

"What are you talking about?"

He put it back and shrugged, leaning a casual elbow on the dresser. "Six months to a year's when it usually goes down. I've been out fourteen months myself. Luckily I knew better than to leave a woman behind, or I'd be living in Dear John City too by now. See ya, wouldn't wanna be ya."

I shook my head. "That's not going to happen."

"Yeah, that's what they all say." Dedman studied the photo again. "*Dang*, she's fine. The finer they are, the faster they fall. Who was your trainer again? Fowler?"

"Yeah."

"*That* horndog," he said sadly. "He doesn't know what's-her-name's address, does he?"

"Why?" I asked, folding my arms.

"I'm just thinking about Elder Snyder, this guy from Seattle I knew when I was a greenie. The poor schmuck. I'm from Tacoma, so he kind of took me under his wing. I liked him, but he was this bitter old fart, all because of his woman. Six months out—only *six months*—was when he got the wedding invitation in the mail. Not even a Dear John, just a wedding invitation. That *was* the Dear John." He sighed. "That was bad enough by itself. No jury would have convicted him, if you know what I mean. But can you guess who the groom was?"

"Not a clue. Who?"

"Elder Sandoval, that's who. His *trainer*. I guess ol' Sandy took a shine to the chick in Snyder's pictures. He must've copied down her address from the mail, then looked her up the second he got to BYU. The rest, as they say, is history."

"Well, that was quick work." Flimsy mental dikes held my panic at bay. Elder Fowler already had a girlfriend, I reminded myself. Katrina would never look at him twice.

"Quick, sure, but not like *my* technique." Dedman picked up Katrina's photo again, addressing it like Yorick's skull. "I call it the Liquid-Plumr strategy—work fast and don't leave a ring."

"Ew." I wasn't sure if he meant actual sex, but either way I was appalled.

"Well, hey, it's been a long day. I better hit the sack." He put the photo back and started undressing. "It's almost midnight, and we start tracting at nine-thirty sharp."

I did get to sleep, but it took me a while. What on earth was I in for?

As good as his word, Elder Dedman led me out the door at precisely at 9:30 the next morning. We did without companionship study, though. When I'd broached the subject after ninety minutes of personal study, Dedman only glanced up from the handheld electronic football game he'd been playing ever since breakfast and said, "I think we'll skip it this morning."

I drove us to a street of drab tract houses where straggling seedlings drooped in a desolate file between the sidewalk and the curb. I opened the hatch and retrieved three copies of the Book of Mormon. Elder Dedman stopped me before I could slam it shut.

"Bring more."

"More?"

"Bring ten."

"*Ten?*"

He smiled at my incredulity. "Did I stutter, Elder? We're going to place ten copies of the Book of Mormon today."

Maybe Dedman's faith was stronger than mine. Maybe he knew some infallible door approach I hadn't learned yet. I just hoped I wouldn't find myself still tracting at 9:30 that night.

"Okay," I said, digging out more books. "Show me how it's done."

At our first door, Dedman took a book from the pile I carried like an awkward stack of pies. A worrisomely cheerful woman in a pink business suit answered. I expected some grand oration on my companion's part, an irresistible spiel to match the boldness of his prediction. Instead he proffered a rather bland rendition of the same door approach Elder Fowler and I had used, never relaxing his vague scowl. The woman's unsurprising response was chirpy disinterest.

"Oh for one," I said as I followed him self-consciously across the lawn to the next porch. Elder Fowler would never have taken a shortcut over someone's grass.

"O ye of little faith. Your door."

On the porch of a whitewashed cracker box no different from any other on the block, I drew out the golf ball, bobbling and almost spilling my books in the process. I opened the screen and rapped on peeling wood. We waited. I knocked again. No one answered.

"Looks like no one's home," said Dedman. I started to turn away, but he stopped me with a hand on my shoulder. "Hang on."

He took the first book from my stack, leaned it against the base of the door, and closed the rusty screen. As I watched in disbelief, he took a blank callback card from his pocket and jotted down the address.

"That's one," he said.

I hurried to keep up with him as he crossed the grass to the next house, dumbstruck. "Hey, what do you call that?" I managed to squeak, indignant.

He stopped and turned, one eyebrow raised. "A book placement."

"That's not a book placement."

"I *placed* a book right where the occupant will find it. That was definitely a book *placement*."

"Not according to the White Bible," I insisted.

"The White Bible's not the most practical guide to life I've ever read." He tossed this over his shoulder as he continued to the next porch, never raising his voice.

That was the way the next forty-five minutes proceeded. We foisted not a single volume of scripture upon the good people who answered our knocks, but every unopened door received its own complimentary copy of the Book of Mormon.

When we ran out of books, Elder Dedman led the way back to the car. I thought we'd retrieve another stack, and I wondered what we'd do the next day when, at this rate, our supply of books was depleted. But Dedman went straight to the passenger door and waited for me to unlock it. The sun peeked out through a rent in the clouds, and the wind ruffled his dirty-blond, center-parted hair.

"Where are we going?"

Dedman shrugged. "Wherever we want. We're done."

"Done?" I shook my head. "We've barely even started."

"We've placed ten books."

"Those weren't solid placements."

"How do you know? How can you judge that?"

"Because—because we didn't even talk to the people at those houses! We just left books inside their screen doors!"

"Wait," Dedman said, tilting his head, "you're saying you can judge those people because we *didn't* talk to them? I don't get it. Doesn't that sound a little backward to you?"

I wanted to stamp my feet. "Judas Proust! You know what I'm talking about."

"I have no idea what you're talking about. All I know is we're done tracting for the week."

"The *week*? We still have eleven hours to do this week."

"We've placed our ten books for the week. We're done."

I looked away and back, at the trees, at the houses. "Those weren't real placements, and you know it. But even if they were, we couldn't quit just because we got to ten."

"Why not? That's our goal."

"Our goal is ten books *and* eighteen hours. Not one or the other."

Dedman folded his arms, his blank face inscrutable. "I've been doing this for fourteen months. Are you telling me I've been doing it wrong all that time? That my trainer taught me *wrong?*"

This was an argument I could not win. "You know how it's supposed to be done," I said sullenly.

"I know I'm the senior companion and you're the junior companion. If you remember that, we'll get along fine. If you don't, I doubt you're going to like me much. Now where are the keys?"

Sighing, I fished them out of my pocket and handed them over. Dedman went to the driver's door and let himself in, then unlocked mine from the inside.

He started the car. "So, where's the nearest bowling alley? This town must have one, right?"

CHAPTER 17

JOSEPH MAY HAVE BEEN CALLOW, IMPERIOUS, AND UNWILLING TO accept criticism or blame, but he certainly did not lack ambition. Almost from the start of his prophetic career, his goal was the establishment of a mighty kingdom of God upon the earth.

His regard for his own stature as an arbiter of God's word was no less robust. After unleashing his "lost" testament of Jesus Christ upon the world, he turned his attention to the Old and New Testaments. In June 1830, he launched into what he thought of as a new translation of the Bible, though in fact it was more of a revision.

Joseph had become convinced that many "plain and precious" truths had vanished from that book over the millennia. "I believe the Bible as it read when it came from the pen of the original writers," he recorded in his *History of the Church*. "Ignorant translators, careless transcribers, or designing and corrupt priests have committed many errors." In this new translation, he set about correcting those errors.

He undertook nothing so prosaic as a survey of the extant Hebrew and Greek source manuscripts. Rather, writes Richard Lyman Bushman in *Rough Stone Rolling*, Joseph "work[ed] his way through the [English] text, straightening out contradictions, correcting errors, and adding lost portions. . . . He sat with a large King James Version, marking passages and dictating changes to Sidney Rigdon and other scribes." Gone was the theater of his Book of Mormon dictation. He had thrown off his seer stones like yesterday's training wheels; the full flower of his translating powers was upon him, divine edits flowing directly into his heart and mind unmediated by magical gadgetry.

Often, his revisions amounted to no more than a few words salted in to redress what he saw as problematic passages. The story of Lot offering up his daughters to placate an angry mob, for instance, is rendered more palatable to Joseph's delicate sensibilities with the addition of a few deft phrases. In fact, he completely reverses the dynamic of the scene, turning Lot from a craven pushover to a mensch. His version of Genesis 19:8 reads in part as follows, with the most crucial additions italicized:

> Behold now, I have two daughters which have not known man; let me, I pray you, *plead with my brethren that I may not* bring them out unto you; and ye shall *not* do unto them as seemeth good in your eyes . . .

In some cases Joseph felt inspired to add entire chapters of his own devising to the Holy Writ, as when he expanded a few throwaway verses mentioning a prophet named Enoch into the long, involved story of a city so righteous it was lifted by God into heaven. In the last days, according to this tale, the city of Enoch would descend again to the earth to mingle and rejoice with the inhabitants of the New Jerusalem. So would commence the Second Coming of Christ, and one thousand years of peace under his personal reign.

This was Joseph's true and most fascinating métier, moralism leavened with pure cosmic science fiction—as would become more and more apparent in the years to come.

THIS WORK OF REVISION PROCEEDED IN FITS AND BURSTS ALL THE way into 1833, when, after nearly three years of labor, Joseph judged his translation complete. Interestingly, the revised text was never published in full during his lifetime—and, curiously, the church has since canonized only select bits. And while the Joseph Smith Translation (as it is known) was never a pillar of my Sunday school education, it played a much more significant role in my seminary classes.

For Mormons, seminary is not the priesthood training-ground it is for Catholics, but rather a paraeducational system designed to give high school students their daily dose of church doctrine. State law in Utah and Idaho allows students to leave school grounds for one class period of religious instruction per day, which is why you'll find small church-owned schoolhouses adjacent to many high school campuses. In other states, Mormon students might attend early morning seminary at a church meetinghouse or even someone's home before the start of the school day.

The four-year curriculum includes a year apiece on the Old Testament, the New Testament, the Book of Mormon, and church history. During our church history year, we studied many of the incidents I've written about here, though from a standpoint that held Joseph and the early Saints rather more innocent in most areas of conflict than objective history would tend to support.

During our Old Testament year, we had frequent cause to dip into the Joseph Smith Translation for clarification of doctrines that otherwise were too complex or contradictory to be plainly comprehended. Joseph's improved Bible gave us the inside scoop on our pre-mortal existence with God, the proper transmission of priesthood power from one man to the next, and the practice of baptism in the millennia before Christ. It taught us that the replacement tablets God gave Moses on Mount Sinai contained only a watered-down version of the law from the original tablets, as the Israelites had become too weak and debased to keep a higher law. And it served up a startling prophecy from the mouth of the Biblical Joseph—he of the many-colored coat—in which God promises to raise up a "choice seer" in the last days. "[H]is name shall be called Joseph," says God, "and it shall be after the name of his father; and he shall be like unto you; for the thing which the Lord shall bring forth by his hand shall bring my people unto salvation."

We leaned on the JST in our New Testament year as well, to straighten out much that was muddy in the writings of Matthew and Paul. But despite the academic trappings of these studies, I remember not taking seminary very seriously. I rarely missed class, and my grades were fine, but since none of it would show up on my actual high school transcript, I didn't feel a need to try my absolute hardest.

One Wednesday afternoon near the end of my senior year, some friends and I ditched school to see *Indiana Jones and the Temple of Doom* on its opening day. Seminary was one of the classes I missed. I figured it was close enough to graduation that my absence would be overlooked, if not excused.

I liked my seminary teacher, Brother Pugh, quite a bit, as did most of his students. He was handsome, goofy, and charming, related well to teenagers, and was even something of a role model to many of us (though I doubt a career in the Church Educational System was high on anyone's list of ambitions). I thought I was a favored student of his too, but when I picked up my report card the next week it included a handwritten note that stabbed me to the heart:

Which is more important—Indiana Jones or Jesus Christ?

THIS WAS THE KIND OF FALSE DICHOTOMY THAT JOSEPH SMITH never worried about. His life took place at the intersection of Indiana Jones and Jesus Christ, packing in more unholy adventure than either one could have handled alone.

Take, for instance, Zion's Camp. On May 5, 1834, Joseph set out from Kirtland on a secret commando mission. Well, it was *supposed* to be secret, but it's not so easy to go incognito when you're leading a troop of two hundred armed men on an 800-mile march.

The displaced Missouri Mormons, now refugees across the river in Clay County, were seeking legal redress for their expulsion from Jackson County. Wider public sentiment was on their side, and Governor Daniel Dunklin's support made it seem likely they'd get their land back. Dunklin had the state militia standing by to escort the Mormons back to their homes when the court proceedings were settled.

At the height of the persecution, two prominent converts, Parley P. Pratt and Lyman Wight, had raced to Kirtland to urge Joseph into action on behalf of the Missouri Mormons. Egged on by his inner circle, Joseph at last issued a revelation that an army of five hundred men should be raised to march to the defense of God's chosen people—and if not five hundred then three hundred, and if not three hundred then no fewer than a hundred. What imaginative youth, after all, could resist the romance of marching at the head of his own army?

As it turned out, recruitment yielded only two hundred men, but that was sufficient to give the mission the green light. Zion's Camp, as they were called, set out armed with "[o]ld muskets, rifles, pistols, rusty swords and butcher knives," according to one account. Joseph's intent was to pass his soldiers off as settlers en route to the frontier lands, but no one was fooled. Word of the march reached Missouri well ahead of the marchers.

Governor Dunklin had been negotiating to establish a federal armory in Jackson County to protect the Mormons, but the news of Zion's Camp threw that plan into disarray. The old settlers preemptively burned all the abandoned Mormon homes that weren't already destroyed so there'd be no place for the refugees to return to. By the time Zion's Camp actually arrived on the scene, Dunklin had judged repatriating the Mormons to Jackson County unworkable.

Worse still, four separate counties were mobilizing their militias to meet the Mormon threat. Zion's Camp had already weathered hunger, privation, and mutinous insubordination on the road. Now it was obvious that if it came to an actual battle they were going to have their asses handed to them. It was time for another revelation, this one stating that the time for the redemption of Zion had not yet arrived, and that the march to Missouri had been a trial of faith. The Mormon soldiers must now return to Kirtland, where God had "prepared a great endowment and blessing to be poured out upon them."

But the trial of faith was not over. Cholera had by then struck Zion's Camp. At first Joseph tried to heal the afflicted by the laying on of hands, but he quickly realized that was fruitless. His excuse was that God had inflicted the disease upon the camp, and that if he continued to try to oppose it he would die himself.

By the time the rampage was over, fourteen of his men were dead.

IF IT SEEMS THAT NONE OF JOSEPH'S FOLLOWERS WERE BOTHERED by his penchant for making things up as he went along, rest assured that such was not the case. For some, like my ancestor Edward Partridge, the moment of clarity was so sharply rebuked by the prophet that it never recurred. Others took much longer sabbaticals from belief. Martin Harris, Oliver Cowdery, and David Whitmer all left the church over differences with Joseph, though Martin and Oliver would both be rebaptized late in their lives.

Still others fell away and came to doubt only after suffering insult or embarrassment at the hands of the prophet. A man named Doctor Hurlbut—"Doctor" was his actual first name—was excommunicated by Joseph in 1833 for making vulgar suggestions to a young Mormon woman. Publicly humiliated, the enterprising Hurlbut parlayed his notoriety into a spot on the regional lecture circuit, delivering anti-Mormon polemics to crowds in Pennsylvania and New York.

At a stop in Palmyra, Hurlbut met several people who recalled Joseph vividly from his money-digging days. He collected sworn affidavits from former neighbors, fifteen in all, testifying to the Smith family's low character and began displaying them at his events.

When Hurlbut arrived in the Kirtland area to lecture, Sidney Rigdon called him a pawn of the rival Campbellite preachers, and called Hurlbut's wife their whore. (Sidney had not been quite the same since taking blows to the head in the mob attack two years earlier.) Joseph joined the fray, and their open war of words escalated to the point where Hurlbut, apoplectic, swore he would see the prophet dead.

Unwilling to take chances with his own safety, Joseph filed for a restraining order against Hurlbut and won. Disgraced again and now forbidden to speak against the Mormons, Hurlbut was forced to give up the lecture circuit and sell his affidavits, which newspaper editor Eber D. Howe published in 1834 as part of the archaically titled exposé *Mormonism Unvailed*.

That book is generally considered our earliest example of anti-Mormon literature, a genre that thrives even today—and which faithful members are encouraged to avoid at all cost. Of course, the line between thoughtful critique and hateful screed can be fuzzy for many Mormons, as it often depends on the observer's level of comfort with material that might contradict the church's teachings or its sanitized version of history. And as church leaders have made very clear over the years, the truth should never be allowed to get in the way of a good doctrine.

At a symposium of church educators in 1981, apostle Boyd K. Packer famously declared, "There is a temptation for the writer or the teacher of Church history to want to tell everything, whether it is worthy or faith promoting or not. Some things that are true are not very useful."

Not very useful if you want to paint Joseph Smith as a genuine prophet, that is. When that's the goal, actual documentary evidence that does not support the thesis becomes secondary, even suspect.

This is why Joseph hit back so hard against Doctor Hurlbut and others like him. Even that early, the prophet knew that to control his church he needed to control his own narrative. And as even he must have recognized after disasters like Jackson County and Zion's Camp, that narrative had serious problems.

CHAPTER 18

Late on a Tuesday night Dedman and I let ourselves into the church. Elder Fowler had finagled a key from the bishop before Pam Laduke's baptism, and we had somehow managed to forget to give it back. Christmas was just over a week away, and the blobby shadow of the fir tree in the foyer, its lights turned off for the night, seemed a fitting token of the dismal holiday season I was having. I pushed my way into the chapel with my sheet music under my arm, not waiting to see if Elder Dedman would follow.

Every passing day had deepened my conviction that I'd fallen in with one of the mission's reigning buckets. I didn't know if Dedman had been like this before Brooks or if this was some protest against an unwelcome transfer, but either way the outcome was the same. My companion had no sense of shame, no fear of punishment, and no desire to do missionary work.

After our first morning of tracting, Dedman had dropped even that slim pretense. Now we didn't bother going through the motions, and what resistance I offered to his slacking was token at best. We did nothing.

Actually, we *did* plenty, just not proselytizing. I could never guess where each new day might take us. My job, Dedman had made clear, was to shut up and tag along on whatever outing struck his fancy. We spent hours in the Badlands, hiking through old dinosaur digs off the designated trails. We explored the 70-year-old ruins of the Brooks Aqueduct, one of the largest irrigation projects of its day. And we returned time and again to the same old haunts—the video arcade, the pool hall, the bowling alley.

I had always loved bowling, but I hated doing it in my whites in that smoke-filled cavern. "What if someone sees us here?" I once asked Dedman, paranoid.

"What if they do?"

"Well, what if they smell all this smoke on our clothing?"

Dedman looked at me like I was mentally deficient. "We say we've been teaching a smoker. Dang, Shunn, use your head."

Many days, after sleeping to ten or eleven, we didn't dress in our pross clothes at all. Scripture study went by the wayside. Some evenings we did still drop in on my favorite families, like the Whitakers or the Montgomerys, but they were far less welcoming toward Dedman than they'd been with Fowler. When he asked them to refer us to their non-member friends, the response was inevitably awkward and vague.

Though I was never alone, I'd never felt more lonely. Dedman didn't talk about himself except to tell me about rad pranks he and his buddies had pulled back home, or to further effuse about Canmore. He brushed off any suggestions that we might go do some tracting with countersuggestions of activities that would be *way* more fun. I never considered ratting him out, though, because I felt complicit in everything we did.

With more time free for fretting over Katrina, my ache for her became a sucking chest wound. I had asked her not to call me since Dedman's arrival—first, because I didn't want to give him more ammunition for torturing me, second, to atone in some small measure for the way I was helping to kill missionary work in Brooks, and third, to remove any thoughts in her mind that I was a chronic rule-breaker.

We had been taught that we would be happiest as missionaries when we were working the hardest. I don't think I'd go *that* far, but not working at all had certainly released whatever brakes were keeping me from plunging into full-blown depression. More than that, even, I was drowning in guilt and paranoia. There I was, robbing God of the labor he had sent me to perform. Not only that, I was flouting the rules so openly it would be a miracle if no one noticed and reported us to President Tuttle. I was constantly looking over my shoulder when we were out and about. All this had taken less than two weeks.

The one thing I enjoyed and which I could talk Dedman into letting me do was playing the baby grand at the church. Among the few personal items I'd brought with me into the field were my favorite books of piano music. Sometimes Dedman would sit in one of the back pews listening to me play as he fiddled with his football game or thumbed through an auto magazine, but that particular night he had flopped down on one of the couches out in the foyer. I was startled to look up from the keyboard after fifteen sausage-fingered minutes of Liszt and realize there was someone else sitting in the shadowy recesses of the chapel.

"Hello?" I said. I had turned on only the lights above the dais, which left me exposed and mostly blind as I peered into the gloom.

The indistinct figure rose and started down the aisle. "Hello, Elder Shunn." I recognized Brother Alvarez's precise diction. "I was doing some work in the bishop's office, and I ran into your companion as I was leaving. I hope I didn't startle you."

"A little."

"You know how much I love your playing." He climbed the steps to the dais and rested his forearms on the side of the piano. He wore, as usual, an immaculately cut suit, this one a dark, rich blue. His smile was reserved. "Late for you elders to be out, though."

"Long day today," I said cautiously. I could never tell quite how to read Brother Alvarez. "I needed to unwind a little before bed."

His eyebrows drew together. "Elder Shunn . . . are you doing all right here in Brooks?"

My stomach clenched. Two dozen indiscretions flooded my memory, most significantly having overslept on Sunday and missed sacrament meeting. "The work's a little slow now, I guess."

"No, Elder, I mean personally. Are you happy here? Do you like the people? Do you enjoy the work?"

"I'm a little homesick." The backs of my eyes burned. "But that has nothing to do with Brooks."

He nodded and looked down at his hands. When he looked up again, it was with an expression of optimistic resolve.

"Our Christmas service is this Sunday. I'm in charge of arranging the program. I wondered if you might not be willing to play a musical number for us."

I swallowed, a grin stretching my cheeks. "I'd love to. But I don't have anything Christmas-y in my repertoire."

"That's fine, Elder. Whatever you choose to play, I'm sure it will be a beautiful addition to the program."

I knew exactly what I wanted to perform—the same Debussy piece I'd been playing the first time Brother Alvarez startled me in the chapel.

I started rehearsing the moment he left. I did it with more enthusiasm than I'd felt for anything in days.

SUNDAY MORNING, DEDMAN AND I ARRIVED AT CHURCH FORTY minutes before sacrament meeting. It was the earliest we'd been up in two weeks, and we were two big bundles of nerves. Before he'd approached me, Brother Alvarez had dragooned Elder Dedman into preparing a talk for the service, a task no missionary could easily refuse.

We both went straight to the dais. Dedman flung himself down in one of the choir seats and buried himself in his notes. I propped up the piano's lid, opened the fallboard, and arranged my sheet music.

There were seven or eight people in the chapel already—Brother Alvarez reviewing his own notes in a seat behind the podium, the ward clerk arranging his roll books, a couple of younger teenage priesthood holders preparing the sacrament, and a scattering of early arrivals—but I figured I could get two run-throughs in while the place was still relatively empty.

I sat, lifted my hands, and began. The music felt *right*, right from the start. Despite the complicated arpeggios, each finger knew exactly where to be at what time without my having to think, letting my hands roll up and down the keys as smoothly as if they were on wheels. And my heart rolled right along with them, buoyed by the river of notes, as light as it had been in weeks.

So consumed was I by the music that I didn't notice Bishop Neuwirth standing at my shoulder until he spoke. "Is this what you're planning to play for us today, Elder?"

He startled me so badly that I laid down a line of clams. I didn't turn to look at him as I tried to recover, an effort that took all my concentration. When I was back on track I forced out a gruff affirmative.

The bishop leaned in over my shoulder, peering at the sheet music and crowding my right arm. "When exactly was this piece written?"

I huffed and stopped playing. "Eighteen eighty-eight," I said frostily. The date was printed clearly beneath the title on the sheet music.

"Eighteen eighty-eight," Bishop Neuwirth repeated, shaking his head. "No, I'm afraid that's not going to work."

Stunned, I turned my head. "Excuse me?"

The bishop rocked back, hands clasped behind his back. "The General Handbook is very specific," he said casually. "Except for certain church-approved pieces, musical numbers performed in sacrament meeting must be at least one hundred years old. You'll have to play something else."

"I don't *have* anything else." A disconnected panic made my hands and my face tingle. "This is what I've been practicing."

"Then play something from the hymnbook," he suggested in a helpful tone. "You can play hymns, right?"

I groped for words. "I can *accompany* anything in the hymn book, but they're not good piano pieces on their own."

"Well, then I don't know what we're going to do." He sounded maddeningly reasonable.

"I've played this a hundred times in church. No one's had a problem with it before."

He folded his arms. "If other bishops don't want to enforce the guidelines, that's their choice. But that's not the way we do things in this ward."

I hated his fussy little mustache and his stupid tweed jacket. "This piece of music is *ninety-eight* years old." I could hear my voice growing shrill. I saw Brother Alvarez heading our way, and Elder Dedman too. "What, in two more years it magically stops being inappropriate?"

Bishop Neuwirth squinted at me in a manner entirely unlike Clint Eastwood. "Elder," he said even more quietly, "I won't allow my daughter go on a date even one day before she turns sixteen. Why? Because that's the guideline the Brethren have given us."

"Excuse me, gentlemen," said Alvarez, laying a hand on the bishop's shoulder. "What seems to be the problem?"

Bishop Neuwirth cleared his throat. If Alvarez wore his Mormonism like an elegant suit, then the bishop wore his like an accountant's green eyeshade and sleeve garters. "I was just pointing out to the elder here that he can't play music under a hundred years old."

Alvarez raised an eyebrow. "Unless the bishop gives his approval."

Bishop Neuwirth coughed a little. "Well, yes. But I'm not familiar with this—" He leaned over me and peered again at the sheet music. "This Duh-*buss*-ee."

"Debussy," said Alvarez gently. "And to be honest with you, Bishop, I was quite looking forward to hearing this number in sacrament meeting. I find it entirely peaceful and reverent, don't you agree?"

The bishop nodded slowly, eyes narrowed.

"So there won't be a problem if Elder Shunn plays this number?"

"All right, yes. I suppose that'll be fine."

Elder Dedman, on the other side of me, touched my elbow. "Smoke break?" he whispered.

Fighting back tears, I nodded gratefully and stood up, shoving my shaking hands into my pockets.

"We'll be back in a few minutes," Dedman said, and I trailed him down the steps from the dais.

When I looked back through a watery veil before exiting the chapel, Brother Alvarez was explaining something to the bishop quietly and furiously, very close to his ear.

IN THE MEN'S ROOM, I WIPED MY EYES AND TRIED TO STILL THE ANGER quivering in my hands. Elder Dedman watched me in the mirror with concern, an emotion I hadn't imagined was part of his repertoire.

He handed me another dampened paper towel. "Are you going to be okay?"

"Yeah, I think so." I plastered the cool towel to my forehead and squinted at myself in the mirror. "Thanks."

Dedman leaned back against one of the sinks, shaking his head. "Man, that guy's a jerk. I don't care if he *is* a bishop. He ought to get punched in the nose. Someone at least ought to give him a swirlie. If he walked in here right now, I'd do it, too."

Picturing Dedman forcing the bishop's head down a toilet, I couldn't help but snort a little. "I don't think he has enough hair."

"It'd work. He combs it over. He'd end up with this one long twist sticking up from over his ear."

I laughed. "Can I be the one to flush?"

"Be my guest."

After another couple of minutes I felt composed enough to return to the chapel. Leaving it, I'd only had a companion. Now, going back with Dedman's hand on my shoulder, I felt like I had an ally.

I DON'T THINK DEDMAN COULD TELL HOW CLOSE I WAS TO A MAJOR breakdown. *I* certainly couldn't, and I was the one clinging to sanity by my fingernails. Brother Alvarez had some inkling, I'm sure, but there wasn't much he could do about it.

Of course, my new sense of camaraderie with Dedman didn't stop me from wincing during the service when he strayed from his assigned topic, "What Christmas Means to Me," and brazenly called the ward to repentance for not supporting our proselytizing efforts.

But at least it was an improvement.

CHAPTER 19

"Now *these* are some impressive numbers," said Elder Tim-
mons that night on the phone. During transfers Elder Garrett had
been promoted to zone leader and moved to Lethbridge, with Tim-
mons brought in to take his place. I didn't know enough about him
to have formed an opinion yet, but he had to be better than Garrett.
"Hang in there, Shunn, because with stats like these you'll be racking
up the dunks again in no time."

The numbers I had just given him were, of course, outright fiction.
Dedman and I had joked that we should start reporting a new set of
stats, including games bowled, high score at Tempest, and hours overslept.

"We'll hang in there, or we'll hang separately."

"Oh, and don't forget zone conference tomorrow. Be at the Lethbridge stake center by three. I hear there might be a visit from Santa."

Zone conference. Like a district meeting, only more so. And with
the added attraction of individual priesthood interviews with President Tuttle.

"Wouldn't miss it."

I hung up the phone feeling drained. With Elder Fowler, at least
our inflated numbers had some basis in reality, even if the expected

standard was all but impossible to achieve. Now there was no way around the fact that I was out-and-out lying. It felt like I was paying out rope and waiting for it to hang us.

I went to the end table and shuffled through the half-dozen small Christmas presents clustered around the base of the lamp. Most were from my family, but even the sweet tag on the one from Katrina was more salt than salve to my wounds.

I sat down on the floor. "Hey, Dedman. Can I ask you a question?"

Dedman glanced up from his comic book. The mask was back in place, and had been ever since our moment in the mens' room at the church. "Hmm?"

I didn't want to come straight out with what was on my mind. "I was just wondering. If we got caught, you know, with all the stuff we've been doing, what do you think Prez would do?"

Dedman looked at me blankly. "Have we been doing anything wrong?"

"Come on, aren't we a little beyond that? How much trouble would we be in?"

"Flip, Shunn." He sighed and put the comic book down. "I'd probably be in more trouble than you would. I might get busted to junior companion, one or the other of us might get transferred, it's hard to say. We'd definitely get ranked on by Prez, though. He'd rank on us hard."

"But we wouldn't get sent home."

"Sent home? No, I doubt it."

"I guess it's kind of hard to get sent home."

"Yeah, you need to screw up big time."

"Whew, good," I said, feigning relief. A dishonorable discharge would not do *any* of my relationships back home any favors, but I did find myself more and more preoccupied with fantasies of getting sent home in ways no one could blame me for. I didn't think misbehaving in some eccentric but ultimately harmless fashion, like Klinger bucking for a Section 8 on *M*A*S*H*, would work. Maybe if I fell and broke my leg badly enough to need months of physical therapy. Or, better yet, if I got cancer. I could go home, get radiation and chemo, and beat it, coming out the other end as everybody's brave, beloved hero . . .

"Tell you a story," Dedman went on. "I heard about this elder in Tahiti or Samoa or someplace—friend of someone here in the mission. This guy wanted to go home *so bad*. He would've just hopped a plane, but their president kept everyone's passports locked up in a drawer. That way you couldn't run off without talking to him first."

"Is that even legal? Wouldn't you need your passport if you got stopped by the police?"

"Who knows if they even *have* police in Tahiti. The point is, this guy was so miserable he finally paid some whore all his rent money to bone him out of his misery. Went to his prez, confessed, and before you know it he was exed." Dedman shook his head in disbelief. "Sure, he got to go home, but he lost his temple recommend *and* his eternal salvation. A package deal, all for two minutes of hide-the-salami."

"That's horrifying," I said, hugging my knees. I glanced up at the dark casement windows with a shiver, as if hell lay just beyond them, closing in. But what I found truly horrifying was that I could understand why the elder had done what he did.

Dedman jumped up from the armchair, suddenly all energy. "Flip, Shunn, why are we sitting here talking? It's been a rotten day, this place is claustrophobic, and you could use some cheering up."

I wasn't sure I wanted to be cheered up. "What do you have in mind?"

He looked around the tiny apartment. "Well, here it is almost Christmas and we're hardly in the spirit at all. Get your snow gear on. I think we need a tree."

WHEN WE GOT IN THE CAR I THOUGHT WE MIGHT BE HEADING TO A tree farm or Canadian Tire, but Dedman drove us only five or six blocks before parking near the mouth of an alley.

"Where are we going?"

"Shhh. Follow me." He turned off the overhead light, exited, and closed his door gently. I did the same.

When he duckwalked down the alley like a suburban commando, I mimicked him as best I could. We kept to the muddy ruts torn in the blanket of snow by knobby winter tires. To our right, behind wooden fences, lay the backs of slumbering houses. To our left was a chain-link fence, and behind that a line of tall, shaggy spruces that bounded the grounds of a grade school. A bright, gibbous moon had just risen.

Dedman stopped far down the alley in a zone of relative darkness, away from any streetlights. Crouching in the weeds and dirty snow beside the chain-link fence, he whispered, "Hold it so it doesn't rattle."

"Hold what?"

In answer he stood, latched onto the fence, and swarmed up it. The sound was like a million sleigh bells jingling. I quickly hooked my gloved fingers through the fence and strained to hold it taut. I expected lights to flick on any moment in the houses behind us, shotguns pumped and ready for a Santa Claus invasion.

The fence was at least eight feet tall. Dedman dropped lightly down the far side, landing in the pristine margin of snow between it and the closely spaced spruces.

He motioned me up. "Your turn."

I seized the fence with both hands, as high up as I could reach. My boots were too big to get a toehold in the links, but after half a minute of huffing and puffing and several queasy seconds of instability at the top, I made it over. I stood stock-still as the rattling of the fence faded out, conscious of the clear night, the bright moonlight, and my own visibility.

I turned toward my companion, but he had vanished.

I pushed my way between the two nearest trees. Their lowest boughs overlapped, clutching at my legs. The scent of broken pine needles stung my nose.

"Elder Dedman!" I hissed as I emerged into the broad, ghostly schoolyard.

A hand touched my shoulder. *"Boo!"*

I yelped as Dedman materialized from the shadows beside me. He shushed me with a delighted grin on his face. "Keep it down, Shunn. You'll get us busted."

"Then don't *do* that. What are we doing here anyway?"

Dedman pointed at the spruce that had concealed him, which had to be twelve feet tall. "Getting a tree."

"Oh, right. Because *that'll* fit in the pit."

He drew his hunting knife and raised it in front of my face. It gleamed in the moonlight, a wicked thing with toothy serrations on the spine of its six-inch blade and a hilt wrapped in rawhide. Dedman, who always carried it when we hiked, called it his coyote-sticker.

"You just stand guard," he ordered. With that, he sheathed the knife and clambered *into* the tree.

It was the platonic ideal of a Christmas tree. Its bushy boughs tapered in a perfect cone from the ground all the way to its apex. Had you draped it in tinsel and capped it with an angel, there'd have been no grander tree in town. Dedman wriggled in toward the trunk and picked his way up from there. About three feet from the top, his head popped suddenly into view. That's where he started sawing at the trunk with the knife's serrated spine. The loud rasp seemed to carry for miles. The teeth weren't made for cutting wood, and the job took forever.

At one point I spotted a distant police car prowling past the front of the school. *"Cops!"* I squealed, throwing myself flat in the snow and cursing the reflective strips on the back of my parka. The car never slowed, and Dedman resumed his work.

After ten minutes or so, I heard a resounding *crack!* as Dedman snapped the trunk. I was so fixed on watching for trouble, the treetop nearly hit me as it shooshed to the ground. It sounded like wind in a wheat field.

Hoisting three feet of heavy, prickly fir over the fence was no simple feat, but we managed it. As we hustled down the alley with our prize slung between us, I glanced back at the ugly gap in the treeline.

It looked to me like we'd knocked someone's tooth out.

CHAPTER 20

IN 1835, JOSEPH SEEMS TO HAVE TAKEN A STEP BACK FOR REFLEC-
tion. Not yet thirty years old, he had accrued nearly 10,000 followers,
most of whom had chosen to uproot their lives and subject themselves
to poverty and discrimination for their beliefs. The personal responsibility for so many souls must have felt like an impossible pressure to
bear.

Accordingly, Joseph began to focus on providing stability for his
flock and administrative structure for his church. He had already
changed its name from the Church of Christ to the Church of Latter-day Saints, at Sidney's suggestion, in an attempt to shed the de-
rogatory nicknames "Mormon" and "Mormonite." (Not that it made
relations with their neighbors any better when the Mormons insisted
on being called "Saints" instead.) Now, early in 1835, Joseph put in
place a new leadership structure for the church. After the First Presidency, consisting of himself and two counselors, came the Quorum of
the Twelve Apostles and Quorum of the Seventy, both of which the
prophet stacked heavily with veterans of Zion's Camp. Though their
duties have evolved over time, this same hierarchy exists in the church
today.

Perhaps it was an increased confidence in his personal authority, or a recognition that his continual prophesying caused more problems than it solved, but around this time Joseph's revelations became extremely infrequent. This two-year period marked a rare time of peace for the Saints in Kirtland. Plentiful credit and optimism fueled a building boom, which included construction of a magnificent temple. Church rolls continued to swell, thanks to vigorous proselytizing and to Joseph's own increasingly accomplished preaching. As biographer Fawn M. Brodie wrote:

> He appealed as much to reason as to emotion, challenging his critics to examine the evidences of his divine authority … The importance of this appeal cannot be overestimated, for it drew into the Mormon ranks many able men who had turned in disgust from the excesses of the local cults. The intellectual appeal of Mormonism, which eventually became its greatest weakness as the historical and "scientific" aspects of Mormon dogma were cruelly disemboweled by twentieth-century scholarship, was in the beginning its greatest strength.

A case in point came in the summer of 1835, when Joseph bought several rolls of ancient Egyptian papyrus from a traveling exhibition of mummies—an expensive purchase toward which he encouraged church members to contribute. After examining the papyri, Joseph announced that they contained theretofore unknown writings of the Old Testament prophets Abraham and Joseph. He had earlier thrown himself into the study of Hebrew, and now, though this was Egyptian, he felt confident in his ability to decipher the hieroglyphs. Over the next several years, he produced a translation of the Abraham papyri that offered a glimpse into the mysteries of the cosmos—including the startling fact that God dwells near a star called Kolob, where a single day equals a thousand years of our time.

The Book of Abraham is now canonized Mormon scripture. The

papyrus rolls were eventually lost and were thought to have burned in the Great Chicago Fire. However, eleven fragments from the Abraham papyri turned up in New York City's Metropolitan Museum of Art in 1967 and turned out to be rather ordinary Egyptian funerary texts.

Mormon apologists today claim that the Abrahamic writings must have been on parts of the papyrus that remain lost—or, that Joseph didn't actually translate them in any literal sense, but rather that the study of the papyri opened his mind to a divine transmission of Abraham's actual first-person narrative.

Thanks to the discovery of the Rosetta Stone, the decoding of Egyptian hieroglyphs was already well underway by the time Joseph produced the Book of Abraham, though this had not yet been widely reported outside of academic circles. Would this knowledge have made Joseph think twice before undertaking his own translation?

It's impossible to know for sure, of course. But given his attitude toward the Bible itself, I think not.

THOUGH THE KIRTLAND OF 1836 LOOKED LIKE A BOOMTOWN, IT was sustaining itself on a growing bubble of debt. The church itself owed $13,000 on its new temple—which did not prevent hundreds of ecstatic attendees from seeing angels on the occasion of its dedication—and church leaders were vastly overextended on credit from various merchants around the country.

As if this looming disaster weren't enough, the Missouri Saints again found themselves in dire straits. Though Clay County had kindly taken them in, now those neighborly folks were ever so delicately suggesting that the Mormons and their weird beliefs might be happier if they just moved on. Why, there was some lovely, barren prairie land to the northeast, in Caldwell County. Why didn't they give that a shot?

At wits' end, Joseph took his older brother Hyrum, Sidney Rigdon, and Oliver Cowdery on a treasure-hunting expedition to Salem, Massachusetts. He recalled a convert who insisted a fortune was hidden in a basement there, and it's a measure of how bad the situation was for the church that Joseph took this to be his best hope. After some time in Salem, Joseph claimed in a letter to Emma that, under cover of missionary work, his cabal had located the house and were now trying to work out how to get access to it. Apparently they never did, because within a month they returned to Kirtland, empty-handed.

Clearly the debt problem required an even bolder solution than a treasure hunt. Thus, in November, Joseph drafted plans for his very own bank, the ironically named Kirtland Safety Society. The state of Ohio, which was trying to clamp down on wildcat banking and the resulting riot of currencies, denied Joseph's charter request. But that didn't stop the Society from opening its doors in January 1837 and issuing its own banknotes. Joseph encouraged landowners in Kirtland to buy into the bank with their well-inflated city lots as backing. Armed with this supposed capital stock, he dispatched banknotes to settle the church's outstanding debts and merchant accounts.

This worked about as well as you might imagine. For a month, Kirtlanders strutted around like the most prosperous society on earth. Then the notes began to be returned, refused, and a run on the bank quickly followed. Cashier Warren Parrish later wrote that they had less than $6,000 in cash reserves.

Joseph's blatant fraud and mismanagement divided an already embattled church. He struck one apostle, the popular David Patten, for the tone of his questions about the matter, and another, Parley Pratt, threatened to sue Joseph when the Kirtland Safety Society tried to foreclose on his property. One of the few apostles who stood by Joseph was the industrious Vermonter Brigham Young, who was enjoying his first taste of affluence.

Joseph faced thirteen separate lawsuits in 1837 and was arrested seven times, racking up a total of $40,000 in bail. In this climate, he sent several of the apostles away as missionaries—ostensibly to spread the good word but also to keep them beyond the reach of the law. Heber C. Kimball was detailed to lead a mission all the way to England.

To make matters worse, Oliver Cowdery, who had been with Joseph from the translation of the Book of Mormon, was now in open rebellion. He tried to wrest away leadership of the church, claiming he had knowledge of "a dirty, nasty, filthy affair" between Joseph and a teenage orphan named Fanny Alger, whom Emma had taken in. Joseph denied the relationship was adulterous, but, tellingly, never quite denied the relationship itself.

Dissenters were soon disrupting church meetings and even brawling in the temple. The capstone for Joseph's troubles came when a vicious anti-Mormon named Grandison Newell, who had already taken him to court over a murder plot, brought banking fraud charges against him. Joseph had lost control of Kirtland, and was in real danger of losing everything. As Kimball famously said of the time, "there were not twenty persons on earth that would declare that Joseph Smith was a prophet of God."

On the night of January 12, 1838, Joseph hightailed it out of town, together with Sidney Rigdon. Emma trailed behind with the children. Their time in Ohio was finished.

CHAPTER 21

WE SET OUT SHORTLY BEFORE NOON, OUR OVERNIGHT BAGS SLUNG into the back seat. Despite the Jiffy Pop we'd threaded and strung around the tree, which was propped up in a cooking pot on the end table, I was happy to leave sight of the wretched thing behind. Dedman, for his part, called our trip "a flippin' waste of a P-day."

Driving southwest under gray skies for two hours brought us to the open, tree-filled city of Lethbridge, on the banks of the Oldman River. We parked in the midst of small fleet of cheap Chevrolets at a large LDS meetinghouse near the University of Lethbridge. Roisterous elders in their P-day finest milled about the halls of the church, and we found a spirited volleyball match underway in the streamer-bedecked cultural hall. The Lethbridge Zone encompassed six districts in southern Alberta, which meant there were about three dozen missionaries in attendance, not counting President Tuttle and the apes.

Zone conferences took place every two or three months. They usually began on a P-day, to give all the missionaries recreation time together, then continued the next day with training sessions, inspirational talks, and a testimony meeting. This particular conference would tackle the added challenge of combating Christmastime homesickness.

As we skirted the volleyball match, Dedman nodded toward Elder Fearing and Elder Hardy, who were playing on opposite teams. "Look at those two. Know how you get to be an ape?"

"Hard work?" I said, not without an edge.

"Superior brownnosing. And the fastest way to climb that ladder's by ratting out your fellow missionaries. What do you bet this clown Garrett's on his way up? Hey, there's Feeley." Dedman lightly punched my arm. "Catch you later, man."

Alone in the crowd, I wandered around until I ran into Elder Stone and Elder Jolley from my MTC cohort. We spent some time swapping tales, after which I was unable to dodge a conversation with Elder Garrett, who couldn't have been more proud of his recent promotion. I let him coax me into playing some volleyball before the local Relief Society served us all a Christmas feast in one of the larger classrooms.

As I ate I kept an eye on the time. A roster had been posted with everyone's interview times, and mine was coming up. I slipped into the dim hallway as the plates were being cleared. While most of the other missionaries were scarfing down cookies and hot apple cider, I sat fidgeting in an upholstered folding chair outside the stake president's office. Indistinct murmurs came from behind the door; sickly fluorescent light flickered overhead. I checked my watch repeatedly. A sense of foreboding roiled my full belly.

Elder Dedman emerged from the office at last, with President Tuttle's hand on his shoulder. "You keep up the good work, Elder," said Tuttle. "There's gold still in Brooks. I know you can dig it up. And don't forget to take a little more off around the ears next time. You're starting to look like a mop."

Dedman tossed me a quick wink before heading off in search of dessert. Apparently he hadn't come clean in his worthiness interview about anything that might trip me up during mine—and apparently President Tuttle's gift of discernment had taken another night off. I released a pent-up breath, but I also felt vaguely let down. It would have been a relief to have the question of whether or not to confess my shiftless ways taken out of my hands.

"Elder Shunn!" said President Tuttle, motioning me inside. "Good to see you. Come right in, please!"

My conscience and I joined him in the small borrowed office as he took a seat behind the neat desk. The walls were whitewashed cinder block, decorated simply with a portrait of Ezra Taft Benson and his counselors. President Tuttle looked somehow out of place there, like something that had emerged from the shadows. I felt out of place myself, in part because I was in sweaty P-day clothes while President Tuttle wore his suit, tie, and name tag. Out of my armor, I was at even more of a disadvantage.

"So how *are* you, Elder Shunn?" His smile was frighteningly magnetic. I wondered if he had to go through interviews like this in austere rooms with *his* superiors.

I wanted so badly to go home. But at that moment, I wanted even more badly to preserve the illusion that I was strong and capable, a righteous missionary. In my weakness, I had nailed myself to that cross. "I've never been better."

"Aren't you just loving the work? You and Elder Fowler found some great success in Brooks. I *knew* things there needed shaking up."

"It's been amazing," I said, bobbing my head, feeling the cracks inside. Driving the nails in deeper.

The usual worthiness questions took us only a few minutes to run through, though I didn't dispatch them with quite the confidence I had three months earlier. When Tuttle started digging into my performance as a missionary, I felt myself on even less certain ground. Still, while I hinted that my proselytizing habits could stand some improvement, I came nowhere close to spilling the awful truth about the big fat nothing we were getting done in Brooks.

After ten minutes of this, President Tuttle leaned forward in his chair, hands clasped on the desk. "Elder Shunn," he said, his voice gravid with concern, "how are you *really*? What's wrong?"

I froze, my eyes turning hot and wet in their sockets. Was my misery that obvious? My mind raced, trying to figure out if there was any way I could tell him something that would get me sent home without making trouble for my companion.

I must have hesitated too long. In a voice sodden with sympathy, President Tuttle asked, "Elder Shunn . . . are you having a problem with masturbation?"

A window into my soul opened just enough to admit a thin ray of light. Though in retrospect it seems ridiculous, my heart leapt at the possibility that this, at last, was my way out—a sexual transgression of sufficient seriousness to get me sent home.

Though hope lifted my shoulders, I lowered my head meekly and in a small voice said, "Yes."

"I'm very sorry to hear that, Elder Shunn." Tuttle shook his head sadly as he placed a briefcase before him on the desk. "It's an insidious habit, and it must have been weighing you down horribly."

"It is." I tried to lock my remorseful expression in place. "It has."

President Tuttle drew a thin sheaf of papers from the briefcase. Discharge forms?

"I'm sure you feel like an irredeemable wretch right now," he said, "but that's exactly how Satan *wants* you to feel. It is, unfortunately, such an easy way for him to attack young missionaries and kill their effectiveness that this is probably the most common confession we hear as mission presidents."

He passed the stapled pages across the desk to me. "The good news is, it's a habit you can fight, and a habit you can break. What you have there in your hands is a guide from the apostle Mark E. Petersen, with plenty of suggestions for how you can overcome the temptation to masturbate. It won't be easy, but I know you're strong, Elder Shunn, and I know you can do it. Just remember to pray, and never lose faith."

STEPS IN OVERCOMING MASTURBATION, proclaimed the typescript, a grainy copy of a copy of a copy. I flipped through it with a sinking heart. A few of the helpful tips jumped out at me: *Avoid spicy food. Don't drink water before bed. Wear bulky clothing instead of pajamas. Sleep with a Book of Mormon clutched in your hands.*

I felt like an idiot.

President Tuttle offered an encouraging smile when I looked up again. "Don't worry, Elder. I know right now it may seem like the end of the world, but you're not finished as a missionary, I promise you that. Not by a long shot you're not."

CHAPTER 22

I APPROACHED CONSCIOUSNESS ON CHRISTMAS MORNING STILL smarting from my interview with President Tuttle. Santa's visit to the zone conference later that evening had not helped, nor had a night in a comfortable bed furnished by a Lethbridge member family, nor had two subsequent days of bucketry.

The clock read 7:00. For the first time ever at a single-digit hour, Dedman was up before me. I could hear him puttering around in the kitchen. I lingered in bed, unable to summon the will to struggle up. I was remembering a prostitute named Daisy with a startling wistfulness. My cousin Marky had introduced me to her in June, at his sister's wedding. After Marky told her I was a virgin, she in so many words offered to rectify that condition free of charge. I of course had turned down her kind offer, but now a big part of me, in a kind of sweet agony, regretted it. If only I'd taken her up on it, I, like that poor dope in Tahiti, wouldn't have to be here.

I drowsed in bed for what seemed like ages until my painful erection subsided. I put aside the Book of Mormon I'd slept with and dragged myself upright. What got me moving was the prospect of talking to Katrina.

I pulled on a pair of sweatpants and shuffled to the bathroom to the accompaniment of blips and bleeps from Elder Dedman's football game. I felt like I was wrapped in plastic, at one remove from the world, but also brittle, as if a tap in the wrong place might shatter me. I couldn't stop looking for my loophole, my Section 8, my ticket home. I knew there was a way—there *must* be. Sometimes I could sense the shape of a plan just beyond my grasp, like the solution to a difficult math problem, or a dream you can't quite call back upon waking. I was obsessed beyond the point of mania. Imagining my way home was my newest chronic thought-crime.

Leaving out God and President Tuttle, whose disappointment I figured I could live with, there were still three variables I couldn't factor out of my equations—my family's disappointment in me, my home ward's disappointment in me, and Katrina's disappointment in me. Three points to define a plane, three legs to prop up a stool. No way around them. But there *must* be a way . . .

Without those three forces holding me back, I would have bought a bus ticket already.

After stalling as long as I could, I emerged from the bathroom and dropped into the armchair. "Early for you," I said to Dedman.

"Just waiting for you to drag your lazy butt out of bed." He set the game down next to him on the couch, eyes alight in his unshaven face. He was fully dressed. "It's nearly eight, dude. I think that's time for presents!"

He reached for the gifts crammed around the cooking pot that held the tree. I felt guilty that I had six presents, while he had only two. I felt guilty about the tree itself, and about the fact that I didn't want to be there with Elder Dedman. I felt guilty that I wasn't looking forward to talking to my family on the phone, on one of the rare days when it was allowed.

Dedman passed me my presents one by one. From my parents and siblings I received two new ties, a sliding-15 puzzle, and some stationery and a nice pen. From Grandpa and Grandma Partridge I received the same fifteen-dollar check they sent every year (though it would go about a third further in Canada than it would back home). Katrina's gift I saved for last—a slim paperback, I could tell through the wrapping. I tore eagerly at the paper but sat back nonplussed when J. D. Salinger's *Nine Stories* emerged. I'd been expecting a science fiction novel, not some mundane literary snoozefest.

Dedman had received a tie from his widowed mother and a fancy compass from his uncle and aunt. As I was gathering up my wrapping paper, he put the compass aside and handed me a red envelope. "Merry Christmas, Elder."

The card was simple but beautiful, green with the silhouette of a Christmas tree in red foil on the front. Inside he had written:

Shunn,

Thanks for being my Companion. I hope this is your best Christmas ever!

Drew Dedman

PS We are Mighty Xmas Tree Hunters!

I stared at the words without blinking. "Thanks, Elder," I said, not looking at him. "Thanks a lot."

He waited expectantly, as if I would now produce a card for him, but I didn't have one. It had never crossed my mind. I burned with shame as I tried to figure out what to say to him, but nothing came. I set his card aside and wadded up the wrapping paper.

Dedman stood suddenly, dusting his hands on the back of his pants. "Well, hey," he said brightly, collecting his gifts, "I'll just get out of the way here so you can call your family and stuff. It's an hour earlier in Tacoma, so I don't mind waiting until you're done." He went and closed the bedroom door behind him.

I held my head in my hands for a few minutes, still frozen in embarrassment. Why was I always such an idiot? Why couldn't I function like a normal human being?

I heaved a sigh and picked up the phone. I realized that, for most of the 30,000 other missionaries in the world, this call was probably the highlight of their year. But I'd had one conversation with my parents already as a missionary in the field, and I wasn't looking forward to another.

My mother answered and put me on for two or three minutes with each of my seven siblings. They were all excited to talk to me, which was nice. When my mother came back on, she told me that she and my father had attended Marty Fowler's homecoming in Ogden, and how impressed they were after meeting him and hearing him speak from the pulpit. "He must have been a great influence to have as a trainer."

"He was really something," I said.

When my father came on the line, he told me "that McCormick girl" had dropped by earlier in the week, bearing goodies.

"How was she?" I hated to sound so avid, but I was hungry for independent confirmation that she was well.

"I couldn't tell you. I turned the dogs loose on her."

"I'm glad to hear you're still Mister Hospitality."

"The cookies were good."

After forty minutes I said my goodbyes and hung up. I barely had the dial tone back before I was punching in Katrina's number. My stomach churned as the line rang.

There was a click. "McCormick residence."

Damn. It sounded like Katrina's mother. I didn't know how she'd feel about me calling. "Hi, Sister McCormick? It's, uh, Bill Shunn."

"Oh, hello!" To my relief, she sounded genuinely happy to hear from me. "I thought it might be you. How's your Christmas?"

"Fine. A little quiet. How's yours?"

"Chaos, thanks for asking. Listen, I know this is long-distance, and

I'm sure you didn't call to jabber with me all morning. I'll see if I can't round up Katrina for you."

I heard the ambient sounds of a house with three teenagers on Christmas. Katrina yelled at everyone to hold the noise down.

"Hi there," she said, her voice turning liquid as she picked up the phone.

My nerves crackled with cool fire. "Katrina, how are you?"

"I'm good. Oh, Bill, oh, gosh, it's so wonderful to hear your voice again."

Hearing my name from her lips was still surreal to me, an honor that couldn't actually be mine. "Yeah, I know. I've missed your voice too."

"I love you so much."

"I love you too."

"Did you get the book I sent?"

"Yes. It's—wow. I can't wait to read it."

"That's one of my favorite books in the world, very personal to me. I know it's not science fiction, but Michelle and I were fifteen the summer we read it. Let me tell you—all we wanted was to do was hitchhike to New Hampshire, knock on that man's door, and throw ourselves at his feet."

"Gosh." I felt a pang of the kind of jealousy only another writer would know. "Man. Well, I can't wait."

"You'll have to let me know what you think."

"I will. I will. So, yeah. Hey, did you get the magazines?"

"Yes. My gosh. Where did you *find* those?"

Part of her gift consisted of three issues of *Galaxy* from late 1972 and early 1973 that I'd found in a local used bookstore. Together they contained *Project 40*, a serialization of the Frank Herbert novel later published as *Hellstrom's Hive*.

"Oh, just digging around."

"They're great. And the picture you sent—that was just amazing."

She was talking about a photographic collage of found objects that spelled out BILL LOVES KATRINA FOREVER. "I'm glad you like it."

"I *love* it. How long did it take you?"

I grinned, happy to elaborate on my own ingenuity. "Elder Dedman and I spent a whole day out taking pictures, trying to find a gate that looked like an E, or a hose we could set up like an S. When I got the roll developed, I then had to arrange all the photos and try to get one good picture of the whole montage. I shot an entire roll using different apertures and exposures, just hoping to get one that worked."

"It did work. It's wonderful. Speaking of which, how *are* you getting along with this new companion? You haven't said much about him in your letters."

"He's—" I glanced at the bedroom door. "Well, he's hard to get to know."

"You like him, though? You get along?"

"Yeah, I guess."

"Well, keep working hard. You're my missionary."

I squirmed in my chair. "I will, yeah." I started pacing, carrying the telephone with me. "Oh, do I ever miss you, Katrina. It's so bad, sometimes I ache."

"I miss you too, Bill. A lot." She paused. "But you know, I think I've finally gotten to point where I've—adjusted? You know, to the fact that you're going to be gone for another twenty months."

My lungs constricted. This span of time was not real to me. I had lost the power to believe that my mission was truly finite. "You have?"

"Well, yes. I mean, what choice do I have? It's not like there's anything I can do about it."

"No, not really, I guess." This was a more practical perspective than I wanted to hear. I wanted to hear that Katrina ached like I did. That she was going as crazy as I was.

Her voice brightened. "But just because I'm getting used to the idea doesn't mean that if you turned up on my doorstep tomorrow I wouldn't get over it in a heartbeat. If that happened, I'd be *thrilled*."

Spots swam in front of my eyes, and my hands began to tremble. In my head, one leg of the stool had just collapsed.

CHAPTER 23

No matter how many questionable ventures Joseph Smith undertook, how many lives and fortunes he ruined, how many high-profile defectors he lost, the majority of his people stuck fast by him.

Part of this was due, no doubt, to his natural and contagious exuberance. No amount of tribulation could keep him down for long. He had come to believe utterly in his divine calling—and why not, since he was collecting followers the way a bear in the woods collects burrs?—but he rarely conducted himself in a solemn or morose fashion. His high spirits and lust for life were always on display, and that couldn't help but be infectious. (Josiah Quincy, Jr., a future mayor of Boston, met Joseph in 1844 and wrote that he seemed "endowed with that kingly faculty which directs, as by intrinsic right, the feeble or confused souls who are looking for guidance.")

Moreover, Joseph had concocted for the Saints no stultifying afterlife of harps or hellfire. His heaven was a realm of ever-evolving hope and wonder, where the righteous and diligent could continue to acquire knowledge and power, and where none but a handful of the uttermost wicked would face eternal damnation. It was a vision of opportunity ideally tuned to the optimism of America, one that flattered everyone who bought into it.

After fleeing Ohio, Joseph and Sidney rendezvoused in Indiana with the fiercely loyal Brigham Young, who was also on the lam. When the group arrived in Far West, Missouri, they were greeted not as fugitive criminals but heroes. The Missouri Saints had been busy, building themselves a new city in Caldwell County, which the state had set aside exclusively for them. Joseph's return was a great boon to these long-suffering souls, who were jealous of Kirtland's supremacy and now felt that the promised gathering to Zion must be at hand.

As if to ratify this perception, more and more Kirtlanders straggled into Missouri over the next few months, disgusted by the antics of the apostates. Even dissenters like Oliver Cowdery quietly took up residence, preferring the company of these Saints to the chaos of Kirtland.

So many new arrivals meant that even more land was required. Joseph was out on a survey of neighboring Daviess County when one of his companions ran across a grouping of rocks that resembled an ancient altar. Joseph named the site Tower Hill and declared it the place where Adam offered sacrifices to God after the Fall (the Garden of Eden being located in Jackson County). The valley below he named Adam-ondi-Ahman, a phrase from the Adamic language. (Mormon lore tells us that Adamic, Earth's original tongue, is so pure and compact a language that the Book of Mormon could be rendered in it as a pamphlet.) The Saints wasted no time establishing another town there.

Converts new and old, gathered through successful missionary efforts, continued to stream into Far West, and Mormons were making significant inroads into four surrounding counties. Mindful of their history with the original settlers, Joseph and Sidney authorized a physician named Sampson Avard to organize a clandestine military force for the defense of the Saints and their property. Called the Danites after the Biblical tribe of Dan, the group swore oaths of brotherhood and knew one another by secret signs and passwords.

They took cleansing the church of dissenters as their first order of business, quite possibly at Sidney's urging.

Avard was a ruthless piece of work. He preached deception, theft, and murder as righteous tactics against the gentile threat. As Avard told his Danites, were any man foolish enough to speak against Joseph, he would not hesitate to get that person drunk and lure him into the brush where, he swore, "I will [slash] into his guts in a minute and put him under the sod."

On June 17, 1838, Sidney Rigdon gave an angry, rambling speech suggesting that the unfaithful should be hanged or trampled. Shortly thereafter, the Mormon dissenters received a letter from Sidney—signed also by Hyrum Smith and dozens of other leaders—accusing them of trying to destroy the church through lawsuits and lies. The letter gave them three days to leave Caldwell County. While Oliver Cowdery, David Whitmer, and other dissenters were away seeking legal assistance in countering Sidney's ultimatum, the Danites besieged their houses, robbed their wives and families of all worldly goods, and ran them out of the county.

Joseph would later try to distance himself from the Danites and their depredations, and would even excommunicate Sampson Avard. But by then the damage was done.

WITH THE INTERNAL PURGE UNDERWAY, SIDNEY RIGDON TURNED his attention to the church's external enemies. He had already been heard to rail against their neighbors who refused to embrace the gospel. Now, at a Fourth of July pageant in Far West, he ranted that the Saints were tired of turning the other cheek and would fight a war of bloody extermination if any dared molest them again. The crowd roared its approval, though some among them were chilled by Sidney's rhetoric. The speech was soon printed as a pamphlet, and public sentiment, which had generally been in their favor, began to turn against the Mormons.

In August, on the day of a hotly contested election in Daviess County, a large group of old settlers tried to prevent thirty Mormon men from voting in Gallatin. After one Mormon was knocked to the ground, the rest seized clubs and cudgeled their way into the polls. Though no lives were lost on either side in the mêlée, breathless reports of two dead Mormons winged their way to Far West. Sidney Rigdon and Sampson Avard marched their newly expanded forces into Daviess County to retaliate.

Accompanying them, Joseph learned that reports of the brawl had been greatly exaggerated. He managed to turn the marchers toward the home of Gallatin's justice of the peace, Adam Black, where Avard extracted a promise that the Saints' constitutional rights would be respected.

Though Joseph was only peripherally involved in the intimidation, Black brought suit against him for threat of murder. Tensions ran high on both sides. Vigilante camps formed up among the settlers of Daviess and several other counties. Joseph agreed to turn himself in, but only on condition that he was tried in a court where his own men, together with state militia troops under General David Atchison's command, could guarantee his safety. Accordingly, he and Lyman Wight appeared before a judge on September 7. The judge found sufficient cause to order a later trial and set the two men free on bond.

This did nothing to defuse tensions between the Saints and the old settlers. Raids against isolated Mormon farms became so frequent that all who could in Daviess County fled to Adam-ondi-Ahman and settled in for a siege. General Atchison and his subordinate Alexander Doniphan did their best to break up the vigilantes and broker a peace. But in Carroll County, the Mormon river port of DeWitt was also besieged, and houses were being put to the torch. Under continual gunfire, and starving, the Saints there finally agreed to sell out and leave. They loaded their wagons and fled to Far West.

On October 14, Joseph rallied the Saints in Caldwell County with the declaration that they were done suffering the injustice of mobs. As a duly chartered arm of the state militia, Mormon troops must march to the defense of Adam-ondi-Ahman. All men were required to join the fight, and those who refused would have their property seized to support the war effort.

"If the people will let us alone, we will preach the gospel in peace," Joseph swore. "But if they come on us to molest us, we will establish our religion by the sword. We will trample down our enemies and make it one gore of blood from the Rocky Mountains to the Atlantic Ocean."

Joseph's troops entered Daviess County the next day, where the old settlers now abandoned their homes and fled. One company under apostle David Patten went looting in Gallatin and burned several buildings. Other companies rustled livestock and herded it to Adam-ondi-Ahman. As word spread of these raids, more Mormon homes were burned. One rogue militia company took three Mormons prisoner on the border of Caldwell County; apostle David Patten was killed, along with two others, as his men tried to rescue them.

News of this skirmish, known as the Battle of Crooked River, came wildly distorted to the ears of Missouri governor Lilburn Boggs. He had studiously ignored the pleas of the Saints as they were harassed and assaulted. Now that they were taking matters into their own hands, Boggs on October 27 issued the executive order that would make his name a synonym for evil among the Mormon people for the rest of time. It read, in part:

"The Mormons must be treated as enemies, and must be exterminated or driven from the state if necessary for the public peace—their outrages are beyond all description."

The Extermination Order, as it became known, remained in force in the state of Missouri for nearly 138 years, until it was rescinded by Governor Kit Bond in 1976.

THERE IS NO EVIDENCE THAT THE EXTERMINATION ORDER HAD reached William Jennings by October 30, three days later, when he led the most heinous and bloody action of the conflict.

While nearly all other Mormons in Caldwell County had taken refuge in Far West, the people of tiny Haun's Mill stayed put. They either failed to receive or failed to heed an order from Joseph Smith to fall back with everyone else. When Jennings and his militiamen rode in, the Saints took refuge in a blacksmith shop. The militia encircled the structure and, through gaps in its log walls, turned it into a shooting gallery. Women and some children were allowed to escape, but the men and boys were not. One old man, wounded, gave up his weapon only to be hacked to death. Sardius Smith, a boy of nine or ten, was dragged from hiding and shot in the head.

At the end of the massacre, at least seventeen men and boys were dead and around fifteen injured. When it was finally safe for the women to return, they could do little more in the way of burial than dump the dead down a well before fleeing with the wounded.

When Joseph received news of the massacre, Far West was already under siege by a huge militia force. Alexander Doniphan, who had some sympathy for the Mormon cause, was begging Joseph to surrender before a larger militia force could arrive to enforce the new Extermination Order. When Joseph approached the militia encampment on October 31 for what he thought would be negotiations, he was instead taken as a prisoner of war. The militia commander, Samuel Lucas, convened a hasty court-martial and found him guilty of treason.

Lucas ordered Doniphan to execute Joseph the next morning, but Doniphan refused, which sent the militia into spasms of confusion. Still, the leaders of Far West surrendered, whereupon Lucas's troops entered and began a reign of looting and rape that lasted most of a week.

Joseph and several associates, including Sidney Rigdon, Lyman Wight, and Hyrum Smith, were taken to Richmond, Missouri, and indicted on such charges as treason, murder, arson, and robbery. The witnesses against them at this inquiry included two apostles, Orson Hyde and Thomas B. Marsh, but the most incendiary witness was surely Sampson Avard himself, who blamed all the excesses of the Danites on Joseph and Sidney.

On November 30, after three weeks of imprisonment in Richmond, Joseph and the others were moved to Clay County's Liberty Jail to await trial. There they would remain for the next four months.

ONE OF THE MOST FAMOUS STORIES OF JOSEPH'S LIFE ORIGINATES in the jail at Richmond. When I was a child, this incident was held up time and again in illustration of the importance of standing up for what's right—and of not using bad language.

The Richmond guards were anything but kind. They constantly taunted their prisoners with tales of their evil deeds after the surrender at Far West. When Sidney Rigdon grew feverish, the guards took sport in mocking his fits and spasms.

One night, according to Parley Pratt, the guards' stories grew so coarse that Joseph could take it no longer. Leaping to his feet, he cried, in a voice that brooked no argument, "Silence, ye fiends of the eternal pit! In the name of Jesus Christ I rebuke you, and command you to be still; I will not live another minute and hear such language. Cease such talk, or you or I die this instant!"

As the tale was told to us children, Joseph could have used his powers to kill the guards, or to bring the prison crashing down around them all. Instead he chose to use his words, and the guards fell silent at his command, unable to speak. Of course, what was represented to us as their swearing—something that had never much bothered Joseph—was actually their boasting about rape and murder. But one should never let historical accuracy get in the way of a good moral.

Parley Pratt, for one, never forgot that moment. He had seen many things in his life, he later wrote, "but dignity and majesty I have seen but once, as it stood in chains at midnight in a dungeon in an obscure village in Missouri." The same apostle who had so recently tried to sue Joseph over a bank foreclosure could now, anew, have no doubt that he sat in the presence of a prophet of God.

EARLY IN JOSEPH'S INCARCERATION, EMMA WAS ABLE TO VISIT HIM on a few occasions, together with their eldest son. So was the resourceful Brigham Young, one of the few Mormon leaders to evade capture or death after Far West. Brigham, an organizational genius, was already setting up supply depots across Missouri to feed the thousands of Saints relocating to temporary quarters in Quincy, Illinois.

Joseph wrote frequent letters from prison, and he and the others tried more than once to escape. They knew they were sitting ducks for a lynching, and in fact someone at the jail did succeed in poisoning most of them, though not fatally. Sidney, meanwhile, between his seizures and his bellyaching, became such a nuisance that the others were relieved when a writ of habeas corpus set him free.

At last, early in April 1839, the men were brought to trial in Daviess County. Their lawyers argued successfully for a change of venue to Boone County, which had not been involved in the Mormon War. This seemed like good news, but Joseph knew that mob justice was still a real danger, however the new trial might turn out. En route to court, he and the others bribed their guards, purchasing their freedom and several horses with a few bottles of whiskey and the promise of eight hundred dollars.

Mounting up, they made good their escape.

CHAPTER 24

SUNDAY NIGHT, AT THE END OF THE LONGEST FOUR DAYS OF MY life, I sat up late reading in the living room. Every piece of my escape plan was in place. All I needed was for Dedman to go to bed—and he wasn't budging.

With one sweet sentence, Katrina had removed the biggest obstacle still keeping me in the field. The social and familial cost of going home early was so high that it had always seemed like an insurmountable barrier. But if Katrina would welcome me back despite the fact that I hadn't completed a full mission, I could deal with the whispers and pitying looks, the recriminations, the ostracism, even the opprobrium of my parents. If she was still willing to pick up where we left off, none of the rest of it could touch me.

I couldn't leave openly, though—not without kicking off a massive intervention. Dedman might be the king of all buckets, but he was still a missionary, and every missionary knew how things worked back home. He would try to talk me out of leaving, and if that didn't work then he'd call President Tuttle. There was nothing else he could do without getting in serious trouble himself. I didn't trust myself to face Dedman without caving, so I had to leave quietly and get beyond his reach before he found out I was gone.

My best option, as I had learned by calling a helpful Greyhound ticketing agent, was a westbound bus that rolled through Brooks at three o'clock every morning. I'd reach Calgary at six, then catch a southbound bus at nine. That was three hours longer than I wanted to spend in Calgary, but if I could sneak out without waking Elder Dedman, then he probably wouldn't even be awake to report me missing until well after I'd made my connection. And with a Monday morning departure, the staff at the mission office might just be out for P-day and that much harder to reach.

I resolutely did not think beyond making that bus. If I let myself dwell on what would follow, I knew I'd lose my nerve.

With a plan in place, a weight lifted from my shoulders. I saw freedom dawning on the southern horizon. My prayers made my heart even lighter. I often scanted my personal prayers, rushing through them with rote gratitude and mechanical entreaties, but now I poured my soul out to God. I followed all the steps we outlined for our investigators: studying the issue out in my mind, weighing the arguments, making a decision, and asking for confirmation that it was the right one. Just as I had when praying at the MTC about whether to propose to Katrina, I rose from these earnest sessions on my knees flooded with the warm, tingly assurance that the course I had charted was right. God and the Holy Ghost always came through for me when it counted.

In retrospect, I can see how I was brainwashing myself into doing what was too difficult to justify otherwise. The mission field was driving me crazy, but I had neither the strength nor the self-awareness to stand up and forthrightly resign.

There on my knees, I was braiding a lifeline for myself from wishes and fantasies.

My biggest immediate problem was prepping for my escape without tipping off Elder Dedman. It was simple enough to find a pretext to drop by the library and return my books, and simple also to pull a wad of Monopoly money out of a Royal Bank ATM, emptying my account. Packing, though, was a different matter. Late on Christmas morning, while Dedman was on the phone with his mother, I had started stuffing clothes into my suitcases, but it didn't take me long to realize that I couldn't pack everything yet or the empty closet and drawers would give me away.

Until that long weekend, I'd perceived Elder Dedman as a fairly unintrusive companion, one who spent hours wrapped up in his own pursuits and left me to my own devices. Now, though, he seemed to attach himself to my elbow. I couldn't change my tie without him tagging along, nattering on about the Edmonton Oilers or the skiing in Banff or the time he offered a Book of Mormon to a hot babe who gave him her phone number. On those rare occasions when the bathroom door closed behind him, I rushed like a demon to jam two or three more items into the suitcases in the closet. I tried never to open my drawers when Dedman was around.

By ten o'clock Sunday night I was ready to bludgeon him to death with his football game. He'd been sitting on the couch playing it since eight. The continual bleats tapped at my skull like a jeweler's hammer. I sat in the armchair trying to read until finally its batteries ran down. As I was murmuring a prayer of thanks, Dedman grabbed a fresh pair of AA's from the refrigerator. My torment was far from over.

At half past ten, having read the same page of John Varley's *Millennium* at least seven times, I started yawning—deliberately—and did it again every few minutes. After fifteen minutes I upped the frequency. Soon Dedman was yawning too. I kept turning pages, eyes fastened to the type, with no idea what I was reading.

An eternity later, Dedman finally put the game aside. He rubbed his eyes. "I think I'll turn in. Anything special you want to do for P-day tomorrow?"

I shrugged. *Eat dinner on American soil?* "Not really. Maybe a burger at that place downtown. You know, I should probably hit the sack too."

While Dedman stretched his arms, I stood up and slipped past him into the bathroom. I took my time washing up, scanning the medicine cabinet to make sure all my toiletries and other supplies were bunched together for easy packing. I didn't take out my contact lenses.

After relinquishing the bathroom to my companion, I stripped off my sweatpants, tossed them into the closet, and pulled on jeans and a sweater. By the time Dedman emerged, I was in bed with the lights off and the covers pulled up to my chin, fully clothed.

"Companionship prayer, Elder?" asked Dedman, his voice loud in the claustrophobic darkness. His bedsprings squeaked. "Elder?"

I kept my face to the wall and played dead.

I DIDN'T SLEEP. I KEPT MY EYES ON THE DIGITAL CLOCK ON THE dresser, running the remainder of the night's tasks through my mind like a mantra. I tried not to think about my imminent reunion with Katrina—the feel of my arms around her waist, the taste of her sweet breath in my mouth—knowing a retreat into fantasy was the surest route to drifting off.

The minutes dragged themselves by like dying men in a desert, but I forced my eyes wide. By midnight, Dedman's breathing was deep and steady, but I gave it another half hour just to be safe. Another eternal half hour. There was too much to do to leave it any longer.

I skinned the covers back and swung my legs cautiously to the floor. I slid the closet door open ever so slowly and over several painstaking minutes ferried my two suitcases and my hanging suits and shirts into the living room. I packed the last of my clothes, then slipped Katrina's photo into my shoulder bag along with Opus. Catching sight of my notebook inside, I realized I hadn't updated my countdown calendar since Christmas Eve, when it stood at 619 days. I'd found a shortcut to zero.

I put on my sneakers and zipped up my parka. Stealthily I carried everything up the stairwell to the parking area, my pulse hammering so hard I could barely hear anything else. A sullen snow sifted down, sparse flakes like volcanic ash. I shoved my luggage into the back of the car, disconnected the extension cord from the heater on the engine block, and climbed into the driver's seat. I blew out a short, nervous breath.

This is it.

I backed slowly out of our spot and shifted into drive, gravel crunching under the tires. As I pressed the gas, I saw a shadow detach itself from the house in the rearview mirror. Huge and dark, it slammed against the back of the car.

I yelped and stomped on the brake. I jumped out, heart pounding.

I realized two seconds too late that this was a mistake. A fully clothed Elder Dedman had leaped spread-eagle onto the hatchback. He pushed off it and planted his hands on his hips.

"Where do you think you're going?" he said, not even panting.

"*Shit,*" I hissed. I wanted to vomit. "Away."

I turned back to the car, but Dedman darted past me and blocked the door. "You think I didn't know you were packing your stuff? You think I'm stupid?"

I tried to shove past him, but he pushed me back like I was a child.

"No. Tell me where you're going."

"Home, okay?"

His brow furrowed. "What—in a mission car? Are you crazy?"

"Of course not! I was going to the bus station. I was gonna leave my shit there, bring the car here, and walk back."

"What's that, two miles?"

"Mile and a half," I said sullenly.

"While someone steals your luggage? What kind of stupid plan is that?"

"Just let me *go!*"

I tried shoving past him again. He pushed me so hard I fell down. "No."

I climbed to my feet. "I'm so sick of this shit." My hands balled into impotent fists. "Why don't you just let me leave?"

He folded his arms. "Yeah, right. And what am I supposed to tell Prez?"

"Tell him I sneaked out! I just vanished! I don't give a shit. Just let me *go*."

We stared at each other, me breathing hard. The miserly snow fell around us, the idling car the only sound.

"You should pray about this."

"I have."

"Then pray with me, companionship prayer. At the church, Elder. I'm not asking." Dedman climbed into the driver's seat. "Get in."

Tears of rage stung my eyes. I looked at my watch. It was after one o'clock. Less than two hours to the bus. My guts were in knots.

Dedman revved the engine. I sighed and got in.

THE LIGHTS SNAPPED ON IN THE CHAPEL, CHASING SHADOWY ghosts away. Dedman led the way to the front.

"Right here, in front of the podium," he said, kneeling down between the dais and the first pew. "Come on."

Reluctantly I joined him. I'd been watching without luck for any opportunity to snatch the keys and run. Dedman folded his arms, closed his eyes, and bowed his head.

"Our dear Father in Heaven, we're grateful for all our many blessings, including the gift of being able to serve thee as missionaries. Father, pour out thy spirit upon us, to increase our desire to serve thee, and to help give Elder Shunn the desire to stay on his mission before he makes a big, big mistake. Bless us, please, and watch over us, and we say these things in the name of thy son, Jesus Christ, amen."

Grinding my teeth, I kept silent. Dedman wore his Mormonism

like a ratty old bathrobe—there if you needed to cover yourself, but you wouldn't want to wear it outside. I refused to ratify his prayer with an amen.

Dedman shifted around until he was sitting cross-legged, his expressionless mask pointed at me. "Elder, why did you come on a mission?"

"Flip." I stood up, gesturing as I groped for words. "Because—because that's what everyone *wanted* me to do."

My throat tightened. It was the first time I'd said what I really felt out loud.

"Yeah, me too," said Dedman, looking up at me. "But you've got to look beyond that. Why you came doesn't matter. What matters is that you're *here*. What matters is finding your own reasons to stay. Not anyone else's reasons. Your own."

"Why do you stay?" I demanded. "You don't *do* anything. It's like when the apes told us to 'Kick and take,' you heard 'Kick back and take it easy.'"

I'd been waiting for a chance to use that line.

Dedman looked at his hands. "I'm not such a good missionary right now, I know. Maybe—maybe I just need some help. A little push."

What occurs to me now is that the mission field made each of us crazy in his own special way. What occurred to me then was how little I knew about this companion of mine, how little I *knew* him, how little I had tried to find out. But I ruthlessly stamped out any glimmering of sympathy. "I *tried* to push!"

"Maybe I need you to push harder."

"Criminy." I turned and walked away.

Dedman jumped to his feet. "Shunn, wait."

I stopped halfway up the aisle, throwing my hands in the air. "Where can I go? You have the keys."

"Elder Shunn, what's the problem?" he pleaded. "What's so bad about this? What can I do differently?"

"You can't *do* anything. This isn't *about* you. I'm miserable. I hate being a missionary. I don't want to be here. I want to go to school and write stories and sleep in my own bed and listen to music and see movies."

"We can see movies if you want."

I gave a rueful snort. "*This* isn't what I want, Elder. I want to go home."

"You really want to go home."

"I really want to go home."

"You've thought this through."

"I've thought this through."

"There's nothing I can do to talk you out of it."

"Nothing."

We stared at each other across the pews. I refused to look away.

Dedman finally nodded his head. "All right, man." He rubbed his eyes like he couldn't believe what he was saying. "How much time do you need me to buy you?"

HEADLIGHTS PIERCED THE SNOW IN THE DISTANCE. DEDMAN AND I stood up from the plastic chairs outside the darkened depot. We hadn't talked much as we waited in the cold for the bus to arrive.

"Listen," Dedman said, hands in his pockets. "Did you ever hear about Runaway McKay?"

I shook my head. All I wanted was to be gone. "No."

"He's this elder a few months ahead of me. He tried to go home too. A couple of things you should know. First is that nickname. He changed his mind, ended up *not* going home, but the name stuck with him anyway. That's what everyone calls him, okay?"

"I'm not going to change my mind."

"Fine. The way the story goes, he was at the airport waiting for his plane when the apes—not our same apes, this was Mason and Saylor—when they caught up with him. Basically they got in his face and chewed him out and called him a pussy until he broke down and changed his mind. Do you understand what I'm telling you?"

The bus pulled in and stopped amid a welter of chuffs and squeals. Snowflakes swarmed like mosquitoes in the headlights.

I shivered. "Yeah, I get it."

"I'll try to wait until sometime after noon to call Prez. That should get you well clear of Calgary before they start looking."

"Thanks, man," I said, my eyes welling.

The driver emerged from the bus. I bought a ticket from him for eighteen dollars, and he stowed my luggage in the compartment underneath.

I shook hands with Dedman, scarcely believing this was happening. "You take care, Elder."

He crushed me in a quick hug. "Go with God, Elder."

Stepping back, he waved me onto the bus.

Maybe a dozen people were on board. I found a seat near the back and slid across the cracked blue vinyl to the window. As the bus pulled out of the lot, Elder Dedman stood watching with his hands clasped behind his back, a desolate ghost in a field of static.

We drove on, and the gray noise swirled him to pieces.

CHAPTER 25

I DOZED ON THE BUS BUT NEVER FELL COMPLETELY ASLEEP. THE fitful snow tapered off and quit as the barren plains turned to rolling hills, the spectral oil fields to farmhouses and wind turbines. By the time we reached the industrial belt around Calgary, the horizon was brightening at our backs like a blue stage scrim. The city loomed ahead, a gleaming fortress of impenetrable black towers, an Emerald City of oil.

The sky was light by the time the huge downtown station swallowed our bus. I humped my suitcases into the cavernous main concourse. Tinny announcements echoed unintelligibly overhead. I twitched like an insect, flinching at every sound. Every man in a dark business suit made me want to ditch my bags and run.

If Elder Dedman hadn't kept his promise, this was where they'd collar me.

At a Greyhound window I bought a ticket to Salt Lake City for $160. I lugged my suitcases to the men's room, and then to a tiny interior McDonald's. Munching a Sausage McMuffin, I watched from my Samsonite bunker as the Monday morning crowd thickened. There was no guarantee I could spot mission personnel at a glance, not if they were in P-day clothes, but they wouldn't take me unawares if I could help it. It wasn't as if they could do anything more than stand in my way, and if they did I could scream bloody murder. But they still scared me, because I wasn't immune to talk. Talk or shame.

After breakfast I found a bench tucked away in one corner of the main concourse and waited for my departure announcement. I watched the hordes through gritty eyes over the top of my paperback, getting no more reading done than I had the night before. Shortly before nine, weary and aching, I joined the line to board my bus. My neck prickled every moment with the certainty that someone was about to grab my shoulder. I didn't feel secure until the doors of the bus had closed and our tunnel had squeezed us out onto a curving exit ramp.

EARLY ON A FRIDAY MORNING THE PRECEDING AUGUST—THE DAY after I turned nineteen—I filed into the Salt Lake Temple's Creation Room with my father and mother and a hundred other shuffling supplicants. Murals covering the walls and ceiling depicted scenes from the organization of the earth: clouded skies, heaving oceans, rocky shores. The carpet underfoot shimmered a pale sky blue, matching the upholstery on the rows and rows of otherwise white theater seats.

We were clad head to toe in white. Shirts, pants, and ties for the men, long gowns for the women, soft white shoes or slippers for us all. We each clung to a large square packet made of white cloth or plastic. In my wallet I carried my new temple recommend, and on my chest I wore a yellow square of paper indicating that I was receiving the endowment for the first time, on my own behalf, in preparation for mission service. Other young people wore pink squares, indicating an imminent temple marriage. The rest were experiencing the rite for their tenth, hundredth, or thousandth time, standing proxy for departed souls whose names had been exhumed in the church's neverending quest for genealogical data, and who had passed on without the opportunity to receive any of the earthly ordinances necessary for salvation.

The preparatory class I'd attended the previous Sunday had been maddeningly unhelpful, since it was forbidden to talk about the endowment outside the temple. Our lesson had been more about why certain ordinances are necessary for salvation, and the reverent and open mindset we must bring to the occasion. I still knew little more than what Brigham Young had said in 1853:

> Your endowment is to receive all those ordinances in the House of the Lord which are necessary for you, after you have departed this life, to enable you to walk back to the presence of the Father, passing the angels who stand as sentinels, being enabled to give them the key words, the signs and tokens, pertaining to the Holy Priesthood, and gain your eternal exaltation in spite of earth and hell.

The main thing to remember during the endowment, we had been taught, was not to worry about trying to understand everything the first time. It was a holy experience that we would only begin to grasp after years of repetition, and new insights would reveal themselves every time through.

I had never been part of such a hushed and reverent crowd. As the men filled the seats to the right of the center aisle and the women took seats to the left, the carpeting swallowed the sounds of our footsteps. The silence was preternatural.

Four elderly men and one elderly woman, all in white, sat in squarish wooden chairs before a sea-blue drapery at the front of the room, facing us with bland expressions. One of the men stood and stepped forward.

"Brethren," he intoned, "you have been washed and pronounced clean, or that through your faithfulness you may *become* clean, from the blood and sins of this generation. You have been anointed to become hereafter kings and priests unto the Most High God, to rule and reign in the House of Israel forever. Sisters, you have been washed and anointed to become queens and priestesses to your husbands."

My washing and anointing had taken place thirty minutes earlier in hurried rituals deep in the bowels of the temple. Naked but for a white sheet that concealed less than a hospital gown, I'd stood before two robed priests. The first dipped his fingertips in water and touched them to various parts of my body. The second did the same with a metal wand dipped in consecrated oil. A third priest blessed me with a new name, pulled apparently from thin air, and helped me dress in the sacred undergarment I would be required to wear the rest of my life as a reminder of the covenants I was about to make.

"If you proceed and receive your full endowment," the speaker went on, "you will be required to take upon yourselves sacred obligations, the violation of which will bring upon you the judgment of God, for God will not be mocked. If any of you desire to withdraw rather than accept these obligations of your own free will and choice, you may now make it known by raising your hand."

I felt a clammy cold on the back of my neck. The proceedings so far had been strange and more than a little creepy, nothing like the worship services I'd been attending all my life. I'd never heard such ominous language before a baptism or priesthood ordination.

The man scanned the room. I glanced around covertly. No one else seemed greatly distressed. In fact, most of the congregants looked downright bored. My parents came to receive the endowment every month. Some of the people in this room would probably spend their whole day doing it over and over again, each time standing proxy for a different dead person who had never heard the true gospel in life.

My father patted me reassuringly on the knee. A lifetime's curiosity shouldered my misgivings aside.

The lights dimmed. Our officiators commenced a mystery play that drew heavily on Joseph Smith's reinterpretation of Genesis but included turns of phrase I had never encountered in scripture. After taking us through the six days of creation, the actors playing Elohim the Father and Jehovah the Son put their decrepit Adam to sleep and created Eve from his rib. We men were told to close our eyes as if asleep. After awakening us, our officiators led us all, men and women, through a door into the next chamber, the Garden Room.

The mystery play resumed with Elohim and Jehovah visiting Adam in the Garden of Eden. After instructing him to avoid the Tree of Knowledge of Good and Evil, they withdrew from the Garden, whereupon an actor all in black playing Lucifer swept in to taunt and tempt Adam with the fruit of the tree. After the Fall, when Adam and Eve realized they were naked (though of course the actors themselves were not), we in the audience were instructed to rummage in our packets and put on the green aprons we found there, representing the leaves with which our first parents covered themselves.

Elohim arrived on the scene to banish Lucifer, then explained to Adam and Eve that their disobedience required new commandments to be imposed, the Law of Obedience and the Law of Sacrifice. We were instructed to stand, raise our right arms to the square, and swear to obey each law in turn by chanting "Yes." This accomplished, we sat again.

"We will now," said the actor playing Elohim, "give unto you the first token of the Aaronic Priesthood, with its accompanying name, sign, and penalty. Before doing so, however, we desire to impress upon your minds the sacred character of the first token of the Aaronic Priesthood, as well as that of all the other tokens of the Holy Priesthood which you will receive in the temple this day. They are most sacred, and are guarded by solemn covenants and obligations of secrecy, to the effect that under no condition, even at the peril of your life, will you ever divulge them, except at a certain place that will be shown you hereafter. The representation of the execution of the penalties indicates different ways in which life may be taken."

What? I couldn't quite process what I'd heard. *Life may be taken?* The proceedings so far had been fascinating, if odd, but now I felt a strange dislocation, heard a buzzing in my ears. The buzzing was dread.

My father sat calmly beside me. I wiped damp palms on my white trousers. The veil between the spirit and mortal worlds was said to be thinnest in the temple, which imbued the business transacted here with an overwhelming gravity. I began to feel in my bones a sense of why it would be so wrong to drag these covenants into the light of the world of man.

"The first token of the Aaronic Priesthood is given by clasping the right hands and placing the joint of the thumb directly over the first knuckle of the hand, in this manner." He grasped the hand of a supplicant from the first row of seats, raising the grip high so we all could see. "We give unto you the first token of the Aaronic Priesthood. We desire all to receive it. All arise."

Elohim, Jehovah, and the others circulated through the audience, leaning in and reaching across seats until every last one of us had shared the sacred clasp. Elohim's hand was dry, papery, and solid in mine.

"The name of this token is the new name that you received in the temple today," said Elohim, returning to the front of the room. "The sign is made by bringing the right arm to the square, the palm of the hand to the front, the fingers close together, and the thumb extended. This is the sign. The execution of the penalty is represented by placing the thumb under the left ear, the palm of the hand down, and by drawing the thumb quickly across the throat to the right ear and dropping the hand to the side."

As Elohim recited the words, the officiator at the altar pantomimed slitting his own throat.

"All arise."

I stood a little unsteadily. More lore and rumors were coming back to me, about the doctrine of blood atonement Brigham Young had preached—that forgiveness for some sins could only be achieved by forfeiting one's life—and about secret ritual murders attributed to the Danites. I'd heard that shadowy cohort might still be lurking around, defending God's kingdom from apostates.

"Each of you make the sign of the first token of the Aaronic Priesthood. This is the sign. Now, repeat in your mind after me the words of the covenant, at the same time representing the execution of the penalty: 'I'—think of the new name—'covenant that I will never reveal the first token of the Aaronic Priesthood, with its accompanying name, sign, and penalty. Rather than do so, I would suffer my life to be taken.'"

Now was when I wanted to withdraw rather than taking on these obligations of my own free will and choice. The world felt as upside-down as if I'd just discovered my parents were Russian spies. I *still* wish I'd had enough sense of self to laugh at the absurdity of it all and walk out the door. But everything in my life thus far had conspired to deliver me to this initiation, and so, with a very real sense that I was putting my body and soul in peril, I thought those words in my mind as I drew a shaky thumbtip across my throat. I could imagine the flesh parting like paper beneath my thumb, could almost feel the slow sting and shock as bright blood cascaded from that lipless grin to stain my shirt crimson.

And Elohim said, "That will do."

We dropped back into our seats, a motley collection of bloodless specters.

NOTHING AT OUR BLAND, BORING SUNDAY MEETINGS HAD PREpared me for anything like the endowment. Belying the white finery around me, this was something primitive, savage, primordial. This was real Old Testament shit. It seemed too obscene to be enacted in so sacred a place. And what did it really mean? If should break my oaths, who would show up to enact the penalty? Would I be expected to do it myself? Or was this an example of the torments that would await me in the next life?

It also seemed uncomfortably close to what the Book of Mormon decried as "secret combinations"—murderous cabals bound together by secret signs and blood oaths. "For the Lord worketh not in secret combinations," the scriptures taught us. But if that was true, then what was this happening all around me?

Some historical perspective is in order, perspective I didn't have at the time. In September 1826, hooded men burned a printing press in Batavia, New York, and beat the owner severely. The press had just produced proofs of a book exposing the rites and covenants of Freemasonry. Shortly thereafter, the book's author, William Morgan, was abducted, never again to be seen alive.

Five men, all well-known Masons, were tried for Morgan's kidnapping and presumed murder in January 1827 at Canandaigua, New York, not far from Joseph Smith's home. Three of the five were acquitted, while the two others received light jail sentences. Further trials resulted in more acquittals, sparking an anti-Masonic fervor the likes of which the country had never seen.

It was in the midst of this furor that Joseph Smith began work on the Book of Mormon, so it's no surprise to find evidence of these attitudes in the text. In fact, this was so obvious to readers of the day that one newspaper, in reviewing it, labeled it Joe Smith's "anti-Masonick Bible."

It was a different world, however, in 1842. The Morgan affair had long blown over, and Freemasonry was enjoying a resurgence, its members again making inroads in business and politics. The Mormons were experiencing a renaissance of their own. Under Joseph's leadership in Illinois, they had purchased most of the land on a bluff overlooking the Mississippi River. There they built a fine city and christened it Nauvoo, from a Hebrew term connoting natural beauty.

Joseph's emissary to Springfield, John C. Bennett, had won extraordinary powers for the new city in its charters, as state legislators fell over each other to curry favor with the Mormons. (Not only did the Saints comprise a large and powerful new voting bloc, but Illinois was also eager to prove to the nation how much more tolerant it was than Missouri.) Nauvoo's government was free to enact any laws it wanted, so long as they didn't contravene the Constitution, and the Nauvoo Legion, a military force nominally part of the state militia, was in effect sanctioned as a private army. Joseph, as its head, had taken to wearing a fancy military coat wherever he went, and preferred being addressed as "General."

The church was growing again, as well. After shrinking by almost eight percent in 1839, membership was now expanding by around eighteen percent a year and would soon hit 25,000. Much of the credit was due to the phenomenal success of the missionary effort in Great Britain, where Brigham Young devised an ingenious emigration program that helped new converts relocate cheaply to America.

All this made the Mormons an attractive target constituency for Masonic political candidates. At the urging of a judge in Springfield, the Mormon Masons in Nauvoo, whose number included Hyrum Smith, applied to charter their own lodge. In March 1842, the Grand Master of the Grand Lodge of Illinois, Abraham Jonas, arrived to help initiate new members. Jonas was, not coincidentally, running for the state legislature.

Among the new inductees was Joseph, who became an Entered Apprentice Mason, the lowest of Freemasonry's three degrees, on March 15. The next day, he received the Fellow Craft and Master Mason degrees, though a thirty-day waiting period was normally required before any advancement in rank. Soon there were more Masons in Nauvoo than in all the lodges in the rest of the state combined.

On May 4, a scant fifty days after first participating in the Masonic mysteries, Joseph Smith introduced a new ordinance, the "endowment," to his most trusted followers in a room above his red brick store in Nauvoo. This ordinance, with its grips, signs, and passwords, bore a striking similarity to the Masonic initiation rites—a parallel which could not have been lost on Joseph's inner circle, since most of them were Masons as well.

The rites and symbols of Freemasonry were said to date back to the construction of Solomon's Temple in Jerusalem, though in fact they descended only from the customs of medieval stonemason guilds. Mormon apologists nevertheless insist that Joseph must have sensed eternal principles at work in the Masonic ceremonies, since he borrowed from them so shamelessly.

Learning all this—not to mention seeing the blood oaths and penalties scrubbed from the endowment in 1990—would play a big part in helping me find my way out of the Mormon Church in 1995. Which, frankly, was years too late.

As THE ENDOWMENT CEREMONY WORE ON, WE SWORE FURTHER oaths, learned further secret handshakes, and pantomimed further grisly penalties. We clothed ourselves in robes, sashes, and caps from our packets as we progressed from room to room. The women donned white veils. I pushed my numb horror to the back of my mind.

Our penultimate stop in the temple was the bright, white Terrestrial Room. Its most prominent feature was a gossamer white curtain that stretched along the wall in front of us. One of our temple guides introduced it as the Veil and proceeded to explain the symbols sewn into it at regular intervals, symbols that matched the smaller ones on our undergarments. The L-shaped mark of the square was to suggest "exactness and honor in keeping the covenants." The V-shaped mark of the compass was to suggest "an undeviating course leading to eternal life."

We queued up at various stations along the Veil, where a man on the far side, representing the Lord, would reach through slits to embrace each supplicant. After being tested in all the proper grips and key words, the supplicant was allowed to pass through a hidden rent in the Veil. Those grasping, disembodied arms made for a tableau as surreal as any from Cocteau.

I preceded my father at the front of the line. Locked in a strange embrace with my unseen tester, I regurgitated all the passwords and handshakes successfully, and I was allowed to pass through the Veil.

The Celestial Room, which I now entered, was cold and very quiet, with a soaring ceiling and elegant chandeliers. Silent robed figures were scattered about in ones and twos, some perched on the pale, over-stuffed furniture in meditation or prayer. My mother was waiting for me, as I assumed she would be one day when I crossed the actual Veil. I was linked to her and my father through their sealing in this temple, born in the covenant. That chain stretched back through the generations, and would stretch forward through me. To break that chain, to ever betray my oaths, seemed unthinkable.

My mother hugged me. "It's wonderful, isn't it?" she whispered.

I nodded, dazed. I tried to soak in the atmosphere, but the hush deadened thought. Supposedly some people were visited by dead relatives in the Celestial Room. I thought of my Line of Authority, the chart that traced the provenance of my priesthood back through time. My father had ordained me an elder. He in turn had been ordained a high priest by this name, who had been ordained a high priest by that name, and so on back in very few steps through evocative pioneer names like Heber J. Grant, George Q. Cannon, and Brigham Young, apostles and prophets who might have conversed with angels or even Jesus Christ in this very room. At the bottom of the chart, Joseph Smith and Oliver Cowdery were ordained by the resurrected apostles Peter, James, and John, and they in turn by Christ. Lines of power, lines of transmission, intersecting and weaving backward to the Author of us all, himself an exalted man who had proven true and faithful to *his* God in *his* lifetime on *his* world . . .

The mind reeled.

My father joined us moments later. "I tell you, son," he said quietly, patting me on the shoulder, "you learn something new every time. It never fails."

What had *I* learned that morning? That heaven was a fraternity for old people? That blood oaths weren't just for pirates, or for rich kids from Yale?

And if the endowment was so wonderful, our theology so vast, generous, expansive, and ennobling, then why did I feel so helpless and degraded?

THE WHITE-AND-TAN LANDSCAPE OF SOUTHERN ALBERTA unrolled like a parchment scroll. On our way down Highway 2, we stopped in Okotoks and High River and Claresholm, my pulse quickening at every station. By the time we turned east onto the Crowsnest Highway at Fort Macleod, I couldn't stop hearing one passage from the endowment ceremony in my head. Lucifer, having appeared again on the scene, gets in this last chilling aside before slinking away after his banishment:

"I have a word to say concerning these people. If they do not walk up to every covenant they make at these altars in this temple this day, *they will be in my power!*"

I wasn't having second thoughts, exactly, but I was trying to wriggle out of seeing this flight of mine as a breach of my covenants with God. By undertaking the Law of Sacrifice, after all, I had sworn on my very life to consecrate my time and possessions to the church.

At the very least, I'd made a commitment to God by accepting a mission call, if not a covenant. What would the consequences be for turning my back on it? Were there souls in Alberta awaiting the one messenger able to touch them in such a way as to bring them to a knowledge of the truthfulness of the Restored Gospel? Was I that messenger? Would the sins they committed in their ignorance of the gospel now stain *my* soul?

But weren't there more ways than one to serve God's purposes? Why had he given me a gift for writing and the desire to use it if not for me to exercise it in his name? To redeem my failure as a missionary, I resolved, I would rededicate my life to the mastery of my craft. I would create glorious works of fiction that illustrated eternal principles with subtlety and artfulness, subliminally preparing the minds and souls of all who read them to receive the true word of God from his missionaries.

I would be to science fiction what Donny Osmond was to pop music. This, sleepless, I promised to God.

CHAPTER 26

IN LETHBRIDGE WE HAD A THIRTY-MINUTE STOPOVER. AFTER A PIT stop in the station, I grabbed a burger to go from the lunch counter and devoured it on the bus in sweaty anxiety. This was Elder Garrett's territory, of course, and the headquarters of my zone. It was also a much smaller city than Calgary, and even if by some miracle Elder Dedman had still not reported me missing, the chances of a random street encounter with the local missionaries felt much higher here.

But I cleared Lethbridge without incident, and now we rolled southeast on Highway 4. We'd traveled 220 kilometers since Calgary, or nearly 140 miles, but it was still sixty miles to the border. I pulled *Nine Stories* out of my shoulder bag. I'd been having a hard time with the time-traveling complexities of *Millennium*, I was so jumpy, but maybe short stories would suit my attention span better. At any rate, it would be good to be able to discuss the book with Katrina when I reached home.

I read the first story, "A Perfect Day for Bananafish," with increasing bafflement. Like the very bus I was riding, the narrative carried me further from sense and safety with every line. By the time Seymour Glass took his pistol out and shot himself, I was unmoored, utterly at sea. Alone and unsettled, I put Salinger away and pulled John Varley out again.

Tiny towns with names like New Dayton, Warner, and Milk River ticked past, each with its easily spotted LDS meetinghouse. In Brooks, Mormons had made up less than four percent of the population. Here, farther south, their ratio was much higher because this was the land to which prophet John Taylor had sent settlers in 1887 to establish colonies beyond the reach of the American government. (Others were dispatched to the Mexican states of Chihuahua and Sonora.) I was grateful that we stopped in none of these towns for longer than two or three minutes.

Around two o'clock we finally reached the international border at Coutts. Here two small government checkpoints faced each other across a wide concrete apron. A U.S. Immigration officer boarded the bus and instructed all passengers traveling to the United States to produce their identification and follow him into the checkpoint for processing.

A cold sun sparkled on remnants of old snowdrifts at the edges of the pavement. The land around us was barren and flat. Only a handful of cars were parked near the checkpoint. None appeared to be mission-issue Chevrolets. I looked in every direction as I crossed the open concrete. Not an elder in sight.

Almost home.

I awaited my INS interview with a dozen other passengers in a lounge painted in faded institutional browns and greens. After ten minutes or so, I was ushered into a corner office that looked out on the pavement. Across a sheet-metal desk, a uniformed man squinted at me with prematurely wrinkled eyes. He asked my name, my citizenship, and what business had brought me to Canada.

"Religious," I said self-consciously. "I'm a—or rather, I *was* a missionary for the LDS Church."

"And you're not any longer?"

A mixture of sadness, strangeness, and relief washed over me. "I guess I quit," I said in wonder.

"So you're returning permanently to the U.S.?"

I nodded. "Yes."

"How did you enter Canada? On a passport? On a work visa?"

"Work visa."

"Do you have it?"

I removed the notarized visa from my wallet and unfolded it carefully. As a missionary I was not *exactly* an employee of the church, but I'd still be unable to proselytize in Canada without this piece of paper. I handed it over like Dumbo relinquishing his magic feather.

The officer examined the visa, nodded, and smoothed it out on the desk. "I'm afraid I'm going to have to keep this. You're certain you're leaving for good?"

I swallowed. Time to burn that bridge. "Yes," I said with unexpected force.

"All right, then." He slipped my visa into a manila folder and stood up. "As long as you're not carrying any fruits or vegetables with you in your luggage, that's it. Thank you, Mr. Shunn."

As I left the office, a woman directed me down a short hall and out a door at the far end of the checkpoint. A Trailways bus idled on the American side of the border—Sweet Grass, Montana. Its driver was porting our luggage from the Greyhound. Freedom was unfenced and only a chip shot away.

I was halfway across the concrete beneath a sky of grudging blue, when a commanding voice called out from somewhere behind me. "Excuse me. Excuse me, *sir!*"

Suddenly queasy, I looked over my shoulder.

The officer who had given us instructions on the Greyhound was moving to intercept me. "Excuse me, sir. Are you Donald William Shunn the Second?"

"That's me." This was it. The end of the line. Somehow the bastards were going to keep me here.

"Sir, I've been asked to pass a message along to you." Opaque black sunglasses made his expression unreadable. "I want to emphasize that you are under absolutely no obligation to comply, but we have two representatives from your church back there in the station, and they've asked if they can talk to you."

I didn't know whether to heave a sigh of relief or heave my lunch.

Seeing my hesitation, the officer said, "Once again, sir, you're under no legal obligation. I'm passing this message along as a courtesy. If it's what you want, you're perfectly free to walk onto that bus and ignore these people. I'll be happy to bring them any message you like."

I could only imagine what desperate entreaties the two elders, whoever they were, had breathlessly burbled to the personnel at the checkpoint. I could only imagine what President Tuttle must have told them in the phone call that had launched them south down Highway 4 from wherever they were stationed. I could only imagine the nickname they'd coin on their dejected way north again, which would spread among the missionaries like whooping cough.

Runaway Shunn.

"I don't want to talk to them. Tell them they can't stop me from going home."

"My pleasure." His bristly black mustache twitched with the barest trace of a smile as he shook my hand. "And let me be the first to welcome you back to the United States of America, Mr. Shunn."

He turned on his heel and marched away.

As I walked to the bus, across the American border, I felt lighter than I had in months. In years, maybe. It was like passing through an invisible Veil into a better world.

I took a seat near the back of the bus. When we started to move, I looked through the rear window at the checkpoint. Staring back at me from behind a window of their own were two tiny faces, crumpling in misery above white shirts, ties, and name tags. Dwindling to nothing.

I laughed. I felt like a character in a movie. I felt like I'd escaped from East Germany.

As the afternoon shadows lengthened, I started thinking about what I'd do once I reached Utah. How would I break the news to my parents?

But now that I thought about it, my parents probably knew already—or if not, they soon would. Now that I'd slipped out of his jurisdiction, President Tuttle would *have* to call them. Or maybe he'd call church headquarters and let them break the news instead. Of course, he'd have to call church headquarters no matter what. They were probably on alert already, sending an all-points bulletin to every missionary along my route.

I began to sweat. Maybe taking the bus had been a bad idea. There'd almost certainly be a reception committee in Salt Lake when I arrived, if not at some earlier point along my route. Maybe I should call Katrina and ask her to meet me in Ogden, or Tremonton, or even Pocatello, Idaho. Judas Proust, I hadn't thought this through at all. I should have had an exit strategy from the start. I should have had contingency plans. I should have involved Katrina already. What the hell was I thinking?

I forced myself to calm down. I'd have to face church leaders again at some point. I still had time to work everything out. Shelby and Conrad were behind me, and Great Falls was coming up fast. That was 120 miles south of the border, with nearly 600 to go after that. Maybe by the time we reached Helena or Butte, the church would have organized its American welcoming party. For now, I'd find some dinner in Great Falls, and I'd take some time to *think*.

The sun was touching the bare treetops as we pulled into Great Falls. The bus station was a cramped two-story building, its first floor a clutter of ticket windows and vending machines. We had forty-five minutes to stretch our legs. This would be our longest stop until Idaho Falls.

Two dozen people crowded the lobby. As I made my way across the scuffed gray tile, I noticed a silver-haired man in a black leather jacket, loitering. Had he glanced my way as I walked in? I wasn't sure, but something told me I needed to get out of there.

Don't be paranoid. There wasn't a toilet on the bus, and I badly needed to pee. *You're fine.*

The signs indicated a men's room on the second floor. I climbed the narrow staircase. A casual glance over the railing when I reached the top showed the man in the leather jacket starting up after me. *Shit.*

I took a few steps into the dusty, low-ceilinged hallway upstairs, trying to breathe evenly. I could see no way out but a pebbled window reinforced with chicken wire at the far end. It was the men's room or back down the stairs.

Judas Proust, settle down. This isn't a spy novel. Just do your business, walk out, and get some dinner. This guy's got nothing to do with you.

The men's room was armored in cracked yellow tile. A man in a duster hemmed with dried mud washed his hands at a sink to my left. I walked past him as the men's room door slapped shut behind me. Water deposits stained the four floor-length urinals. I stepped to one of the middle units and fumbled with my zipper.

The door opened as I began relieving myself. I heard the man in the duster walk out, but another set of slow footsteps clicked across the floor and stopped six feet behind me. My chest felt hollow. The urgent, endless torrent splashing the porcelain rooted me in place.

Behind me, the man in the leather jacket said, "Elder Shunn?"

I could have denied it. I could have screamed. I could have turned and pissed on his black cowboy boots. When I think back on that moment, I wish I'd done any or all of those things, but exhaustion, anger, and resignation had wrung all the ideas out of me.

Over my shoulder, I bitterly snapped, "You picked a fine time for a confrontation."

I could just see him, leaning against the tiled wall with his arms folded. "This gives us a chance to talk."

"So talk," I said, shaking off and zipping up. I felt less vulnerable with my dick stowed, but not by much.

"Okay. I'm President Garfield, and yes, I know how that sounds. I'm president of the Great Falls Stake."

I crossed to the sinks. My hands shook as I turned the taps. I was so stupid, so naive. I watched him in the mirror. "You don't look like a stake president."

"I appreciate that." He was short and trim, and wore black jeans and a black T-shirt with the leather jacket. "You've got a lot of people worried about you, you know, Elder Shunn. You've got a mission president back in Calgary who's just sick about this. He's trying to figure out what he did wrong."

I dried my hands and just looked at him.

He shifted his feet. "Listen, why don't you come back to my spread. Just to talk."

"I've got a bus to catch."

"There's always another bus. Your ticket will be good for the next one. We'll give President Tuttle a call, let him know you're okay. Maybe we'll talk Sister Garfield into serving some of her famous lasagna. You must be getting sick of road food."

I made a sound like gears grinding low in my throat. I don't know what kind of Jedi mind trick it was, but I just couldn't help *trusting* church leaders when they spoke reasonable-sounding words. I didn't know how not to. It was my kryptonite.

At the same time, I dreaded the looming confrontation with my parents. Anything that might help put that off a little longer, or might help ease me into it by smoothing the way, sounded pretty attractive just then.

"All right, okay," I said, and I hated myself for it. But I promised myself I'd still be on the next bus.

PRESIDENT GARFIELD HELPED ME CARRY MY LUGGAGE TO HIS CAR, a gleaming black Camaro IROC-Z convertible. He was an attorney, he explained as we roared off. I had told him he didn't look like a stake president, but now I realized that wasn't true. My stake president back home in Kaysville, Hank Clearmountain, was an airline pilot, and Garfield had the same confident air of unquestionable authority. That was no doubt why I'd spotted him so readily at the bus station. He was like a wolf trying to lie low in a pack of dogs.

At their cozy ranch-style home, Sister Garfield fussed over me like any good Mormon mother, and her lasagna was as good as promised. After supper the president and I retired to his study, a room of dark wood and crimson felt bricked over with law books and family photos.

"We've had a lot of missionaries in this family," he told me, waving at the walls as we settled into a pair of red leather chairs studded with brass tacks. "Our youngest is serving right now in Alabama. We know how hard it can be."

I steeled myself, and for the next fifteen minutes resisted every suggestion that I return to Calgary and give my mission another chance. He was earnest, dogged, compassionate, persuasive, but I stood firm. The shoe had dropped—my first major obstacle, a church leader, had appeared. I no longer had to dread its arrival. It was here, in front of me. This gave me the courage to stick to my guns, and I took great pride in doing so.

"I understand completely, Elder Shunn." President Garfield crossed to a gorgeous desk, consulted a note, and dialed his phone. "You've made up your mind, and I respect that. We should just get your mission president on the line so we can let him know."

I shifted in my chair and swallowed as Garfield pressed the receiver to his ear.

"Yes, President, hello," he said after a few moments. "This is Grant Garfield, down in Great Falls. Yes, I do, I have him here with me. Fine, no, he's just fine. We've taken care of him, made sure he's fed. Quite an appetite this young man has! No, he's still fixed on going home. Uh-huh. Uh-huh. Well, I'll sure ask him." He covered the receiver. "Elder

Shunn, President Tuttle wants to know if you'll talk to him for a minute."

I winced. "No, I really don't care to."

"Your president would really like to hear from you, Elder," said Garfield, his furrowed brow a poignant plea. "He's got to talk to your parents, after all."

Reluctantly I stood and took the phone. "Hello?"

"Elder Shunn! Hello! This is President Tuttle!" Even long-distance, his voice was oversized and bright, though that blanket of affability seemed to muffle something wounded. "How are you?"

"I'm okay."

"I'm glad to hear it! We sure miss you here."

"Yeah."

"We'd sure like you to think hard about coming back. There's still a place here for you."

I sighed. "President, I don't think it's for me."

"We can talk more about that, Elder, but if you do really want to go home, at least please come back and let's do it the right way. We'll give you a proper release from your mission and a plane ticket back to Utah if that's what you decide you want. But *please* don't just pick up and run. There's a better way to do this—better for you, for your family. Better for everyone involved."

"Really, no thank you."

"Elder, think about your parents. They're so worried about you. I want to be able to tell them I know you're okay."

"I'm fine, President, I'm just fine." Darkness pressed in against the windows. I looked at my watch. "In fact, I probably need to be catching the next bus soon."

"I don't like thinking about you out there on the road, Elder Shunn, all alone, the middle of the night." He sounded forlorn. "It's not safe out there. The open road, it's no place for a missionary."

That jagged spike was back, driven deeper into my skull with every word. I had nothing to fear on "the open road"—nothing but missionaries and church leaders. I could see it now, what I had to look forward to at every fucking bus stop between here and Salt Lake.

"Elder, stay over tonight with President Garfield. He's offered already. First thing in the morning, you'll get on a bus back to Calgary. We'll do this right, get you an honorable discharge, put you on a plane. What do you say?"

I knew better. I did. But I heard myself agree.

CHAPTER 27

I FOLLOWED ELDER FEARING AND ELDER HARDY INTO THE MISSION office Wednesday morning. President Tuttle was waiting in the entry hall and greeted me with a firm handshake.

"Good morning, Elder Shunn. Beautiful day, isn't it?"

I adorned my mumbled response with a scowl. It had been a long thirty-six hours.

Rather than put me up at his home Monday night, President Garfield had tried to farm me out to two zone leaders in Great Falls. But those elders, busy with appointments, had palmed me off on two other missionaries in their district, Elder Densley and Elder Goff. It turned out Densley and Goff were even bigger buckets than Dedman and I— or kickers, as they told me it was called in their mission. Their first move after they picked me up was to drop by a downtown pawn shop and borrow fifty bucks from the sleazy local member who ran the place. Armed with cash, they took me bowling. Afterward, we stopped by a video store and rented a whole stack of R-rated movies. On a contraband television in their tiny pit, we watched Eddie Murphy curse a blue streak in *Delirious* and Kelly Preston get full-frontal in *Mischief*. It was four in the morning before I stretched out on their couch for some shut-eye. It was six when my travel alarm woke me. My contacts were gritty.

At seven, Densley and Goff drove me to the bus station, where President Garfield met us with my return ticket. The trip took most of the day, but nearly ended before noon at the border checkpoint in Sweet Grass. A pretty young immigration officer grilled me about my business in Canada for fifteen long minutes and seemed to grow more and more skeptical of my story by the moment. Why, after all, would someone who quit a job and left the country want to reenter the country just so he could leave again?

I had to admit, it didn't make a lot of sense to me either. "I just want to go home," I said at last, in utter misery.

The officer smiled suddenly, transforming herself from functionary to confidante. "A mission's a hard thing, eh, Elder?" she said, and winked at me.

My mouth must have fallen open in shock.

She laughed. "I went to Spain on mine. It was tough. And I want to help you, Elder, but the problem is, you surrendered your work visa yesterday, so you really shouldn't be readmitted." She drummed her fingers on the desk. "But let me see what I can do."

She left the interview room for about ten minutes while I wondered if my trip north was destined to end here, despite everything. But she returned triumphant, with my visa in hand. Somehow she'd sweet-talked it out of her opposite number at the American checkpoint.

I suppressed a groan. I'd begun to hope that Canadian bureaucracy would take all further decisions out of my hands.

It was late Tuesday afternoon when I reached Calgary. Fearing and Hardy let me wait an hour at the station before picking me up. I expected to get my honorable release from President Tuttle immediately and be on my way again, but when we reached the mission office he took only enough time to greet me and suggest I spend the night in prayer before rushing off to some other appointment. I had no choice but to accompany the apes on their evening proselytizing rounds. By the time they brought me with them to the office the next morning, I was at the end of my patience.

Even as President Tuttle escorted me past the bullpen where the office staff worked, I was on my guard, ready for the assault to begin. I knew this wasn't going to be easy, but I was determined to stand my ground. I had spent so many miserable weeks dreaming of an impossible escape, I still couldn't believe how close I was to actually making it, and how far away. All the resistance I'd encountered had only hardened my resolve. What had once been unthinkable was now, for me, the only acceptable outcome.

President Tuttle closed his office door behind us and settled himself behind his desk. "Shall we pray, Elder?" he asked, eyes somber but hopeful.

I shrugged. "Sure."

We pushed back our chairs and knelt to one side of his desk. He folded his arms. "Elder Shunn, would you?"

"Sure." I bowed my head and closed my eyes. "Our dear Heavenly Father, we thank thee for all the many blessings thou hast given us. We pray to thee this morning that thou wilt send thy spirit to be with us, that we might conduct our business swiftly and decisively, and with thy blessing upon us, and we do so in the name of thy son, Jesus Christ, amen."

"Amen."

If he had hoped to awaken in me a sense of duty and penitence, it hadn't worked.

"Have you spent time in personal prayer this past night, like I suggested?" he asked when we were both seated again.

"Yes." I tried to control my breathing. I was feeling a little dizzy.

Tuttle leaned forward. "And did you get any answer?"

"I did. The Spirit told me I'm right to go home."

He spread his hands and cocked his head. "Elder Shunn, the Spirit does not work that way."

"I know what I felt," I said, and a thrill of horror ran through me. One does not contradict the word of one's leaders.

His eyebrows drew together. "You know, Elder, sometimes if we're not praying sincerely, or if we're not listening closely enough, we hear only what we want to hear."

"How are we supposed to know the difference?"

He sighed. "We have to ask ourselves whether or not what we're feeling is in harmony with the commandments, with the words of our living prophet."

"That gives us the answer before we even pray, then, doesn't it?"

He nodded. "Often it does. Often we know the right answer from the start."

"Then why bother to pray at all?"

"So that we can gain our own testimony of those principles and commandments."

"But what if the answer we get doesn't match the one we've been taught?"

"Then you keep praying until it does."

I licked my lips. "I know what I felt," I said, though the words left me breathless. I'd never been this frank with one of my church leaders before, nor this combative. "I'm going home, President."

Tuttle clasped his hands on the desktop, exhaling heavily. "Elder Shunn, you're a brilliant young man, but that can work against you as much as it can for you. Satan loves to play to the vanity of the intellect. He can use it to convince you to listen to your head over your heart, your mind over your spirit." He shook his head. "Don't let him do it. Don't let him win here. Don't make the biggest mistake of your life."

I could barely get enough air to speak. My mouth was so dry it crackled. "My mind is made up," I told him, though everything I'd ever been taught told me to capitulate. "There's nothing you can say that will keep me here."

AFTER THAT IT GOT UGLY, THOUGH NEITHER OF US RAISED HIS voice.

President Tuttle tried bribery. He'd heard reports from Brooks, he said, about questionable behavior on the part of Elder Dedman. If I would stay, he promised to set me up in a new city with one of his best, most responsible elders as a companion. I turned him down.

He tried scare tactics. He cited not just the commitment I'd made to God by accepting a mission call but also the Law of Obedience I'd sworn in the temple. He observed that any woman who would have me after I'd abandoned a mission was not the sort of woman who would inspire me to the great achievements of which I was capable. He predicted that my dereliction of duty would cast a shadow as long as my life, impairing my ability to finish what I started, crippling my sense of self-worth, setting a precedent for failure over which I would never triumph. No worldly success, he said, could ever compensate for this one preeminent defeat.

He tried appealing to my sense of ambition and vanity by pointing out how difficult advancement in the church would be without having completed a mission. "I'm not saying that you *couldn't* ever become a bishop or a stake president. I'm just saying it'll be a whole lot harder, and a lot more unlikely."

"I don't want to be a bishop or a stake president."

"If you did, you wouldn't be worthy of the calling."

The conversation was plunging down a rabbit hole, and I was tired—tired of fighting, tired of non sequiturs, tired of jumping through hoops at the behest of people who only *thought* they knew me. Did this J. Matheson Tuttle—this fat, smug businessman who in real life sold *insurance*—actually believe, as we taught our investigators in the second discussion, that the free agency of mankind, the right to make one's own decisions without compulsion, was one of the basic principles of the universe? It didn't seem that way. I felt like Joseph Smith at the siege of Far West. I had crossed enemy lines in good faith, thinking I was only there to negotiate, when in fact my foes aimed to take me prisoner. I wanted it to be over. I wanted my freedom.

"President," I said, "this is pointless. How long do we have to do this?"

He froze, mouth open, hands raised, then slowly let his palms sink to the desktop. He looked me straight in the eyes.

"Elder Shunn—*Bill*. Listen to me. This mission is where your Father in Heaven wants you, where he needs you. It's where he *commands* you to be. Please. Stay."

"No."

He let out a long, defeated sigh. "Well," he said, looking not at me but down and to the side. "Obviously my breath is wasted here. If you want to leave, then by all means leave. I've got the paperwork next door. Let me just go get it."

He shambled past me out the door, face fallen. His slumped shoulders stirred up more guilt in me than I'd felt all morning.

I'D BEEN WAITING ALONE IN HIS OFFICE FOR SEVERAL MINUTES, increasingly uneasy, when I heard a phone ring out in the bullpen. A moment later President Tuttle leaned his head through the doorway.

"Elder Shunn," he said in wonderment, "you have a phone call. You can get it right there." He pointed at the desk and pulled the door shut behind him.

I steeled myself, hoping it wasn't my father. I picked up the receiver and after a moment realized that I needed to press the button beside the blinking red light. "Hello?"

"What is wanted?" asked a distant, static-laced voice.

I would have known that gentle Southern drawl anywhere, even if it weren't impudently quoting from the endowment ceremony. "Elder Vickers?" My district leader from the MTC.

"One and the same! How are you, Shunn?"

"Oh, you know," I hedged, wishing the call were a coincidence but knowing it was not. "How's Yellowknife?"

"It's a real adventure. This town only comes alive in the winter. It's very strange. But listen, Elder Shunn, I hear you're having something of a crisis down there."

"Crisis is over. I'm on my way home."

"I'm sorry to hear that, truly sorry, my friend. You're a good man. We need you here, Shunn."

"I need myself elsewhere."

"No way, not half as much. Don't you remember our district, the way we all hung together at the MTC? Don't you remember how the guys all looked up to you?"

"I don't remember that," I said, my throat clotting.

"Oh, I see," said Vickers, quoting the endowment again, "your eyes are not yet opened. You have forgotten everything."

"No one looked up to me."

"They did. We all did. And when those elders hear that *Shunn* couldn't stick out the tough times, what do you think *they're* going to do when things get bad?"

"Decide for themselves, that's what."

"Your decision has repercussions."

I set my jaw. "I will not partake of that fruit."

Vickers laughed bitterly—a strangled, pathetic sound made all the more harsh by the poor connection. "Is there anything I can say to make you stay?"

"No, not a thing."

For several moments, all I heard was the ghostly static. "I am sorry—very, very sorry. But it was good to know you, Elder Shunn. You take care of yourself. Keep in touch."

My lungs constricted. "You, too, Elder Vickers."

"It shall be done."

A FEW MINUTES LATER PRESIDENT TUTTLE POKED HIS HEAD IN again, interrupting my melancholy reverie. "Would you believe it, Elder Shunn? You have another phone call."

When he closed the door, I gripped my head in my hands. I took a deep breath, let it out slowly, and picked up the blinking line. The booming voice of Hank Clearmountain, my stake president back home, greeted me.

It was like I was trapped in a game of *Punch-Out!!*, squaring the mat against tougher and tougher opponents on my way to some unimaginably bloody championship bout.

"Hello, President," I said, and raised my dukes.

CHAPTER 28

In the building's front meeting room, near the fieldstone fireplace, sat a blond upright piano. While President Tuttle prepared my discharge papers, a seemingly endless process, I ran through every mournful number in my repertoire. The phone, thankfully, had not rung again after I dispatched President Clearmountain, and I couldn't stay cooped up in Tuttle's little office.

Elder Hardy wandered in. Three months earlier, he and Elder Fearing had stood at the front of this room, lecturing to us greenies about mission procedures. He listened to me for a minute or two before coming over and resting his elbows on top of the piano.

"You play beautifully," he said when I finished my number, pushing his hay-colored hair back from his forehead. "What was that?"

"Just a little thing I wrote."

"You *wrote* that?"

I shrugged. "Yeah. It's called 'Stars in My Pocket Like Grains of Sand.'"

"Interesting title. I think it fits."

"I named it after a novel."

He nodded. "I wish I could play. I took lessons when I was little, but I guess I didn't have the patience to stick with it." He was one of those people who always seemed to be smiling, and as he gazed wistfully over my head his toothy grin and freckled cheeks made him look like Howdy Doody. "I sure regret it now. If I could play like you? Boy. Did you take lessons?"

I laced my fingers together, cracked my knuckles. "Yeah."

"When did you start?"

"I was nine," I said.

"How long did you keep studying?"

"Seven years."

"Gosh, that's a long time. I bet it wasn't easy. It was probably hard to get you to practice."

"At first," I said, warming up to the topic. "But then I really fell in love with it. You couldn't get me to *stop* practicing."

"So it took you a while."

"Yeah."

"And it was worth going through that hard period where you didn't like to practice."

Finally it dawned on me what we were really talking about. I folded my arms and glared. "So, were you up all night working that one out? Just itching for the chance to use it?"

My tone erased his smile. "Elder Shunn," he said earnestly, "do you believe in the gospel? Do you still have a testimony?"

"Of course I do," I said, though I felt like a singer in a bad music video, where tepid lip-synching fails to match the emotion of the song. "That's not the issue."

"It is."

"It is not."

"Elder Shunn, I'm just trying to point out to you that—"

"Stop," I said, raising my palms. "All I want to do is sit here and play. I don't want to hear your trite little object lesson."

"Well, that's too bad," said Hardy, more like a scary puppet now. "Maybe I read you wrong. Maybe Fearing and I should have handled you the way Mason and Saylor handled Runaway McKay. Did you ever hear about Runaway McKay?"

"I heard they called him a pussy."

Hardy stroked his chin, looking at the ceiling. "No, I don't think that's one of the names they called him. But they *did* call him names. No fancy tricks. They just badgered him until he did the right thing. So is that what I'm gonna have to do to get you to stay, Elder Shunn? Badger you? Call you names?"

"Sticks and stones."

"You won't be around to hear it, anyway, when people start calling *you* Runaway. That'll make it easier to take." He stared me down without expression. "So you have fun *playing*. It probably *is* what you do best."

He turned and walked out, leaving me to clench my teeth in silence.

PRESIDENT TUTTLE FINALLY SUMMONED ME BACK TO HIS OFFICE, I assumed to fill out those discharge papers he'd been working on. I should have known better. The system was not designed to listen to what *I* wanted, or even to inquire into what was best for me. Or maybe it *was*, early on in the process, and my failure to speak up honestly about my true desires and misgivings had shunted me past all natural exit ramps. Now my only option was backing out over tire rippers rigged to keep me in.

Tuttle waved at the phone on his desk. "Another call for you, Elder."

I rolled my eyes. "President, I'm not interested in any more phone calls."

"I think you'd better take this one." He left the room, pulling the door closed behind him.

When I picked up the receiver, it was not without great trepidation. "Hello?"

Hearing the voice on the far end chilled me to the marrow. "Son, hello. This is your father."

It was a grueling conversation. My father used every weapon in his arsenal. We'd been saving money for this mission all my life. I'd be setting a terrible example for my brothers and sisters. He and my mother hadn't raised me to be disobedient like this. Everyone I knew, right down to the mailman, would be crushed with disappointment. Any marriage I entered into under circumstances like these would surely end in heartbreak and divorce. I'd be killing any chance of converting my non-member cousins.

"We've been working on Claire and Gabe for so long, and they're *close*," my father said. "But if you leave, we'll never get them. Why should they change their lives for something *you* won't even commit to?"

Rarely had I heard my father's voice so enervated, so swollen with emotion. It scared me. If only I'd had the guts to stand up to him before. If only.

But here I was. The day had come. No way was I giving up now.

"It's my choice," I said, with steel I'd never known I had. "I'm done with this."

"Son, I'm begging you, listen to me," he said, sounding strangled. "I know exactly what you're going through."

I barked a laugh. "Yeah, right. Sure you do."

"Just listen to me!" He drew a shuddering breath. "You know I went to Germany on my mission. I've told you and your brothers and sisters the story a thousand times. But I never told you about all the hypocrisy—and I'm not talking about the German people. I'm talking about the missionaries. I had an image in my head of what a missionary was and how one ought to behave. What I saw there did not square with that. I saw elders not working. I saw elders at the beer halls. I saw elders on *dates*, and not with random women, either. I mean with girls from church."

My stomach had clenched like a fist.

"I was appalled. I was sickened. My parents were dead, you know, and Bishop Klein wasn't sending me his money so I could spend thirty months in Sodom and Gomorrah. I was older than the other elders. I had better things to do. I wasn't going to waste my time in a cesspool like that. I only finished six months of my mission. That was it. That was all I could stand.

"And you know? Leaving seemed like a good idea at the time, the best idea. But it wasn't. Do you know why? Because I wasn't there for my own benefit. I was there for the Lord, and I let him down. And what have I felt since then? Nothing but pain and regret. *Nothing* I've done has ever worked out. Because I didn't stick things out in Munich, I've failed at *everything*. Not a day goes by that I don't wish I could go back and change what I did.

"Son, that mistake has followed me through the rest of my life. Don't let the same thing happen to you. You're so much smarter than I was. Stay. Stay on your mission. Don't let your life go to pot like mine."

I sat back, gasping. I couldn't believe my ears, but at the same time the story made terrible sense. I wanted to weep for my father, for this wall he couldn't get past, but even more I wanted to shake him, scream at him. All my life he had lied to me, lied about his mission, lied about who he was. And now here *I* was, the beloved firstborn son, on the verge of repeating history.

I felt used. I felt *betrayed*.

"Son? Are you there?"

"I'm here." I was clutching the receiver in a death grip. "Thanks for filling me in. I'm glad you did, because now I *won't* make the same mistakes as you. I'm coming home, and I won't let it ruin the rest of my life."

I flinched from the most disconcerting howl I've ever heard. My father broke down in sobs. The sound died abruptly as my mother came on the line.

"Bill," she demanded, "*what* did you say to your father?"

I THOUGHT I HAD VANQUISHED THE MIGHTIEST CHAMPION PRESI-
dent Tuttle could throw at me, but I hadn't reckoned on my mother.

I had never particularly regarded her as a spiritual powerhouse, despite that line of pioneer stock stretching all the way back to the begin-
nings of the church, and I knew she was perfectly capable of losing her
temper with me. Nonetheless, for the next ten minutes she proceeded to expound, calmly and convincingly, on all the positive aspects of
mission service, and on why I needed to finish.

At the end of it I was dazed and battered. I could not have repeated
a single word she said to me, nor could I have pinpointed the turning
point in her argument. It simply blew through me like wind, leaving
no impression on my memory as it erased my will and resolve.

I didn't know what had hit me. I burst into tears. "Okay, Mom.
Okay, I'll stay."

"It's the right thing to do."

My father was back on the line with her, his voice still in tatters.
"Obey your mission president, son," he said, no longer combative. "If
you just obey, you'll be blessed. You'll be okay."

"Okay," I repeated, broken at last. "Okay."

BOOK III

THE OCCIDENTAL TERRORIST

12/31/1986 - 3/12/1987

And it came to pass that when Nephi had declared unto them the word, behold, they did still harden their hearts and would not hearken unto his words; therefore they did revile against him, and did seek to lay their hands upon him that they might cast him into prison.

—Helaman 10:15, *The Book of Mormon*

CHAPTER 29

Meekly I crept into the bullpen to find President Tuttle. When he heard my news, he swept me into a joyful embrace, heedless of the office staff. Then he gripped me by the shoulders and studied my face from arm's length. His smile held a certain reserve, as if he wasn't quite ready to believe his good fortune, but his eyes sparkled. "What was it that finally changed your mind?"

I felt shell-shocked and fragile. "It was my mom. I wish I could tell you exactly what she said."

"The words don't matter. She made you feel the Spirit, the way only mothers can. That's what made the difference. Oh, this is such wonderful news, Elder Shunn."

I nodded dumbly, not sure what to say.

"You know," he went on, as if unable to stop himself, "if you were just some run-of-the-mill punk, I'd have given you a plane ticket yesterday. I'd have paid for it out of my own pocket. But you—I've known since we first met that you were one of the good ones, one of the *great* ones. You're going to be one of my leaders, Elder Shunn, mark my words. Oh, I'm *so* pleased. Thank the Lord. This is a miracle."

He left me standing there in the bullpen while he scurried off to round up the apes. I nodded to the Farnsworths, the elderly missionary couple from northern Utah who helped keep the books, and who had watched this scene with nervous eyes. As I did, my glance happened to fall on a sheet of notepaper lying on Elder Fearing's desk—a hand-written table of names, some of which, even upside-down, jumped out at me. Idly I rotated it with my fingertip.

MARTIN FOWLER—TRAINER, was listed first, with a notation of NOT HOME. VERNON VICKERS—MTC DL followed, and HENRY CLEAR-MOUNTAIN—STAKE PRES. Then DONALD SHUNN—FATHER and ANN SHUNN—MOTHER. NEIL PARTRIDGE—GFATHER, PATRIARCH. KEITH MCCORMICK—GF'S FATHER. A phone number accompanied each entry. All but the last two were checked off.

Absorbing that list, I sensed the steel trap around me, already closed.

AFTER I'D ENDURED HANDSHAKES AND HUGS FROM THE APES AND all the hullabaloo had died down, President Tuttle asked me back into his office.

"Like I promised before," he said, "I'm going to put you with one of my very best elders, right here in Calgary so I'll be close by. Elder Dedman's here in Calgary too, and I can't tell you how much trouble he's in. Brooks is in a horrible state, just horrible. The more I hear, the less I blame you for wanting to leave. I have one outraged bishop on my hands, and I've had to close the city to missionary work altogether. It'll be a good while before we can open it again. Do you understand the seriousness of this, Elder?"

Numb, I nodded. How many souls were still waiting in Brooks for the gospel? I felt the weight of them all on my shoulders.

"Good." His face darkened. "If you'll pardon my language, Elder Dedman is number one on my crap list right now. He's busted to junior companion, and his driving privileges are revoked. One more major screwup and he's out of here—I don't care *what* Salt Lake says. But not because of Brooks. I'm sure I have three or four other situations just like it brewing now. Do you know what Dedman's in the biggest trouble for?"

I shook my head, dreading the answer.

President Tuttle held my gaze. "For not doing *everything* in his power to stop you from leaving."

The words seemed to reverberate in the tiny office. I saw Elder Dedman facing our president across this selfsame desk, wincing under the lash of Tuttle's anger, my name a curse on his lips. When he helped me escape, he couldn't have known how much grief he was buying himself. Could he? The White Bible said nothing about what to do when your companion wants to ditch.

My mind reeled. There were more ways to commit sin than I'd ever imagined, ways that weren't enumerated in any book. The only way to negotiate a landscape of such moral quicksand was to keep my eyes fixed firmly on the gospel, and on the White Bible, and on my mission president.

I had come so close to falling. I couldn't come that close again.

"I'm telling you this, Elder Shunn, so you'll understand your own worth in the sight of God. I want you to put this episode behind you and concentrate on serving the Lord. Don't give another thought to Elder Dedman. That's over. Your new companion is Elder Snow, and I think you're going to love him. He's been out less than six months, but he's a district leader already. I want you to pay attention to everything he does and learn all you can, just as if you were preparing to step into his shoes. Okay?"

"Okay," I squeaked.

"Excellent." Tuttle steepled his fingers. "Now, one last thing. We're going to want to keep this little incident under our hats as much as possible. Not that it's anything to be ashamed of, but there are some missionaries who'll want to give you a hard time about it. I'd rather not subject you to that. You can rely on my discretion, and that of the office staff, and I assure you that you can trust your new companion about it. I wouldn't talk about it with anyone else, though. Some people can be awfully cruel, and that you do not need. Does that make sense?"

"Yes," I said, though I wondered how many people had heard about "this little incident" when the APB went out. Could I rely, for instance, on the discretion of the elders who'd tried to intercept me at the border?

"Wonderful." President Tuttle stood and shook my hand. "Your new companion should be here any moment. I can't wait to introduce you."

ELDER ADAM SNOW DROVE THE BLUE CAVALIER ONE-HANDED through Calgary's sunny afternoon streets. "So, Shunn, where are you from?"

"Hmm? What?" I slouched in the soft bucket seat, hypnotized by the postwar homes going by. We were in the southeastern quadrant of the city. "Oh, Utah."

"No shazz, Sherlock," said Snow. "You and everyone else I know. Where in Utah?"

Elder Snow was a striking fellow, if not exactly handsome. He stood about six feet tall, but his boyish face, mischievous eyes, and cowlick made him look like Dennis the Menace. I had liked him as soon as I shook his hand. I just hoped he was everything President Tuttle had promised. I hoped I was done with clods like Dedman or even Fowler.

"Uh, Kaysville. It's kind of near Ogden."

"I've heard of it." His nasal voice gave everything he said a slight sneer. "I think we've got a sister missionary from Kaysville."

Now *there* was a topic I didn't want to touch. It belatedly occurred to me that I could run into Nylund or Youtz in Calgary, not to mention Dedman, and that was the last thing I wanted. Especially Dedman, considering what he'd sacrificed for me. For no reason.

"How about you?" I asked. "Where are you from?"

"Sacramento, most recently. But really I'm from all over. Originally we lived in Snowflake, Arizona, with most every Flake in the church, but—"

I snickered.

"No, really. Snowflake was founded by William Flake and Erastus Snow, so that's where the name comes from. Not many of us Snows ever lived there, but plenty of Flakes did."

"Are you related to Lorenzo Snow?" He was the fifth president of the church, from 1898 to 1901.

"Distantly. Erastus and Lorenzo were apostles together, but they weren't close relatives. Does *your* family go back?"

"My mom's a Partridge. I'm descended from Edward on that side."

"Hey, *my* mom's got Partridges on her side. We're probably cousins."

"Cool." The church could make for a small, small world.

"But yeah, my dad left Snowflake a long time ago. He taught Institute for years, and now he's in charge of the whole Church Educational System for northern California."

"Wow." That would mean administering the Institutes of Religion that the church maintained near most college campuses—where LDS students could delve deep into Mormon history and doctrine alongside their degree programs—not to mention the region's seminary program. Serious responsibility.

"But in between, he got called as a mission president in Australia, so that's where I lived from fourteen to seventeen."

"Judas Proust, that must have been wild," I said, both impressed and intimidated. There weren't a lot of mission presidents in my family's social circle. "Did you go to school there and everything?"

"Oh, yeah, of course. I was more like a missionary than a regular kid, though, or at least that's how I felt. Sometimes it seems like I've been a missionary half my life. I wanted to leave on my own mission as soon as we got back from Australia, but not even my dad could get the church to let me go early. I'm so happy to be here now. I couldn't wait to get back out in the field. We did a lot of splits with the elders in Brisbane, my brother and I. That was the best. I learned so much." He pounded me on the leg. "So I hope you like tracting, Shunn. I really learned to love it."

I was supposed to be turning over a new leaf as a missionary, so I stifled my groan. "That'll definitely be—it'll be a change."

Snow's rubbery face creased with concern. "Prez told me a little about Brooks. That must have been tough."

I wondered how much President Tuttle had told him. "It wasn't easy."

"This won't be either. But it'll be fun. That's my motto—work hard, play hard. You play hoop, right?"

"Basketball?"

"That's what I said."

"I usually hit the piano instead."

"Hey, that's cool too. But basketball—I love it, man. I plan to raise a whole flippin' team, five sons. You come from a big family, Shunn?"

"I'm the oldest of eight."

"Not bad, not bad. I think twelve's the minimum for me. How about you?"

"Not, um, quite that many. Actually, I think I only want two or three."

"Hey, different strokes."

I smiled as I watched the city roll past. My new companion might be weirdly über-Mormon, but at least he didn't seem uptight. And apparently I hadn't lost all capacity for heretical thought.

ELDER SNOW PULLED OVER IN FRONT OF A BLOCKY BRICK APART-ment building in a neighborhood of mostly duplexes and quadplexes.

"Time to meet the district, Shunn," he said, yanking the parking brake. "Part of it, anyway."

I peered out the window. I felt overwhelmed by Calgary's vastness. "This isn't our place?"

"No, this is where the blisters live."

My heart raced. "Please don't say it's Nylund and Youtz."

He gave me an odd look. "It's Roper and Steed. They're great, you're gonna love them. Frap, Shunn, you look pale. Are you okay?"

If what I'd imagined was bad, the reality was worse. "You're kidding. Sister *Roper's* in our district?"

"Yeah. What's the problem?"

"Fowler and I took over from her in Brooks. She was a flippin' *legend*. Everyone there loved her, and I'm the one who got the place shut down. She's gonna hate me."

"Shunn, relax. She doesn't know anything about what happened in Brooks. Anyway, from what Prez said, it was your bucket companion who got the place shut down, not you."

"I sure didn't help."

"Getting some guys to work is like pushing a rock uphill. Now come on." He opened his door.

"But what if she asks me about Brooks?"

Snow looked back over his shoulder. "Just say the work wasn't going very well so Prez decided to close it. It's the truth, right? Let's go."

As I followed him up the walk, he said, "Now, fair warning, they might be a little bugged that Elder Philby's gone and they didn't get a chance to say goodbye. Mid-month transfers suck like that. But they did want to meet you."

I don't think he meant to twist the knife, but I felt it anyway. How many people had my stunt affected? What kind of juggling had it taken for President Tuttle and the apes to make room for both Dedman and me in the city? How many elders had been shuffled to accommodate my selfish agenda? I hadn't spared a thought until now for Elder Philby, who had probably loved this area and now was gone with no warning. I felt sick.

The day was cold and clear. We entered a central breezeway and descended a half-flight of stairs. Snow knocked at the first door we came to. "We know you're in there, you buckets! Throw down your hair dryers and come out with your hands up!"

"You'll never take us alive!" drawled a voice from inside. The door opened a crack. Two women in their twenties peeked out. "Unless you brought chocolate."

"In your dreams, Roper. But I did bring my new companion." He grabbed me by the elbow and pulled me over. "Sisters, Elder Shunn. Elder Shunn, Sister Roper and Sister Steed."

The door opened all the way. Sister Steed, short and round, leaned past her companion to shake my hand. "Pleased to meet you, Elder Shunn."

"Charmed as well," said Sister Roper, gripping my hand hard. She was gorgeous, with an incongruous golden tan. "Now don't just stand there catchin' flies, you two. Get on in here and help us hang our new shower rod."

Snow followed them in, but I dithered at the threshold. He stopped and looked back. "You heard the lady, Shunn."

I shook my head. "Elder, we can't."

The sisters were staring at me now too. "Of course we can," said Snow. "Just move your feet."

I might not always have obeyed it, but I knew the White Bible front to back. "It's against the *rules*," I said in a ridiculous stage whisper. "We're not supposed to go into sisters' apartments."

Snow rolled his eyes in mild annoyance. "Look, there are rules that are crucial to follow, and then there are rules that just get in the way of our work. The way I run my district, we're all friends. We hang out together. We have more fun that way, and we get a lot more done. We're here as friends, not to have an orgy."

After all I'd just been through, I couldn't bring myself to walk through that door. "But, but—"

Sister Roper reached past Snow and seized my arm. "Just hush up and get in here, Elder Shunn. We ain't gonna bite."

I followed the others into the living room, expecting Lucifer to leap cackling from some dusty corner. But there *were* no dusty corners. The apartment was as big as the one Fowler and I had abandoned in Brooks, with plenty of light from sliding glass doors that opened onto a grassy courtyard. Crafty decorating touches made it feel homey, and it was cleaner than any missionary pit I'd seen since Brooks.

"I'll make some Kool-Aid," said Sister Steed, bustling off to the kitchen.

Snow settled against a mound of needlepoint pillows on the couch. I sat down beside him somewhat self-consciously, while Roper took a seat in an armchair across from us.

"So, what happened to Philby?" she asked, crossing her legs and smoothing her khaki skirt. She filled out her pullover sweater like a pinup girl. "God decided he was such a saint for putting up with you that he translated him?"

Gospel humor! A translated person was someone God changed directly into a perfect, immortal state without tasting of death. Guiltily, I developed a small crush on Sister Roper.

"Bite me," said Snow with bored detachment. "Philby's over in Red Deer now, and Shunn just got here from Brooks. Roper, you served in Brooks, right?"

"Brooks? That was my *town*," said Roper, beaming. "How are things there, Elder Shunn?"

Had my laser vision worked, my new companion would have slumped to the floor as a pile of charred meat. "I hate to say it, but things in Brooks aren't so great. Fowler and I had a couple of baptisms in November, but it's been pretty dry otherwise. I guess President decided we'd done all we could, because now it's closed. He pulled us out."

"Oh, no," said Roper, leaning forward with such a look of concern in her green eyes that I forgot to breathe. I could understand why every-one loved her in Brooks. "You reckon he was right?"

I tried not to look where her name tag was pinned. "I really do think the work was at a standstill."

Roper shook her head, setting cascades of auburn hair in motion. "I'd have sworn there was more gold in Brooks than that. But at least you got a couple of dunks, right? Anyone I'd know?"

"Pam Laduke was first." At her blank look I said, "Teddy Laduke's wife. It was basically a shotgun wedding."

"Oh, yeah, I remember him. Never met her, though."

"It was a righteous dunk. But then right before Fowler died, we got Buddy Van Rijk."

"You got Buddy? No kidding?" She slapped her knee, grinning. "Hot dang, that was good work. We tried so hard with him."

For the first time in weeks, I felt some pride. I straightened in my seat. "It was mostly Elder Fowler."

"He couldn't have done it alone, Elder Shunn. Dang!"

Sister Steed placed a tray of iced cherry Kool-Aid on the coffee table. "Here you go, Elders," she said, handing me one. She was older than Roper, I realized now, more like thirty, her dark hair curly and short. "And when you're done, Elder Snow, let me show you what we need done in the bathroom."

"Oh, right, I keep forgetting." Snow picked up the other glass, drained it in one heroic swig, and let out a long *Ahhh*. "Okay, let's do it."

Snow followed Steed to the bathroom. The moment they left us alone, Roper's expression hardened. The piercing look she gave me peeled me open. "So, what's *your* story, Elder Shunn? How long you been out?"

"Four months almost," I said defensively.

"You have a girl back home." It was less a question than an accusa-tion.

"Uh, yes."

"Huh." She sniffed. "Why are you on a mission?"

Shit. She knows all about Brooks. I couldn't have felt more exposed with a Klieg light shining in my face. The story of Runaway Shunn was spreading like the plague, I just knew it.

"You know, the usual." I was the lamest excuse for a missionary on the face of the planet. "I figured it was the right thing to do."

"Uh-huh," she said. She stared at me for so long I could barely keep from babbling my every crime.

Snow's voice saved me. "Hey, Shunn, we need your help!"

Relieved, I skedaddled down the hallway. Sister Steed waved me into a tiny pink bathroom, where I found Elder Snow standing in the tub—fully clothed, thank goodness—holding a heavy shower rod. "Grab that end, Shunn? Help me get it in place."

I climbed into the tub with Snow. Roper had followed me into the bathroom and now she crowded between us, directing us imperiously with her hands on her hips as we tried to get the rod level and securely braced.

We had it almost in place when Steed cried out, "*Cheeeeeese!*"

Arms above my head, I looked toward the doorway just in time to see the flash go off.

"Ha ha ha!" Steed cackled, waving her camera. "Blackmail pictures! Two elders in the shower with a sister!"

Roper nearly fell over laughing. "Your turn, your turn! Trade places with me!"

Elder Snow shrugged at me. "Welcome to the district, bucko. Get used to it."

CHAPTER 30

THE YOUNG WOMAN WHO PEEKED OUT THE DOOR GLANCED FROM MY
name tag to Elder Snow's with a expression of distaste. "Yes?"

"Good morning, ma'am," I said. We were tracting in a development
on the southern edge of Calgary so new you could practically smell
last year's cow manure. Every beige house looked the same, and our
luck had been just as uniform. "My name's Elder Shunn, and this is
my companion, Elder Snow. We're representatives from the Church
of Jesus Christ of Latter-day Saints, and we're visiting your neighborhood today with news of another testament of Christ. We—"

She scowled. "No, thank you."

As she began to close the door, I said, "Ma'am, do you believe in the
Bible?"

She opened it again. She wore a long peasant dress and bounced a
baby on her hip. "Yes, I do. But I don't believe in your Mormon book."

"Have you read it?" The snide edge to her voice was getting my back
up, though I tried not to show it. "We have a copy here with some of
the best passages marked."

Her eyes narrowed as her baby began to squall. "Boys, I don't need
to read your book to know what you're all about." She reached for something out of the sight, then thrust a pamphlet at me. "It's all right here."

On the cover was a drawing of two shadowy men standing at someone's front door. I raised my hands like the pamphlet was a snake. "No, thank you."

"What—are you afraid of the truth? You people preach that Satan was Jesus's *brother*."

I mustered my sweetest poison smile. "That's true, ma'am. We do believe that. And we believe Satan was *your* brother too."

The woman let out a gasp and slammed the door.

"I've got to say, buckfart," said Snow as we started for the next house, "that was certainly *one* way to handle things."

I shook my head. "I shouldn't have said that." My breath steamed in the cold morning air. "But she really got under my skin. I don't know why."

"Maybe it was her welcoming and Christlike attitude."

I laughed. "Could be."

"I thought you kept your cool pretty well, at least, and that was a good comeback. Maybe not very constructive, though."

It was a Friday morning. I'd been in Calgary a little over a week, and I was still dazed. Brooks felt like a bad dream, my road trip like something that had happened to someone else. I was trying extra hard to fit in, no longer sure exactly what I wanted for myself. I could feel the manic edge to everything I did, and I told myself this was joy. If sometimes late at night I berated myself for not getting back on that southbound bus in Great Falls—well, missionary work wasn't supposed to be an easy sacrifice.

We encountered a more sophisticated kind of opposition in Calgary than I'd seen in Brooks, but Snow always handled it with equanimity and dry wit. Nothing rattled him, whether it was a Jehovah's Witness telling us we didn't understand the Bible or an evangelical minister berating us for poaching good Christians. He could debate scripture with the best of them, but he never let himself be drawn into an unproductive argument. The only quality I didn't admire was that he never seemed to tire of tracting.

"That lady was definitely ready for us with the pamphlet," I said. "What do you think was in it, anyway?"

"Oh, that one's all hung up on the War in Heaven. Makes the missionaries look like complete numskulls too."

"You've *read* it?" The White Bible was very explicit about avoiding such material.

"Sure. It's just a dumb little comic book."

I was startled. "But it's anti-Mormon."

"Shazz, Shunn, if you're going to preach the gospel, you need to know what people are going to throw back at you. These little books, they're just full of half-truths taken out of context. It's designed to confuse people and make us look like we're coming to, I don't know, kidnap their children. We have a few back at the pit."

"Children?" I said in mock-horror.

He snorted. "No, dork. Pamphlets."

I was curious, though the idea of looking at anti-Mormon literature made me feel squirmy and ill.

We climbed the next porch. "Hey, all this reminds me of a joke," said Snow. "It's a good one."

"Shoot."

"These two Mormon missionaries are walking down the street one morning, and they meet this Catholic priest coming the other way."

"Okay..."

"So the Catholic priest says, 'Good morning, sons of Satan!' And the missionaries, not to be impolite, say, 'Good morning, Father!'"

Good thing it was Snow's door, because I was still laughing when it opened.

HEADING HOME FOR LUNCH WAS ALWAYS A WELCOME BREAK FROM the tracting grind. Our pit was a marvel, a huge one-bedroom in a monstrous building reserved for low-income households. In typical missionary fashion the place was barely decorated, but it was roomy enough for tennis and never ever ran out of hot water.

We lived in a commercial part of the city's southeast quadrant, just off Macleod Trail. The busy thoroughfare was thick with fast-food joints, oil-change parlors, and drive-up banks. Our fellow tenants, who must have numbered in the hundreds, seemed mostly friendly and innocuous.

We ate dirt-cheap. Our staples were corn flakes or oatmeal for breakfast, cold cuts or peanut butter sandwiches for lunch, and ramen noodles or generic macaroni and cheese for dinner on nights when we didn't have better plans. Snow was a wizard with the Mac-'n'-Shazz, as he called it. He would slice in boiled hot dogs for Wienie-Mac, stir in onion soup powder for Onion-Mac, or, grandest of all, mix in a whole can of chili con carne for his infamous Chili-Mac.

As Snow busied himself in the kitchen that afternoon, fixing ham sandwiches and heating tomato soup, I sat staring at the stationery and pen I'd received for Christmas. I had a difficult letter to write, and I'd been putting it off for days.

My parents hadn't told anyone else about my unfortunate episode, least of all my brothers and sisters, and they wanted to keep it that way. I was still supposed to be setting an example. But I felt I owed it to Katrina to come clean. If we were going to get married in a couple of years, we shouldn't be keeping secrets from each other. She knew I'd been transferred to Calgary, but not why. I was embarrassed to admit how weak I'd been. I had no idea how she might react, and I was afraid to find out.

I let myself get distracted by my countdown calendar—which now stood at 603 days—before turning back to the letter. I'd only gotten as far as *My dearest Katrina* when Snow called out, "Oh, hey, Shunn! We haven't prank-called the sisters today."

I was happy for an excuse to put down my pen. I crossed to Snow's desk. I felt a manic edge coming on. "What's it gonna be today?"

"I don't know. Um . . . okay, be someone who just saw one of those commercials on TV and really wants to get baptized, like, right now. Leave them an awesome message."

Snow and I were way ahead of the sisters in tracting hours—legitimately—but they had more investigators and were looking at a couple of baptisms soon. If we couldn't beat them where it counted, at least we could yank their chains.

After two rings, the line picked up. "LDS missionaries, this is Sister Steed speaking. Can I help you?"

"Um, yeah," I said, startled, in a shady-sounding growl. I hadn't expected them to be home. "I'm, like, totally I've always been an atheist and stuff, but I just saw this commercial about how there's a Heavenly Father and he has a plan, and I'm like, I'm crying, and I wanna come join your church. Are you the ones I talk to about it?"

The church was testing a new marketing campaign in Calgary, and we'd been prepped to start receiving referrals from it. "Well, I'm glad to hear you're interested," said Steed in her gingham-and-lavender voice, "but there are a few steps you need to go through first. We have a series of six lessons that two of our best representatives will need to teach you."

"Um, how much does that cost?"

"Oh, it's absolutely free. Let me get your name and address and I'll send them right over. They're two great, smart, handsome young men, and their names are Elder *Lienhard* and Elder *Kopp*."

Those were the two other elders in our district. "You're, um, sure they're the best ones you've got? I don't want any second-rate goofballs teaching me. This is important stuff."

"Well, you definitely don't want Elder No and Elder Dumb."

I snorted. "Elder No and Elder Dumb?" I said in my normal voice. "That's the best you've got, Weed? You and Doper need to try harder than that."

I had coined their nicknames, much to Snow's glee, and the sisters had been having a heck of a time coming up with ones as good for us.

Steed was laughing. "Yeah, well, did you think we'd fall for that atheist bit? The commercial gives an eight-hundred number, Elder *Dumb*."

Snow was standing over me, holding out his hand for the phone. I gave it to him. "Steed? We're still on for pizza tomorrow, right? Yep, the whole district. Cool, we'll swing by before five. Now you buckets get back to work." He hung up, an evil glint in his eye. "Tonight, we fill their car with t.p."

I giggled. "*Yes*."

He went around the chair where I was sitting and rifled through one of the desk drawers. He pulled out a couple of tracts and tossed them in front of me. "These are the guys we should *really* prank."

I picked them up like I was handling toxic waste. The one the woman had tried to foist on me that morning was called *The Visitors*, and the other was called *Are Roman Catholics Christians?* The heavy black ink and stark typeface made the tracts look foreboding. In a blank area on the back of each, "Saints Alive in Jesus" and a Calgary phone number had been stamped in blue.

"What's Saints Alive in Jesus?"

"It's an apostate group, mostly people excommunicated for teaching false doctrine. It's Ed Decker's organization—you know, the guy who made that movie, *The God Makers*."

I dropped the tracts and stood up. *The God Makers* was an infamous movie that taught lie after lie about the temple and the endowment ceremony. Evangelical churches would host showings of it to whip up anti-Mormon fervor. I hadn't seen it, of course, but the very mention of the title chilled my blood. It was our *Protocols of the Elders of Zion*, or so we Mormons tended to feel. "Are they based in Calgary?"

"No, I think the headquarters are somewhere like Seattle, but they've got a chapter here. The local chief's a guy named Valiant Brewer, and from what I hear he *loves* to tangle with the missionaries."

"Valiant Brewer? That's his name? Are you serious?"

"It's got to be a family name from pioneer days. He *is* an ex." He took my place at the desk, spun one of the tracts around with his finger, and dialed the phone. "Let's just see if he's in."

I watched in thrilled disbelief. Were we really about to prank an anti?

Snow drummed his fingers on the desktop. "Answering machine," he said to me after a few moments. He cleared his throat. "Yes, hello. This is Lucifer calling, hoping to speak with my brother? So if Val's there, have him give me a ring. He has the number. Thanks."

"I can't believe you did that!" I chortled as he hung up. "I want to do it, I want to do it!"

"Knock yourself out."

Shaking with silent laughter, I dialed the number from the back of the tracts. This was like bearding the devil himself in his den. As the line rang, I tried to think of the most cutting thing I could say to a turncoat son of perdition.

The line clicked. "You've reached Saints Alive in Jesus," said a man's voice. "Please leave us your testimony after the beep, and praise God!"

Beep!

Jolted by adrenaline, I said, "Valiant Brewer beats his wife!"

Before I could hang up, I heard another click.

"Now, what would make you say a thing like that?" queried the voice from the recording.

I slammed the phone down, trembling, and stared wide-eyed at Snow. "Oops."

CHAPTER 31

ELDER LIENHARD AND ELDER KOPP WERE NOT ASSIGNED A CAR, SO we'd scheduled our district outing for a pizza joint near their pit. Snow and I picked up Roper and Steed in the late afternoon, but before climbing into the back seat they had to sweep aside books, pamphlets, index cards, blue planners, soda cans, fast-food containers, and grease-smeared paper towels.

"Good hell, Elders," said Roper, kicking through the garbage and dirt at her feet. "This car is *filthy!*"

Steed waved a hand in front of her nose and rolled down her window. "I think you've got mold in your floorboards. I'm going to be sick."

"Seat belts, please," I said, looking over my shoulder.

Roper flapped her hands in disgust. "I don't wanna touch anything I don't have to." She batted at something near her hip and plucked gingerly at the seat belt. "Good gravy, this is repugnant."

"You know," Steed said, "if you need something to wipe up all this *crap* with, we have loads of *toilet paper* at home."

Snow and I exchanged a look and burst out laughing.

"Yeah, we appreciated your thoughtfulness," said Roper sourly, "but next time you could at least fill our car with Charmin."

"Don't look a gift horse in the mouth," Snow said, sniggering, as we pulled into traffic.

Roper sniffed audibly. "That was a *lot* of t.p. Do you know we were late driving Lienhard and Kopp to their discussion this morning? Come to think of it, we're always giving rides to those two, or loaning them our car, while you keep yours to yourselves and don't even take care of it." She kicked the back of Snow's seat. "You elders don't *deserve* a car."

We cackled, and Snow wiped his eyes. "Shazz, Roper, we give those buckets plenty of rides. But I'm a district leader. I need a car to do my job."

"Some *humility's* what you need, boy. A little gratitude for your blessings."

We probably shouldn't have laughed so hard when she said that.

THE NEXT TUESDAY MORNING, ELDER SNOW AND I WENT TO THE mission office for our individual weekly conferences with President Tuttle. This was part of my rehabilitation process, since I was more or less on probation as a missionary. Prez would first interview me to assess my mental and spiritual state of being, then talk with Elder Snow to find out how *he* thought I was doing. This meant Snow was essentially spying on me and reporting to Prez, but since we all knew what was going on it didn't bother me that much.

I had drunk the Kool-Aid but maybe not a full glass. In our conference that morning I tried to present a portrait of growth, steady improvement, and cheerful diligence, telling President Tuttle what he wanted to hear. He put on such a show of friendliness and concern, though, that I had a hard time remembering why he had ever seemed like an enemy. At the very least, if I kept thinking of him as an enemy it was going to be a long twenty months.

When Elder Snow's conference was over, President Tuttle invited me to join them both in his office. I entered warily, pulling the door closed behind me.

"Don't bother shutting that, Elder Shunn. As long as we have a few extra minutes, I thought we'd do a little car inspection."

Snow glanced up at me worriedly. "Well, President," he said, "we washed it just yesterday, like we do every week. And we're not due for inspection until the next zone conference."

Tuttle stood up, shrugging into his suit coat. "Like the five wise virgins in the parable, we never know the hour of the bridegroom's arrival. Best to keep our lamps trimmed at all times, right?"

Helplessly, Snow and I followed him out front. "See?" said Snow while we were still yards away from our gleaming blue Cavalier. "She's in fine shape. Washed and waxed yesterday."

Tuttle pointed at the driver-side door. "Can you open this up for me, Elder? I need to check the mileage too, you know."

Snow hesitated only briefly before unpocketing the keys. "Sure thing, President."

Once the door was open, Tuttle didn't so much as glance at the odometer. He squatted and reached for something on the floor beneath the steering wheel. He straightened up, frowning, with what looked like a scrap of withered brown leather pinched between two fingers. "Now this is interesting. What do you think it is?"

I reluctantly identified it as a scrap of mummified orange peel. We would gladly have traded the angry scowl this elicited for the tongue-lashing President Tuttle bestowed upon us when he saw the mess in the back seat. You would have thought cleanliness was not next to godliness but twenty stories higher. We took it meekly, shivering in the cold, though we were thinking colder thoughts about the ones who'd ratted us out.

"When we're done here, Elders," Prez finished up, "I want you to drive this car straight over to Elder Lienhard and Elder Kopp, and you'll take their bikes in exchange. You've lost car privileges for a week."

"But, President—" Snow protested.

"Should I make it two weeks, Elder?"

Snow looked down. "No, sir."

"Good."

We followed President Tuttle inside so he could write a note for us to deliver to Lienhard and Kopp along with the car. We were on our way out again when I spotted Elder Dedman and his new companion hanging out near the apes' desks.

I tried to look away, but Dedman had spotted me too. For a split-second, raw, scalding hope suffused his face. He raised his chin as if preparing to acknowledge a hello.

For all Dedman's faults, he'd taken a big one on the chin for my sake, and I had thanked him by ratting him out. Too mortified to look him in the eye, I turned my head and kept going, pretending I hadn't seen him.

But I knew that he knew that I had.

THE PHONE RANG ONE NIGHT LATE THAT WEEK AS SNOW AND I were reading. He handed me the receiver with a grim, disapproving expression. "For you."

Shit. My heart stuttered, and not in a good way. It had to be Katrina.

I'd finally gotten that impossible letter written and in the mail. After praying for guidance and wisdom, I had picked up my pen and spilled my guts. I held back nothing, from my utter misery in Brooks to my mortifying confession at zone conference, from my abortive run for freedom to my father's staggering revelation about his mission. By the time I was done I had twelve densely scribbled pages, sodden with the zeal of a sinner reborn. Katrina had told me she wanted to share my struggles. Well, here they were, in all their moth-eaten glory.

Could I possibly be understood and still loved? That was my wild hope as I committed my epistle to the post. But like the letter to my parents in November, the instant it was out of my hands I wished I'd never written it.

Snow left the room as I licked my lips and put the phone to my ear. "Um, hello? This is Elder Shunn."

"I can't believe you *did* that!" Katrina shouted without preamble.

Eesh. "Apparently you got my letter."

"Yes, I got your *letter.* What the hell were you *thinking?* How could you run away from your mission?"

Wincing, I forced the receiver back to my ear. I should have known that including this new phone number in the letter was a bad idea. "I thought you wanted me to," I said, bracing myself.

"I want you to be a missionary! I want you right where you are!"

Her words were a giant boot, grinding my heart. "You sure made it sound like you wanted me to come home."

She let out something between an exasperated sigh and a snarl. "Bill, I can't believe we're having this conversation. I thought you were doing so *well.*"

"I'm doing much better now. But I told you, I was so *miserable* there in Brooks."

"It scares me to think how close you came to throwing everything away, it really scares me. Is that what's going to happen every time you get unhappy? You'll run away?"

"Look, I'm back, aren't I?" I blurted in a frantic rush. "I'm here, I'm doing fine. I wouldn't even have left in the first place if you hadn't said you wished I were home."

"Of course I wish you were home! I *miss* you, Bill. But I need you *there.* I need you to finish your mission and *then* come home. I need you to take me to the temple." Her voice softened, cracking. "Oh, Bill. This—this stupid love thing is so *hard,* and you're *scaring* me. What am I supposed to do if you can't keep this commitment either? Will you leave *me* when things get tough?"

Words jammed up in my throat. Was she even hearing a thing I said? I was working on *fixing* my problems. Was my father right about her? Was she only interested in me as her ticket into the Celestial Kingdom?

I strangled the thought. "Katrina, I'm *sorry.*"

"And do you know what else?" she demanded, as if my feeble apology were all it took to set her off again. "I can't *believe* you told me about"—her voice withered to a self-conscious hiss—"about doing the *M-word!* Ewww! I can't even *think* about it!"

I clutched my burning forehead so my brain wouldn't explode. I wanted to curl up and die.

CHAPTER 32

IN CALGARY, A CITY WITH MORE THAN FORTY MISSIONARIES AND limitless recreational opportunities, basketball ate up nearly every P-day. This was no fun for me but even less fun for the sisters, who had to watch from the sidelines if they wanted to hang out with the gang. (Church ball did not exactly have a strong coed tradition.) That's why, late in January, Sister Roper organized a P-day activity everyone could enjoy—paintball.

More than a dozen missionaries converged that afternoon on a converted warehouse on the west side of the city. Layered in thick coveralls, quilted headgear, goggles, and gloves, we divided up into teams and fanned out through a maze bathed in ultraviolet light, each of us armed with a compressed-air pistol and a tube of varicolored projectiles. For nearly two hours, we ran, ducked, and fired like our lives depended on it. Getting shot with a paintball hurt like a son of a bitch, even through all the padding, but I'd never had so much fun as a missionary. As we stripped off our paint-spattered coveralls at the end of the afternoon, everyone else seemed to feel the same way. It was hard for me to remember how alone I'd felt just a month earlier.

Elder Snow, unfortunately, had to miss the outing. Every month President Tuttle held a two-day leadership conference in Calgary that started on a Monday afternoon. Every district leader and zone leader in the mission was required to attend (which was a big incentive for me to *not* want to become a district leader). I felt bad for Elder Snow, but I wouldn't have traded places with him for anything.

My temporary partner for the duration of the leadership conference was Elder Stewart Finn, whose companion, Elder Roland, led our neighboring district. Since Snow and I were still on our car suspension, Elder Finn drove, and I spent Monday evening with him at a dinner appointment in his proselytizing area. Finn was built like a wrestler, and he didn't strike me at first as someone I'd have much in common with. As we talked about things like girls and movies, though, we uncovered a mutual interest in new wave music. Finn, in fact, was a bit older than I was and had worked at a radio station in Fresno before his mission. Deejaying was one of my many dream jobs, and I ate up his colorful stories.

Finn was something of a legend in the mission, despite having only been out since October. His first month in the field, he and Elder Roland had tracted out a golden family named the Dawsons, and by the time Christmas rolled around Dad, Mom, and all three children had gone under the water. The Dawsons were now minor celebrities in the Calgary Mormon scene, in high demand as speakers at evening services all over the city.

"How the heck did you manage it?" I asked, desperate to unlock the secrets of the supermissionary.

"Just lucky, I guess. The family was ready, and Elder Roland knew what he was doing. A monkey could have done my part."

But when Elder Roland dropped off Snow at our apartment late that evening, at the end of the first day of the leadership conference, he told me a different story. "It was all Elder Finn," he said. "There's real power in the rosy-cheeked innocence of a simple greenie."

Finn flashed him a middle finger. "Sit and spin."

Elder Roland sighed. "And innocence is all too fleeting."

IF I WAS AMAZED BY THE SUCCESS ROLAND AND FINN ENJOYED, then I was downright flabbergasted by the letters I received from Andy Kilmer in Brazil. My high school chum was hauling people into the water at a rate of three or four a *week*. I knew stats like those were par for the course for Latin America, and I tried not to measure my own performance against that yardstick, but I sometimes felt as if God had called me to Calgary as punishment for a lifetime of tenuous faith. I was there because I wasn't worthy of serving in a mission with a higher baptismal rate. (Though neither, come to think of it, was Andy.)

Snow and I did have a couple of good investigators, but they were carryovers from Elder Philby's term. While I was enjoying Calgary far more than Brooks, I still felt fragile—not to mention ambivalent about my mission service. Finding new investigators, golden investigators like Finn's, would make me feel better about myself and what I was doing, or so I imagined.

Failing that, I could at least snatch temporary satisfaction from pranking that snake Valiant Brewer. I'd been flipping through the little comic book from Saints Alive in Jesus, and I was offended at its portrayal of a missionary so easily argued by a combative woman into questioning his faith. If I took pride in one thing as a missionary, it was my intellectual understanding of the gospel.

One afternoon on lunch break, I dialed Saints Alive in Jesus with a terrific zinger at the ready, but instead of getting the answering machine, a man picked up. "Hello?"

I froze. The quip I'd prepared boiled away in the heat of my discomfiture.

"Hello? Is anyone there? No one, eh? Are you calling to tell me again that I beat my wife? That wasn't very nice of you."

That pricked my conscience. "I, um, I'm sorry about that," I mumbled.

"He speaks!" said Valiant Brewer. "Apology accepted. I forgive you. Not the best way to win friends and influence people, though."

"No, I guess not."

"I wouldn't be speaking to a missionary, would I?"

Now I felt like I'd shamed my entire brotherhood. Snow had wandered over from the kitchen with a question on his face. I pointed at the tract on the desk and shrugged. He gave me a cautionary look.

"Guilty," I said. "How did you know?"

"Let's just say the odds were good. Now, was there something I could help you with?"

I swallowed with a dry throat, screwing up my courage. I'm sure I wanted to demonstrate, to myself if no one else, how bold and, pardon me, valiant I could be in defending the faith. "As a matter of fact, there is. I just wanted to know why you feel like you have to help spread lies about the church. I mean, if you disagree with us, why not be honest about it? Why spread all these pamphlets that make us out to be these evil schemers, coming to steal your soul?"

"I don't think you're evil, Elder. Just misinformed, the same way I used to be."

"I think I'm very *well* informed about the gospel."

"Did you know that Joseph Smith was a Master Mason? That's where he borrowed all the elements of his Satanic endowment ceremony, from Masonic rituals."

"That's not true." I knew next to nothing about Freemasonry yet, but I knew my father had once told me their fancy lodge in Ogden was the Church of the Devil. That didn't sound like something Joseph could have been involved with.

"Look it up. Learn your history. Haven't you ever wondered why, if the Book of Mormon contains the fullness of the gospel, there's nothing in it about an endowment ceremony? It's because Smith didn't make that up until later."

He was trying to do to me what the woman in the comic book did to that missionary. "The endowment's too sacred for outsiders to read about," I said, though in truth I *had* asked myself that very question.

"Elder, don't take my word for it. Do some studying, pray about it. But if you're like me, you probably already have questions about a lot of these things."

Elder Snow, who'd been frowning down at me, was now snapping his fingers. With relief, I handed over the receiver.

"Brother Brewer? This is Elder Snow. Yes, nice to talk to you too. Now what's all this you're saying about the temple? Mm-hmm. Mm-hmm. No, actually that's where you're wrong. There's no contradiction with the Book of Mormon at all, especially when you take into account what we learn from the Pearl of Great Price . . ."

I quietly took over fixing our lunch.

ON THE FIRST OF FEBRUARY, A SUNDAY EVENING, ELDER SNOW AND I met the sisters at a "fireside"—an evening service featuring a couple of inspirational speakers—held at a huge stake center near the University of Calgary. Young adults from all four of Calgary's stakes crowded the building. It was quite a scene. Seeing all those college-age kids in their Sunday best, joking and flirting and knotting up in cliques before the service, made me as trunky as I'd been in a month. I missed Katrina, and I missed normal things.

After the fireside, Roper and Steed invited us to meet back at their apartment for some hot chocolate. It was dark by then, and in the vast expanse of Calgary we were miles from their pit. The sisters set off at a good clip, and I tried to keep their red Cavalier in sight as we sped down the wide, unfamiliar streets.

The rivalry between our companionships was escalating to reckless levels. The previous P-day, the sisters had challenged us to a round of five-pin bowling at the mall, losers to buy dinner at the food court for the winners. They thought they had a lock on victory since neither Snow nor I had bowled five-pin before, but we mopped the floor with them and then stuffed ourselves on their dime with teriyaki chicken. It was only as we were sopping up the last bits of sauce and belching in contentment that Snow looked at his watch and announced in horror that he and I had a dinner appointment with the Kent family in thirty minutes. We had completely forgotten.

It is a basic tenet of Mormon culture that elders must eat everything their hosts set in front of them. It is another basic tenet of Mormon culture that mothers must pile plates for the elders sky-high and insist they go back for seconds, if not thirds. The Kents were a wealthy, influential family in the ward, and we didn't dare insult them. When we left their home three hours after arriving, neither of us could stand up straight for the pain. We shuffled to the car bowed like hunchbacks over our distended bellies. It was torment snatched from the jaws of victory.

The memory of that endless dinner may have been why I found myself racing to overtake the sisters' car. It may be why Snow egged me on to drive faster and faster. Racing down one of Calgary's broad thoroughfares, I gunned the engine and pulled abreast of the red Cavalier. Roper and Steed taunted us with rude gestures and tried to shake us by peeling off into a mazelike neighborhood. Were we sublimating some instinct toward flirtation and courtship? Was this how Fowler and Nylund had found themselves on the wrong footing?

A good ten minutes later, Snow and I found ourselves stopped behind the sisters in a left turn lane a few blocks from their apartment. The light was red. "Chinese fire drill!" Snow shouted.

Giddily I jammed the gearshift into park. Snow was already out his door.

I pounded on Roper's window while Snow rousted Steed. "Chinese fire drill!" we cried. "Chinese fire drill!" Within moments all four of us were running figure-eights around the two cars, waving our arms and whooping it up.

When the light turned green, Snow gave me a diabolical look and jerked his chin at the sisters' car. I understood instantly.

Without a word, the two of us hopped into their car, slammed the doors, and squealed away. Roper and Steed, in the few moments I could still see them in the rearview mirror, gaped after us.

"Hah!" I shouted. "Take *that!*"

Four or five blocks later, we parked behind their apartment building and got out of the car to wait for them. We waited, and we waited, and we waited.

We were pacing with worry, breath steaming in the cold night air, when our blue Cavalier finally careened into the parking lot and screeched to a halt. Nearly twenty minutes had passed. The sisters, white-faced and breathless, scrambled out the doors and ran straight toward us.

Sister Roper grabbed Snow by the lapels. "Oh my Lord," she babbled, "oh my Lord, oh my Lord, we're getting sent home, all of us. We're getting sent home for sure. Oh, I can't believe it, we're gonna be in *so* much trouble, so much trouble."

"Hey, hey, slow down," said Snow, extricating himself from her grip. "What the shazz happened?"

"Oh my word, it's a nightmare is what it is."

"We got stopped by the *police,* thank you," said Sister Steed.

I felt a stab of fear. "The *police?*"

Snow folded his arms and drew himself erect. "What did you two do?" He was trying to project authority, but I could tell he was rattled.

"What did *we* do?" said Roper, flapping her hands in dismay. "We took off after *you*, that's what we did. But there was this pedestrian crossing on the next block. I was all mixed up from the Chinese fire drill, and the lights started flashing yellow, but it was too late for me to stop so I went through the crosswalk. But there was a car behind us back at the red light, and it turns out it was a *cop*, and he flipped his lights right on and pulled us over."

Snow was shaking his head. "Oh, Doper, you've got to be kidding. A *pedestrian crossing?* That is one serious ticket."

"You're telling *me!*" said Roper, her face a mask of desperation. "But it gets even better. When the cop asked to see my driver's license, guess where it was?"

"Where?" I asked. "In your pit?"

She whacked my shoulder. "No, you idiot! It was in my purse on the front seat of the car. The car *you* were driving!"

I clapped a hand to my forehead. "Oh, no. Roper, I am so sorry."

The look she gave me would have pulverized granite. "Tell me that tomorrow when I have to take my license down to the police station. I'll be lucky if I don't get arrested. I'm lucky I'm not in jail *right now.*"

"At least we had *your* registration," said Steed. "That helped. Of course, the officer took down the address, which is the mission office. So guess who's getting a visit from the police first thing in the morning?"

"Oh, shazz," Snow moaned, clutching his hair.

"Like I told you," Roper said. "Tomorrow that cop's gonna tell Prez I ran a light without a license in *your* car, and do you think he's gonna believe us when we say there's nothing funny going on? I'm telling you, we're all getting sent home."

"My father's gonna be *so* cheesed off," said Snow, eyes closed, fists clenched at his sides. "Flip, flip, flip."

I couldn't stop shaking my head, seeing all my hard-won progress evaporate. What was wrong with me? Why did I always have to be so *stupid?*

But at the same time, I felt the stirring of a tiny mutinous hope. Might we really get sent home?

Roper and Steed exchanged a look. Their mouths trembled, and suddenly they both cracked up. Steed doubled over, and Roper had to lean against her to keep from falling down.

Huh?

"What is this?" Snow demanded. "Hey, what the shazz is going on?"

"Oh, boy, Elders," said Roper, pounding Steed on the shoulder. "We really had you going!"

Steed held her heaving stomach. "You ate it up, every bite! You two looked so terrified I almost peed myself!"

"Wait, you didn't get pulled over?"

"We *did* get pulled over," said Roper, wiping her eyes, "but we only got a warning. The cop said the Chinese fire drill was kind of cute, but when we ran the light he had to make sure we weren't drunk. Well, we weren't."

She and Steed dissolved in fresh peals of laughter. Pretty soon I was laughing too, and after few minutes even Snow cooled down. Hot chocolate around the sisters' kitchen table went a long way toward repairing the breach.

As we were rinsing our mugs, Sister Roper said to me in her most serious tone, "Don't you forget what we've all been through together, Elder Shunn. You need to write a book someday and put all this down for posterity. People need to know what it's *really* like to be missionaries, and how we got through it. You hear me, Elder Shunn? I expect to see that book someday."

I promised her she would, though I couldn't for the life of me see how to write such a book and keep my temple recommend.

CHAPTER 33

AROUND THIS SAME TIME, I ATTENDED MY FIRST MISSION CONFER-
ence. Every six months or so, the entire mission was summoned to
Calgary for one full day of meetings, activities, and inspiration. *Almost* the entire mission, I should say. Travel was prohibitive for the
remotest elders, including Elder Vickers, whom I had most hoped to
see.

Late that afternoon we started filing into the chapel at the stake
center hosting the conference to hear an address from President Peter
G. Murdock, a General Authority visiting us from Salt Lake. I felt a
gentle hand on my elbow as Snow and I were about to pass through
the doors.

It was Sister Nylund. "Elder Shunn, I need to talk to you for a minute," she said quietly.

For a moment I panicked, looking around for Sister Youtz, but the
only other woman nearby was someone I didn't recognize. Apparently
Nylund had a new companion.

"Save me a seat," I told Snow. I stepped aside with Nylund to the far
corner of the foyer. Her companion waited a discreet distance away,
arms folded impatiently.

Nylund frowned. She looked haggard, her makeup caked on like

plaster. "Elder Shunn," she whispered hoarsely, "you haven't told anyone anything about Mar—about Elder Fowler and I, have you?"

"Of course I haven't. I haven't even told my girlfriend."

"Are you *sure?*" she pressed, leaning toward me in an intimidating
way. "I've heard there's a rumor."

I tried to lean away. "Of course I'm sure. Jeez."

"You haven't said anything to President?"

"Nylund, what is this? Why would I want to get you in trouble?"
I glanced around, afraid of being overheard. "I haven't said anything
to anyone, ever. And don't you think if I'd said anything to Prez you
would have heard something from *him?*"

She sagged, and all she looked now was sad. "Well, don't, *please,*"
she said, staring at the floor. "I—I broke things off with Marty. After
he went home."

I'd had a couple of letters from Fowler, but he hadn't mentioned
that—at least, not if I'd deciphered his handwriting correctly.

Nylund must have seen the shock on my face. "It was wrong—
wrong," she said fervently. "I don't think I really realized that until
after he'd gone home already. I'm trying to figure out now whether or
not I should tell President."

I had to get away from her. "I'm sure you'll figure out the right thing
to do. I, uh, listen, I think they're gonna start in there in a minute."

I turned and hurried into the chapel. An elder I didn't know was
playing prelude music on the organ, and a soothing murmur of conversation rose from the pews, filled to half capacity by nearly two
hundred missionaries. I saw Elder Snow waving at me from a seat
near the front of the chapel. As I made my way over, I anxiously
scanned the room for Elder Dedman—the better to avoid him after
the meeting.

President Murdock took the pulpit after short, fluffy talks by President Tuttle and the apes. Murdock was a member of the First Quorum of the Seventy, the governing body next in authority after the

Twelve Apostles. He was also top man in the church's Missionary Department. And as I discovered when he began to speak, he was the closest Mormon equivalent to a hellfire-and-brimstone preacher I'd ever heard.

Most General Authorities were mild and soft-spoken. Not President Murdock. With his broad shoulders and square jaw, he might have played a convincing older Superman—if Superman seethed and snarled when he spoke, that is. There was no joy in President Murdock's delivery, though he lectured of joy, no charity in his pitiless gaze nor love in his flinty heart, though he invoked a God of love and charity. His method was not to inspire or ennoble his stripling warriors but to terrorize us into docile, slavish execution of our duties. I thought he might pound the pulpit to flinders.

Like Patton minus the profanity, Murdock harangued us with the story of an elderly woman whom missionaries in Germany had baptized into the church a few years earlier. "After she came out of the font, Elders and Sisters," he spat, "the bishop laid his hands upon her head, and in the course of conferring upon her the gift of the Holy Ghost he was inspired to tell her that she might have joined the church *forty years earlier* if only the missionaries back then had paid attention to the promptings of the Spirit and *not bypassed her door,* and that those elders would surely suffer the pains of *hell* for the sake of those unnecessary *decades* of darkness and sin!"

This story chilled me, as I'm sure it was meant to, but it was nothing compared to the arctic freeze that engulfed the chapel as Murdock ranted about the quicksand awaiting those of us who took a single ill-considered step off the straight and narrow path. "You *watch* yourselves out there," he barked. "You *gird* up your loins with the armor of God, *especially* you young elders, because this world is just *crawling* with women who would love nothing better than to *drag you down.*"

We might have been spared any elaboration on that dire pronouncement if it weren't for Sister Roper. Into the space at the end of Murdock's sentence, Roper coughed a harsh and disbelieving laugh, loud as a gunshot. She was sitting behind Snow and me, and I turned my head just in time to see her clap both hands over her open mouth, eyes wide with shock.

A stunned silence reigned for two short seconds, which is all the time it took for President Murdock's face to suck every remaining particle of warmth out of that chapel. He went from white to molten red before most of us could remind ourselves to breathe. Mouth quivering with rage, he thrust his steely head as far over the pulpit as he could and thundered, *"Do you think this is FUNNY, Sister? Do you think it's a JOKE when a district leader and his companion tract into a house with only a mother and her teenage daughter at home, and within five minutes the daughter is performing oral sex on one elder in the bedroom while the mother does the same to the other in the LIVING ROOM? Maybe YOU'D like to be the one who has to listen to stories like this EVERY WEEK, and then explain to the poor, tithe-paying parents why you had to EXCOMMUNICATE their idiot sons! WOULD YOU LIKE THAT?"*

I think there were tooth marks in the pulpit when the tirade was over. I'm not sure what the sisters were thinking as they left the chapel after the closing prayer, but I'm pretty sure I know what was on every elder's mind:

How come stuff like that never happens to me?

WE CAN PERHAPS FORGIVE PRESIDENT MURDOCK HIS HYPERBOLE when we remember that women did in fact bring down Joseph Smith. Not deliberately and not directly, but it was this predilection of his that set him on the path that ended his life.

Brigham Young is surely the most famous of all Mormon polygamists, but the first was of course Joseph himself. Historians have long known that Joseph secretly took as many as forty wives, possibly more, though the church did not officially admit this until 2014. Critics sometimes charge that Joseph concocted the whole plural-marriage scheme to cover up and sanctify marital infidelities, but if so he did some careful advance planning. The first hint of his unconventional philosophies can be found in the Book of Mormon, in the second chapter of Jacob:

> [T]hey understand not the scriptures, for they seek to excuse themselves in committing whoredoms, because of the things which were written concerning David, and Solomon his son.
>
> Behold, David and Solomon truly had many wives and concubines, which thing was abominable before me, saith the Lord....
>
> Wherefore, my brethren, hear me, and hearken to the word of the Lord: For there shall not any man among you have save it be one wife; and concubines he shall have none...
>
> For if I will, saith the Lord of Hosts, raise up seed unto me, I will command my people; otherwise they shall hearken unto these things.

This passage seems to imply, if you squint at it sideways, that God can when necessary suspend the law of monogamy—presumably so that his chosen people can start having more babies. In any event, when we recall that Biblical figures besides David and Solomon practiced polygamy with God's blessing, we see that even this early in his prophetic career Joseph was trying to reconcile problematic aspects of the Old Testament with the conventional Christian morality of his day.

Even so, Joseph was hardly unique in his drive toward a redefinition of marriage. Other antebellum sects, most notoriously the Oneida Community, would experiment with sexual mores that were far more unorthodox. But Joseph's teachings were destined to outlive and overshadow the others, both in actual implementation and in the nation's thrilled and horrified popular imagination.

Starting in 1831, Joseph may have secretly entreated girls as young as twelve to become his "spiritual wives." Some of his apostles later attested that he first told them about "plural marriage" that year, and that God had commanded righteous men to take multiple wives. But it wasn't until 1834 or 1835 that his first well-documented polygamous marriage took place, when he wed Fanny Alger, a teenager working as a serving girl in the house where he lived with Emma and their children in Kirtland, Ohio. Joseph's clandestine proposal may have been relayed to Fanny by her uncle, Levi Hancock, who is also reported to have officiated at the ceremony. Though Emma knew nothing of the marriage, she did suspect a relationship between Fanny and Joseph and, by one account, eventually threw the girl out of the house. (This is the same relationship that Oliver Cowdery later decried as adulterous. His accusation against the prophet got him expelled from the church in 1838.)

Whatever the cause, the relationship ended, and in 1836 Fanny moved to Indiana with her parents, Mormon converts who reportedly took pride in calling the prophet their son-in-law. It couldn't have been comfortable for Fanny to stay in Kirtland after being linked with Joseph, but we may never know more of the story than this. She went on to remarry and raise nine children, and even when asked directly she never divulged a word about her time with her first husband.

Though it's possible that Joseph took another wife in the interim, his next well-documented marriage didn't come until April 1841, several years later, when he wed Louisa Beaman in Nauvoo. (It was a surreptitious outdoor wedding, and Louisa wore men's clothing in case they were spotted.) Why did it take him so long to tie another knot, particularly if plural marriage was a principle he'd been commanded by God to practice? And why the secrecy?

Perhaps he dragged his feet because his experience with Fanny Alger made him realize how hard it was going to be for people—particularly his beloved Emma—to accept this new order of marriage. In fact, if hearsay can be believed, it was hard for *him* to accept. Several acquaintances reported Joseph telling them it took three visits from an angel for him to get his act together and start practicing plural marriage again. On the third visit, the angel threatened to slay him if he continued to disobey.

If Joseph truly believed he saw this angel, it suggests he was conflicted enough about plural marriage to manufacture himself a forceful mental prod. Whatever helped him over that hump, the wedding to Louisa Beaman seems to have opened the floodgates. Brigham Young officiated at two of Joseph's early 1842 weddings, as the prophet commenced secretly propositioning and marrying an astounding number of women. Many were young and comely—the youngest being fifteen—but a few were much older. Some, lovestruck, were easily convinced. Others took more persuading, sometimes over a period of months. Nearly a dozen were married to other men—some of them his trusted lieutenants—when Joseph proposed. It's possible these men assented to these "celestial" marriages in order to ensure the proximity of their links to his in the great dynastic chain Joseph was forging in the world to come. (It's probable that these particular marriages were never consummated.)

As Joseph's plural marriages proliferated, so did the rumors in Nauvoo of his sexual malfeasance. He had only instructed a few of his most faithful friends in the doctrine, but those men too were wooing extra wives. With so many people privy to the secret, it was inevitable that word would leak.

In fact, it was two women who spurned polygamous proposals that figured in the biggest scandals. The first, Martha Brotherton, rejected persistent advances by Brigham Young, whereupon her shocked parents whisked her away and helped publicize her story. The second was Sidney Rigdon's daughter Nancy. Joseph pressed her so hard to marry him that she ended up going to her father. This was the first Sidney had heard about plural marriage, and it nearly drove him out of the church. In both cases, Joseph denied having anything to do with polygamy and was only able to clear his name through smear campaigns discrediting the young women involved.

Emma staunchly refused to believe the rumors of plural marriage, though she certainly suspected Joseph of serial infidelity. Their conflict came to a head when the poet Eliza R. Snow, secretly married to Joseph, came to live and work as a teacher in their home. In February 1843, echoing the Fanny Alger affair, Emma's jealousy of Eliza reached such a pitch that she angrily ejected the other woman from the house. One account claims Emma actually pushed Eliza down the stairs, causing the other woman to miscarry Joseph's child.

Joseph was finally forced to let Emma in on the secret, lest she murder his other wives on suspicion of adultery. Emma never entirely accepted the revelation on plural marriage, but she did reach an uneasy truce with the idea when Joseph agreed to let her select and approve his new wives from then on. He evidently still hadn't told her the whole truth, however, because the first girls Emma chose for him, sisters not long out of their teens, had already been married to him for two months. These were Edward Partridge's daughters Emily and Eliza—my great-great-great-great-aunts. (Edward himself had been dead for three years, but were he still alive he would no doubt have borne this fresh indignity with mild Partridge stoicism.)

Joseph, not wanting to make Emma more angry and humiliated than she was already, staged a second marriage ceremony with Emily and Eliza, after which the girls moved into the house. Another pair of sisters selected by Emma—Maria and Sarah Lawrence, nineteen and seventeen—soon joined them.

But Emma never truly embraced polygamy. She found the necessity of living under the same roof with other wives nearly intolerable. She begged Joseph so fervently to disavow the practice that when he finally issued a revelation from God making plural marriage an official commandment, it contained a side note for Emma, telling her, in so many words, that if she didn't shut up and get with the program, "she shall be destroyed."

Joseph caused a furor when he introduced the new revelation to his full leadership council in August 1843. After much debate the council accepted the revelation, but a few of the members remained resolutely opposed to the practice, and factions began to form. Even then, the truth about plural marriage remained concealed from most of the citizens of Nauvoo, particularly the new converts still pouring in from England.

But it wouldn't stay hidden much longer.

CHAPTER 34

IN MID-FEBRUARY, SNOW AND I FOUND OUR GOLDEN INVESTIGA-
tors. Or rather, as it happened, they found us.

We were home for lunch when we picked up an answering-machine message from Bishop Tomlinson of our ward. *He* had received a call the evening before from a couple, Sandor and Cherilyn Marek, who'd seen the church's television commercial and wanted to know more. Instead of dialing the 800 number, they had called the nearest LDS meetinghouse. We promised the bishop we'd contact them right away.

The Mareks happened to be home when we called, and we arranged to come right over. They didn't actually live in our proselytizing area, so technically we should have turned their contact information over to the appropriate missionaries. In fact, there is a word in the mission field for what we were doing, and that word is "poaching." We justified it, though, because the Mareks had called our bishop, and our bishop had called *us*. To our missionary brains, this meant that God obviously intended for us to be the ones who taught them. (To be fair, the elders we were poaching from would surely have seen it differently.)

The middle-aged Mareks, holding hands on their couch, looked at each other hesitantly when Elder Snow asked why they had wanted to contact us. "I was raised to be a Catholic," said Sandor in a thick Hungarian accent.

"And I grew up Baptist," said Cherilyn.

"We had both left our faiths far behind and had felt never any need to replace them."

Cherilyn looked fondly to the corner of the room where a tow-headed baby rocked happily in an infant swing. "But that was before Dorian came along."

"Yes. When the little one came, we realized we needed a church that would provide him a strong moral foundation."

"We've been looking for more than a year. We've tried everywhere, but we just ..."

"We had no good feeling from any of them. At last we simply ..." Sandor shrugged.

"We gave up. We figured we'd just have to do our best and teach him ourselves."

"But then we saw your commercial on the television."

"The one that talks about how families can be together forever?" I asked.

Cherilyn clasped both hands to her heart. "Oh, yes. That's the one."

"We had not heard of your church before. We are new to this area."

"But we found you in the Yellow Pages," said Cherilyn, squeezing her husband's hand.

"Yes, and now we are ready to learn."

An hour later, when Elder Snow passed Cherilyn a copy of the Book of Mormon inscribed and donated by a church member in Utah, she turned it this way and that as reverently as she might a fragment from the hem of Jesus's robe. Sandor had Dorian in his lap, and he passed the baby to Cherilyn as she handed him the book. He put on a pair of reading glasses and gently opened the front cover.

A few moments later, Sandor looked up from the inscription. "You boys are sent by God," he said, nodding. "I truly believe you are sent by God."

OUR DISTRICT LOST NO ONE AT TRANSFERS, BUT WE DID PICK UP an extra member. Sister Herzog was a five-foot spitfire with blue mascara and frosted hair—the selfsame Herzog that Fowler used to call Mad Dog. She joined Roper and Steed in a three-leg, the awkward result of an odd number of sisters in the mission. Happily, Herzog fit right in with the gang, the biggest change being that Snow and I were now at an even greater disadvantage in the battle of pranks.

Not that all was rosy in my world. Around that time a thick missive from Katrina landed on the doorstep with a thud, and while it wasn't the Dear John that I'd been dreading, it was in many ways much worse.

My confession to her having gone so well, Katrina had decided it was time to unburden *her* conscience. Thus was I treated, to my mounting horror, to a sordid tale of alcohol, drugs, and sex that began sometime in high school and only ended a few months before she and I connected at the bank, with a tearful confession to her bishop:

> Telling that smug awful man about all the things I'd done was the most humiliating experience of my entire life. But I had to get my life back together. It was hard, the hardest thing I ever did. The temptation to go back to that life was so unbearable. But then you came into my life. That was my sign from God that I was back on the right track. YOU, Bill.

I set the letter aside. I didn't want to keep reading. I felt like I'd been punched in the gut. I wanted to throw up.

It may seem like a quaint belief to people who weren't raised with it, but I was taught from a young age that your virginity was the greatest gift you could bring your partner on your wedding day. Nobody wants to eat off a used plate, we were told. No one wants a wad of gum that's already been chewed. Boys were told to stay clean and avoid girls who were too aggressive or dressed immodestly or did not attend church. Girls were told to defend their precious virtue with their lives. Any deviation from the straight and narrow would destroy lives and reverberate through eternity.

So, Katrina thought she could give it up to persons unknown while cranked on coke, and I was her *reward* for kicking the lifestyle? What about *my* reward for never having so much as copped a feel or sniffed model-airplane glue? What about my reward for always doing everything I'd been told, for putting my life on hold for this stupid mission? I'd been told all my life I'd be the first man to touch my wife "that way." How the hell was *this* fair?

But I couldn't leave it there. I had to keep reading:

> Now I have to confess something else. Remember the first time you told me you loved me, when we were sitting out on my front porch? I liked you a lot but I wasn't in love with you. But I said it back to you anyway. I was so surprised and shocked when you said it, I didn't know what else to do. The funny thing was, as the days went by, I started to realize it was true. I did love you. I do love you. I always will. You're such a wonderful, amazing guy. I'll understand if you can't, but I only hope you can forgive me for everything. Please.

I couldn't breathe right. I hadn't thought it could get worse, but it had. She had lied to me, lied to my face, while I'd made a fool of myself pouring my heart out to her. I wanted to tear her letter into little pieces and set the pieces on fire. But Elder Snow was sitting calmly at the other desk, oblivious, so all I did was refold the pages, slide them carefully back into their envelope, and put the envelope in a drawer. I sat with my clenched fists trembling in my lap.

First my father, now Katrina. *No one* in my life was honest with me when it really counted. They hid the truth from me until I, in all good faith, had done exactly what they wanted me to. Until after I was in too deep. And now Katrina wanted my *forgiveness?*

Here's the thing about forgiveness. I'd been taught—I *had* taught—that when God forgives a sin after sincere repentance, that sin is wiped away as if it never happened. I was expected on the one hand to embrace this doctrine with all my heart, but on the other to hold out for my virgin and not settle for anything less. When I weighed those competing imperatives in the balance, which was supposed to win?

Hell no, I would not forgive her.

I WAS BEING IMMATURE AND OVERDRAMATIC, I KNOW. BUT THAT'S the thing. I *was* immature. As much as I wanted to think of myself as knowing and worldly, I was just a sheltered nineteen-year-old kid who was too intellectually overdeveloped and emotionally underdeveloped for his own good. I shouldn't have been engaged, let alone serving a mission. I should have been making all the classic life-mistakes of college, where *my* soul was the only one at stake, not shaking the trees of some foreign city thinking I could save the untethered souls who fell to the ground around me. It was the wrong business for any nineteen-year-old, let alone this one. I didn't know a goddamn thing about how the world worked.

Or rather, I *knew* plenty, but my knowledge was mostly theoretical. I'd never had the chance to put it to any practical use—and the mission field was hardly the best environment for that.

ALL THROUGH THE WEEKEND I STEWED OVER KATRINA'S LETTER. Elder Snow could tell something was wrong, but I couldn't talk about it. I didn't know how. On Saturday he and I taught the Mareks their first discussion, and on Sunday we brought them with us to sacrament meeting, but all the while my mind was elsewhere.

I couldn't bring myself to simply write Katrina off. I kept smacking up against the fear that she was my only chance at finding a Mormon bride who was nerdy and nubile in equal measure. If she wasn't the virgin I'd been taught to aim for, well, at least I could extrapolate that she liked having sex. There might be something to be said for a wife with more experience than I had—or with any experience at all.

This argument seemed especially compelling late at night, in bed, at those moments when I caught myself imagining what positions Katrina had done it in, how much or how little she'd been wearing, and what sexual intercourse with an actual woman was going to feel like. It seemed less compelling when I woke up nauseated in the morning.

I seesawed from one extreme to the other, unwilling to cut my losses but unable to purge my jealousy and righteous indignation. At last I decided to punt. I took a cue from Katrina herself, from the night when she told me she loved me too. I wrote to say I forgave her. It wasn't true, but I hoped over the coming weeks and months I would come to mean it.

THE MAREKS COULD NOT HAVE BEEN MORE RECEPTIVE TO THE GOSpel. Snow and I taught them three more discussions that week, and on Sunday night we drove them to our stake center for a special churchwide fireside on the subject of families. Snow and I sat with the sisters in the pew behind the Mareks as some of our most beloved leaders spoke live via satellite from Temple Square on a huge projection screen.

A hush fell over the congregation as the evening's final speaker, Ezra Taft Benson, approached the pulpit in the Salt Lake Tabernacle. We members all held our breath. President Benson, our prophet, was 87 years old, and it was a crapshoot whether he'd be able to say more than a few quavering words. Once upon a time he had been a vigorous political firebrand, serving as U.S. Secretary of Agriculture throughout the Eisenhower administration and frothing about Communism every chance he got. Benson had been a member of the Quorum of the

Twelve Apostles since 1943, and a common joke held that if he ever became prophet, every Mormon Democrat would leave the church.

Now that he *was* prophet, it was obvious that he was a mere shadow of the man he used to be. In fact, things were even worse than we realized. In the year 2001, I spent two fascinating hours on the phone with his grandson, the Pulitzer Prize–winning editorial cartoonist Steve Benson. Steve very publicly left the church in 1993, accusing its leaders of covering up his grandfather's increasing senility. Far from leading the church, Steve told me, his grandfather was, more often than not, propped up at the pulpit like the corpse in *Weekend at Bernie's.*

Having brought our golden investigators to hear him speak that particular night, Elder Snow and I breathed sighs of relief when President Benson began speaking in a reasonably steady voice. His impassioned address called upon faithful Mormon couples to stop putting off having children, to have as many as possible as early as possible, and to do it on a single income. "'Numerous divorces can be traced directly to the day when the wife left the home and went out into the world into employment,'" he said, directly quoting his predecessor, Spencer W. Kimball. "'I beg of you, you who could and should be bearing and rearing a family: wives, come home from the typewriter, the laundry, the nursing, come home from the factory, the café. No career approaches in importance that of wife, homemaker, mother— cooking meals, washing dishes, making beds for one's precious husband and children.'"

I could see Cherilyn Marek nodding and growing ever more rapt as the prophet drove his point home. I could also see the sisters, particularly Roper, growing fidgety and impatient.

At the end of the fireside, after the Tabernacle Choir had sung a closing hymn, Cherilyn popped right up out of her pew, Dorian snug in her arms, and turned to Snow and me. "Oh, Elders, thank you so much for bringing us here tonight! That was the most wonderful talk I've ever heard!"

Sandor had stood up beside her. "Not a lot of men are willing to speak so plainly and with such boldness."

"I agreed with every word of that talk," Cherilyn affirmed, pugnacious. "That man is *so right*."

By now we were all standing, and the hum of voices had risen as people began shuffling toward the exits. Sister Roper opened her mouth to say something, but Elder Snow shot her a warning glance. "That man is a prophet of God," he said to the Mareks. "His words are living scripture for our times."

Sandor shook his head in rueful wonder. "How could we have lived so long and never known this?"

Snow walked ahead with the Mareks as we exited the chapel, leaving me to trail behind with the sisters. I could practically see the steam venting from Roper's ears. "That was the biggest load of manure I ever heard," she seethed. "What year is this, *eighteen* eighty-seven? No one's telling me what *my* place is."

I shuddered. I certainly didn't want *my* wife—be it Katrina or whoever—stranded like a slave in the house squeezing out Shunns for a living. But to contradict the prophet of God? Out loud? In a *church*?

I let the sisters get a few steps ahead of me and tried not to look like I was with them.

CHAPTER 35

FEBRUARY 23, 1987, IS A DATE I WILL NEVER FORGET, THOUGH THE day began with only a minor aggravation.

The first stop Elder Snow and I made that morning was the office. For missionaries in Calgary, the apes held any mail that came directly to the office for district leaders to pick up and distribute. Elder Snow normally collected the mail on Tuesdays, but this week our individual meetings with President Tuttle had been canceled because of the leadership conference starting that afternoon.

Elder Hardy, dressed like us in jeans and a pullover, had a small stack of envelopes ready, but before we could leave, President emerged from his office and caught sight of us.

"Elder Shunn," he said, sounding unhappy. "As long as you're here, could I see you in private? This should only take a minute."

Oh, no. I followed him into his office. Our weekly visits had been going so well. What had I done wrong now?

Tuttle took a seat behind his desk. "Close that behind you. Elder Shunn, I'm not sure how to bring this up, but you received a rather, well, interesting piece of mail here the other day. Elder Fearing brought it to my attention."

I sat, racking my brain for what the offensive item might be.

"A manila envelope," Tuttle said, answering my look of puzzlement, "with the address of a magazine rather unsuitable for the consumption of priesthood holders stamped in the corner."

Oh, shit. That had to be *Playboy,* returning a short story I'd submitted a couple of months earlier. I hadn't written any new fiction since entering the field, but I *had* brought along manuscript copies of all my old stories. I didn't see any reason I should stop trying to sell them just because I was a missionary, so occasionally on a P-day I'd Xerox one and send it off in the mail, together with the requisite self-addressed envelope and a couple of international reply coupons for return postage.

It might still seem odd that a nominally good Mormon kid like me was submitting work to *Playboy,* but at the time it was the most prestigious market for science fiction stories. They published two or three a year and paid in the four-figure range. My father, in fact, had encouraged me to send my work there. Once he'd resigned himself to the fact that I was going to write science fiction at all, he did a little market research for me and decided that was the place to be. (It was one of my father's strange quirks that he had no problem with me submitting to *Playboy,* but years later when I published a poem in *Sunstone,* a leading journal of Mormon studies, he fretted that I was well down the road to hell. *Sunstone* was a place for dissidents and radicals, not for his son.)

"President," I said, "it's not what it looks like."

He stalled my protest with an upraised palm. "Now, Elder, just listen. There are some pursuits a missionary simply *must* put behind him while he's in the field. I know you want to be a writer, but this is not the time or place for commercial pursuits."

Huh? How could he know what the letter was about? Unless—

I groaned. Unless he'd opened it.

Tuttle folded his hands. "I've sent the contents on home to your parents, so it'll be waiting there for you when you finish your mission. Until then, let's not have any more story writing, all right?"

I didn't even have a typewriter. "But, President, I didn't—"

"No buts. I don't want to have to tell you this again. Now go on, enjoy your P-day."

I was shaking with anger as I walked out to the car with Elder Snow. That envelope was addressed to *me!* It was *illegal* for President Tuttle to open it! It would have been illegal back home, anyway. I didn't know about Canada.

"What was that all about?" Snow asked.

"Nothing," I said, slamming my door and slumping in my seat with folded arms. The worst part was, now I was going to have to write my parents to find out whether or not my rejection slip had included a personal note. I had to know.

As we drove away, I fantasized about calling the police. I didn't care if he *was* my mission president. J. Matheson Tuttle had just crossed a line.

OUR P-DAY WAS FREE UNTIL TWO, WHEN WE HAD TO MEET UP AT our zone leader's apartment to make our split-offs for the leadership conference. Since Snow was attending the conference, I'd be partnering up with Elder Finn again for twenty-four hours. Finn had called me a couple of times over the preceding week, wanting to make sure we were on for splits.

Snow and I spent an hour playing video games at the mall, after which we dropped by the sisters' pit for lunch—unannounced, of course. Sister Steed, unflappable, put on some extra tomato soup and grilled cheese sandwiches.

As we ate, Sister Roper fulminated about a run-in of her own with President Tuttle. "I swear, who does he think he is to tell me I can't go tanning or to the gym?"

"You fake-and-bake?" said Snow around a mouthful of sandwich. "Imagine that."

Roper threw her cloth napkin at him. "I'll have you know I can't feel good about myself when I'm fish-belly pale and ten pounds overweight. And when I can't feel good about myself, I'm not a good missionary. I tried to explain this to Prez, but he just didn't listen."

"Hey, I get it," Snow said, tossing the napkin back. "Black girls are foxes. It's hard for Paleface to compete. When polygamy comes back, my second wife's gonna be black."

We all stared at him.

"What?" He shoved another bite into his mouth. "How else am I gonna raise my basketball team?"

"Pig," said Roper.

SNOW AND I WENT HOME AFTER LUNCH SO HE COULD GRAB A SHOWer and change into his suit, then we drove across town to Elder Quimby's pit. He and Elder Titus lived in an apartment complex that looked like a Swiss chalet on stilts. A handful of mission cars were already parked in the fire lane under the elms out back. The third-floor apartment was crowded with a dozen noisy elders, some in their whites, some in P-day clothes. Not for the first time, I was glad Elder Dedman was stationed in the Calgary North zone.

"Oh, good, Snow, there you are," said Elder Quimby. "I think this is everybody. Hey, stop that!"

This was directed across the room at Runaway McKay and another elder, who were grinning into the fancy camera McKay held out at arm's length. The flash went off to the accompaniment of cheers and laughter. McKay bowed to the crowd and returned the camera to Elder Quimby.

"You dicks," said Quimby, advancing the film by hand. "Aw, well. I've been trying to finish this roll off anyway."

Elder McKay was a district leader, and Finn's new companion since Elder Roland had been promoted to zone leader. I'd crossed paths a couple of times now with McKay, and he always made me uncomfortable. It was nothing about *him*, exactly. It was the stigma of that nickname of his. His presence reminded me that I was a runaway too, and that I didn't know how many of the people around me might know it. Though come to think of it, I realized, I'd never heard anyone but Dedman and the apes call him "Runaway," and he seemed to be getting along just fine in the mission field, even thriving.

Quimby set his camera on a bookshelf. "All right, Elders, let's listen up here!"

Elder Finn stepped in from the balcony. I tapped Elder Snow on the arm, nodded my goodbye, and made my way around the edge of the room.

"For the district leaders," said Quimby, "we'll head out in two cars. Aguerra and Hutchins are driving. For the rest of you, Elder Titus has a miniature golf outing all planned. But don't forget that P-day ends at six-thirty! Everyone not at the conference should be back out proselytizing by then. Okay? Okay, let's move out."

As the district leaders funneled out the door, I touched Finn's shoulder. "Hey, dude. You up for some mini golf?"

"Not really." Finn was grimacing as if the noise hurt his head. "Let's get out of here, all right? I've been playing hoop all day, and I really need a shower."

"Uh, sure, okay," I said, though I'd been looking forward to going out with the gang.

We threaded our way across the room. Finn slipped out the front door without a word to anyone.

"Hey, Shunn," Elder Titus called out. "Aren't you guys coming for putt-putt?"

"We, uh, made other plans," I said. "Next time, though."

I followed Finn down the stairs. He shambled ahead of me, tired and surly. Out back I headed for the blue Cavalier, fumbling the keys out of my pocket. Finn was heading for his gray Aries K.

"Hey," I said, "don't you want to take mine? It's nicer."

"No, let's take mine. I want to drive."

Finn was acting weird, and I didn't want to get into a scene. I bit my tongue and followed him to his car.

CHAPTER 36

WE DROVE SOUTH ON MACLEOD TRAIL. THE SUN WAS A QUEASY shimmer behind a thin glaze of clouds.

"You got any errands to run, Shunn?"

"I should grab some cash. And as long as we're not out with the gang, I should take care of some laundry. I promised Snow I'd try to get it done."

Finn's face twisted. "Screw Snow. Don't let that asshole tell you what to do. Let him wash his own dirty G's."

This was not the Finn I'd had so much fun with a month earlier. "Dude, he's not *making* me do it. I *offered*, so he wouldn't have to spend his free time this morning at the laundromat. He even gave me a roll of quarters. Judas Proust."

"Okay, okay, flip. Anything else you need to do?"

"No errands," I said brightly, hoping to dispel his black cloud, "but I *did* set up a d.a. for us tonight. It's this really cool family in our ward, the Blanchards. They've got this awesome daughter, Louisa, who's seventeen. *Damn*, is she gorgeous. Like Michelle Pfeiffer. You know, from *Ladyhawke?*"

Finn pursed his lips as he stared down the road. "Yeah, okay, whatever."

I'd have thought he'd be salivating at the chance for dinner with a girl like Louisa. "It's at seven."

"Great," said Finn without enthusiasm. "I can grab that shower, and maybe a nap. You said you needed cash, right? Me too."

He turned into the parking lot of a small Royal Bank branch. It looked enough like the bank where Katrina worked to make me feel not just homesick but physically ill. I wondered what she was doing right at that moment. I hoped it didn't include booze, booty, or blow.

Inside I went straight to an ATM, but Finn crossed the lobby to one of the teller windows. As my machine spat out a pair of twenties, I glanced across the lobby and saw Finn's teller forking over a thick wad of bills. It wasn't Monopoly money, either. It was hard green U.S. currency.

That was odd.

FINN AND MCKAY LIVED ON THE FAR SOUTH SIDE OF CALGARY IN A concrete monolith that jutted with two or three others from several acres of paved-over wasteland. We rode to the ninth floor in a metallic elevator etched with graffiti. The apartment itself wasn't bad—a little messy, but not foul.

"Pit sweet pit," said Finn, gesturing around the small living room. "Make yourself at home. I shouldn't be too long."

Like most missionary apartments, there were tracts and books piled everywhere, and a street map pinned to one otherwise bare white wall. I noticed a portable cassette player and headphones on the coffee table beside a brown vinyl briefcase with DRAMATIZED CHURCH HISTORY stamped in gold foil.

I pointed to the case. "Hey, are those your tapes?"

"They're McKay's, but knock yourself out. He doesn't like me touching his stuff, but what he doesn't know won't hurt him." Finn disappeared down a short hallway.

I stepped over a set of barbells and a box of pamphlets to one of the windows, which looked east over a flat landscape of tract housing and industrial grime. Only by flattening my cheek against the glass could I catch a glimpse of the smudgy downtown skyscrapers.

I toed a dirty T-shirt aside and sat down on the couch. There were three dozen cassettes inside the brown case, each in its own slot. I had studied my share of church history, but the life of Joseph Smith was so complicated that I could never keep straight where he and the early Saints had been persecuted when. I sorted through the tapes until I found one with a title that interested me. The script was by Orson Scott Card—an idol of mine, and the only Mormon science fiction writer I'd ever heard of.

Eagerly I popped in the cassette, slid the headphones over my ears, and settled back to listen.

LEGAL TROUBLES DOGGED JOSEPH THROUGHOUT HIS YEARS IN Nauvoo. Though Missouri had been excoriated in the national press for its treatment of the Mormons, Joseph was still a fugitive from its courts. He managed to elude the sheriff who arrived to arrest him in September 1840, but he wasn't so lucky in June 1841. On his way home to Nauvoo from a meeting with Governor Thomas Carlin, he was arrested by officers from Illinois and Missouri, possibly with Carlin's complicity.

Joseph found an ally in Illinois Supreme Court Justice Stephen A. Douglas (who would run for president against Lincoln in 1860). Douglas heard the case and invalidated the Missouri warrant on a technicality. The Mormons had been largely liked and tolerated in Illinois until then, but when Joseph declared the Democratic Douglas a "tried friend" of the Latter-day Saints, Whig newspapers decried Nauvoo's rising political power. The tide of public opinion was beginning to turn against the Saints yet again. A persistent rumor that Joseph had prophesied the violent deaths of both Governor Boggs of Missouri and Governor Carlin of Illinois did not help matters.

Haunted by the fear that he could be locked up or lynched at any moment, Joseph had undertaken a project to dictate his life story as he wanted it to be told. It was here that his First Vision, which had been recounted in various inconsistent forms over the years, took on its final, canonical shape, the version every Mormon child knows today. It was here he took pains to ensure that his history would be synonymous with the history of his church—and succeeded.

Begun in 1838 after his flight from Kirtland, this work would proceed in fits and starts over the remainder of Joseph's life. The Mormon War and the long imprisonment in Liberty Jail disrupted the project, of course, and it had to be suspended again in August 1842, when a fresh legal nightmare forced Joseph into hiding.

On May 6, an unknown assailant shot former Missouri governor Lilburn Boggs in the head through the window of his home. Boggs, through gravely wounded, was not killed, and it didn't take him long to label the attack an assassination attempt by the Mormons. He was encouraged in this suspicion by John C. Bennett, the former mayor of Nauvoo. Bennett had been expelled from the church for seducing women under a claim of authority from Joseph, then become well-known for his lurid, widely published exposés of Mormonism (one of which included Martha Brotherton's account of high-pressure advances by Brigham Young). Now he claimed he'd heard Joseph promise a huge bounty to any Danite who could fulfill the prophecy that Boggs would die.

Warrants were issued for the arrests of Joseph and his most trusted bodyguard, Porter Rockwell. Porter had joined the church at the age of sixteen, on the day it was founded, and he never swerved from his fierce loyalty to the prophet. He had just returned from a mysterious trip to Missouri, and that fact, together with Bennett's testimony, made him the top suspect in the shooting. However, the Nauvoo city council had just voted itself the power to invalidate any arrest warrant from another jurisdiction that it found "malicious." When Joseph and

Porter turned themselves in to an Illinois sheriff, Nauvoo's municipal court freed them immediately with a writ of habeas corpus. Before Missouri could pull a legal response together, Joseph and Porter disappeared.

Joseph remained in hiding in and around Nauvoo until December, moving from house to house by night, frequently risking his freedom to rendezvous with Emma. At least once he narrowly escaped capture. Despondent, he was considering a run to Wisconsin when word came that U.S. District Attorney Justin Butterfield believed his extradition to Missouri on charges of conspiracy to commit murder would be illegal. Joseph traveled to Springfield with a vigilant retinue, where, in a circus of a hearing, the U.S. Circuit Court invalidated Missouri's warrant.

Porter Rockwell, meanwhile, spent a harsh winter alone in Philadelphia, only to be captured in Missouri in March 1843 en route home to Nauvoo. He languished for nine months in prison—a period enlivened by an escape and recapture—before a grand jury failed to indict him for attempted murder.

It was Christmas day when a dirty, long-haired stranger pushed his way into a lavish party at Joseph and Emma's home in Nauvoo. Guards tussled with the intruder before Joseph entered the fray and recognized him. "It's Porter!" he exclaimed.

After Porter had recounted his adventures, Joseph declared before the assembled guests that the bodyguard, like Samson, would enjoy the Lord's protection so long as he remained faithful to both the church and one commandment more: "Cut not thy hair and no bullet or blade can harm thee!"

Porter would later achieve infamy as a Wild West gunfighter and lawman, with rumors constantly swirling about his busy secret life as an assassin for the Mormon Church. But from the day of Joseph's prophecy, writes biographer Harold Schindler, "through thirty-five violent years in which [he] encountered hostile Indians, desperadoes, and other characters on the western scene, he managed to avoid a single physical injury at the hands of another man."

When Porter Rockwell died of heart failure in 1878, he had belonged to the church longer than any other living person.

EVEN DRAMATIZED CHURCH HISTORY COULDN'T KEEP MY MIND from drifting. I was thinking ahead to that evening. Maybe Finn wouldn't mind if I called Katrina after dinner. She'd been sending me weird letters, asking questions about the temple ceremony and what the symbols on her parents' garments meant. I wondered if someone had handed *her* an anti-Mormon tract. In any case, hearing her voice might help me get over my lingering bile and truly forgive her.

Toward the end of the thirty-minute program, I realized that the shower, which had been vaguely audible earlier, was no longer running, and hadn't been for some time.

An angry mob was shouting on the tape. Just as a volley of gunshots sounded, Finn appeared from down the hallway. He had on jeans and a purple sweater. His wet hair was neatly combed. His shoulders sloped like a gorilla's, his posture morose but still threatening. He said something I couldn't hear. I slipped the headphones down around my neck.

"What's that again?" I asked warily.

He didn't look me in the eye. "I said I'm about to freak you out, Elder Shunn."

My blood froze. "What? How?"

Finn indicated the bedroom with a jerk of his head. "I've, um, been in there packing my stuff. I'm flying home tonight, Shunn. And you're gonna drive me to the airport."

CHAPTER 37

I STARED AT ELDER FINN WITH MY MOUTH OPEN. ALL I COULD think was how flipping unfair this was—and how fitting.

Finn snapped his fingers. "Shunn, *hello*. Did you hear me?"

"Uh, yeah. Yeah, I heard you." Hands shaking, I took the headphones from around my neck and lowered them to the coffee table. I never took my eyes off him. I was no physical threat, and I didn't want him to mistake me for one.

He stared me down from across the room. "Well?"

I clasped my hands between my knees, trying to stay cool, but my stomach hurt. What was it going to look like if Elder Finn ran away on my watch? Was this what Elder Dedman had felt like, confronting me? "Why are you doing this? What makes you want to go home?"

Finn threw his arms in the air, pacing frenetically. "I *hate* my mission! I can't stand it here one more day!"

"It, uh, from my point of view it looks like things are going pretty well for you." A trickle of hot sweat ran down the small of my back. "I mean, look at the Dawson family. Look what you did for them."

"Oh, please," he said bitterly. "That didn't have anything to do with me. They were ready. A monkey could have baptized them. I was just the first warm body to come along."

"Maybe they *were* ready. But they still needed *you* to point it out to them."

He jammed his hands in his pockets, chin nearly touching his chest. "So maybe I did one good thing on my mission. At least I've accomplished that. Doesn't mean I have to stick around and be miserable for another twenty months."

"It might seem bad right now," I said, beginning to plead, "but it gets better. I promise it does get better." Did I believe that, or was I just saying it? I didn't know.

"I'm not waiting around for it to get better."

"But Finn, look at your companion. *He* wanted to run away, but he stayed. That was a year and a half ago. Did you know that?"

"Everyone knows that. He stayed because the apes called him names."

"Uh, well, I guess. But obviously things got better for him. He's a district leader now."

"He's a dick," Finn snarled. "I hate that son of a bitch. I wish he *had* gone home."

I recoiled. "I thought he was kind of cool."

"You don't have to be with him all day, every stupid day." Finn's fists clenched and unclenched. He paced like a bull in a tiny pen. "You don't have to put up with his self-righteous bullshit. That flippin' asshole."

"So is that why you want to leave? Because your comp's an asshole? I know what a difference a bad companion can make, but you can't let one guy ruin everything for you."

Finn looked at his shoes, and his chin began to tremble. "That's not all of it," he said huskily. "It's my mom. She's really sick." He knuckled his eyes. "They might have to amputate her foot."

"Oh, shit, man." I helplessly flexed my hands. This water was over my head, and I was flailing. "Finn, I'm so sorry. Listen, though. Some things are just more important, okay? Your commitment to the Lord is more important."

He glared a warning from under lowered brows.

"Just listen for a second," I said. "My cousin Lauren was on her mission in Nebraska when my uncle Doug died of leukemia. Her father. He *died*, and she still stayed out on her mission. She didn't even go home for the funeral."

"That's wrong," said Finn, his face twisting. "That's just *wrong*. Why would God want that? Why would he ask that?"

He had a point, which put me in the weird position of arguing against something I agreed with. "That's the commitment you make when you come on a mission. But your mom, she's not going to die, right?"

Finn sniffled. "No. I guess not."

"Well, there you go. There's no real reason for you to be there. In fact—" I spread my hands. "In fact, I think you just want to go home, and this is the justification."

"Screw you, Shunn!" he spat, punctuating his words with angry thrusts of his finger. "I want to be there for my mom! Maybe the surgery won't kill her, but she doesn't want to *live*, okay? She's losing her *foot*. I have to be there."

Palms up, I spoke in the most placating tone I could muster. "All right, all right, I understand. I'd want to be there too. But the question is, is that what your *mom* wants?"

He ran a hand through his hair. "As much as she wants anything. Which isn't much."

Criminy. "Well, what about the rest of your family? Don't you think *they'd* rather have you here? Don't you think they'll be disappointed if you come home early?"

Finn flung himself down in an armchair near the couch. As he stared at the ceiling, he might have been blinking back tears or he might have been counting to ten.

"Shunn," he said at last, "did you grow up in the church?"

"Well, yeah."

His eyes bored into mine. "I didn't. You had that whole expectation growing up that you'd go on a mission, but I didn't. I'm a convert. My mom and I joined when I was twelve. She never pressured me to go on a mission. And my dad, he's not even a member. He doesn't understand why I'm here. He supports me, but he doesn't get it."

"Do you *wish* he were a member?"

"Of course."

"Well, Elder, what does it say about your commitment to the church if you *do* go home? What kind of an example does that set for your dad? Do you think he'll ever find it worth joining if you don't even find it worth sticking out your mission?"

"If I *don't* go home for this, it might turn him against the church forever." Finn shook his head, his expression darkening, and stood up. "Shit, Shunn, I don't have time for this. Look, my original plan was, my buddy Patrick would fly in today from Fresno, but at the last minute he couldn't ditch work. He was gonna keep you busy, sit on you if he had to. But he's not here, which means I really need your cooperation. You can either be cool or be a dick, but I gotta finish packing and roll out of here, and if you're gonna be a dick then I'm gonna have to get mean, okay? I don't have time to keep talking shit."

He turned away. Desperate, I jumped to my feet. As long as I could keep him talking, I figured there was a chance I could bring him around, but the sand was slipping between my fingers. "Just one question, Elder. Have you prayed about this?"

He looked back with gritted teeth. "Of course I have."

"And what was your answer?"

"Go," he said, turning away again.

It was so much like me two months earlier, it made me dizzy. But I couldn't think about that.

"Wait, wait, wait," I said, rounding the coffee table and reaching for his arm.

Wearily, Finn rubbed his face. "What?"

"Have you talked to President Tuttle?"

He let out a sullen laugh. "Oh, flip, Shunn," he said with what sounded like pity.

"Finn, you've got to talk to Prez. If you're going to leave, at least you should leave the right way."

"You're gonna make a good ape someday, you know that?" He checked his watch. "Now shut up and listen to me. I'm leaving in fifteen minutes. You can come with me to the airport or not, I don't care, but until then I want you to stay right here. I'll hear it if you try to leave, and I'm not kidding—I won't let you."

He started toward the bedroom again. I turned my head toward the phone, a wall unit that wasn't mounted but instead, with typical missionary laxness, was propped up on a chair near the windows.

Finn turned around before I could think about taking a step. "And forget about calling anyone. I've got the extension in the bedroom off the hook."

I plopped down on the couch, head in hands. I was being punished for my sins as a missionary, I just knew it. Now, if I didn't do everything in my power to keep him here, I was in deep shit.

I went to the phone and picked up the receiver. No dial tone—just dead air and faint rustling noises.

A clattering sounded and Finn spoke, his voice eerily loud on the line. "I *hear* you, Shunn. Nice try, though."

It was four o'clock in the afternoon. I hung up and sat down again to think.

TEN MINUTES LATER I WAS HELPING FINN LUG HIS BAGS OUT TO the car. The gray sky lay heavy overhead. I had considered trying to sneak out of the apartment while he was still in the back room, but I didn't know where to go and I had no idea what he might do if he caught me. At least if I stuck with him, I could keep tabs on him until there was a chance to find a pay phone.

Finn had seemed relieved and grateful when I agreed to ride to the airport with him, and he loosened up even more once we were on the road. He grew expansive enough, in fact, to elaborate on the many and varied ways in which Elder McKay and President Tuttle, among others, were flaming assholes. He navigated a maze of streets that played hell with my sense of direction, and before long we were headed north on a freeway just starting to clot with rush-hour traffic. To the southwest, the sun trickled earthward.

"Finn, listen," I said when his diatribe had run its course. "You may not like Prez, but I really think you should talk to him. You don't ever want to look back on this day and regret it."

"Damn right I don't," said Finn, his face clouding. "Flip, you don't let up, do you?"

"I *can't*." My throat clogged with the mass of my ambivalence and regrets. It was time to bring out the big guns, time to speak from experience. "Finn, I, I've been exactly where you are right now. I tried to run away. I got as far as Montana, but—but—"

I broke off because Finn was smiling, his mouth twitching on the verge of laughter.

"What's the matter? What's so funny?"

He practically cackled with glee. "Oh, my *God*, Shunn! I know that. *Everyone* knows that! What, did you think it was a secret? Not even."

I was suffocating in a cloud of humiliation. "But—"

"You haven't figured out why I did this today of all days? How dense *are* you? Shunn, I've been planning this for *weeks*. You know why I wanted you on splits with me? *Because* you've been through it. I figured if anyone would be sympathetic, it'd be you. I'm going to need *time*, Shunn. I have to be long gone before the word gets out, you know? Do you get it? Can you do that for me?"

I wondered if Finn knew that Dedman had done the same thing for me. "Finn, I—I—"

He turned pleading eyes on me. "Can you do that for me, Shunn?"

I sagged against the vinyl seat. "Yeah," I mumbled, not looking at him. "Yeah, I can do that."

He let out a long breath, nodding with relief. "Okay, thank you."

We drove on in silence. Signs for Calgary International Airport began to appear.

"Now here's a thought," said Finn, as if it had just occurred to him. "I do have two seats reserved on this plane. Patrick was supposed to have one of them, but he's not here, so . . ." He shrugged. "Um, if you want it."

The thought made me ill. Even if I did want still want to go home—and part of me certainly did—I couldn't go through an ordeal like that again. "Thanks—I guess? But no thanks."

Finn raised an eyebrow. "Not tempted? Not even a little?"

"Not even a little."

"Well, hey, suit yourself." He said it offhandedly, like he didn't want me to know I'd hurt his feelings.

Something nagged at me about Finn's offer, but I couldn't put my finger on it, and our off-ramp was coming up. I looked at my watch. 4:35. I hoped there was still time somehow to shift this burden to President Tuttle. "So when's your flight?" I asked.

"Oh, in a little while."

"What airline?"

Finn shook a finger at me, smiling slyly. "Ah-ah-ah, Shunn. I don't think I'm ready to tell you that." He frowned, looking twice his age, and grumbled, "But I *am* changing planes in the worst of all possible cities."

It clicked then, why Finn thought his friend's plane reservation might tempt me. I'd have no reason to want to fly with him to Fresno, but if he was making a connection in Salt Lake City . . .

I kept my face carefully composed. This was the break I needed.

CHAPTER 38

FINN PARKED IN A FIFTEEN-MINUTE LOADING ZONE IN FRONT OF the main terminal. "You shouldn't have to be here any longer than that," he said as we exited the car.

It was 4:40. Auto traffic at the airport was light. The sky continued to darken, and the stiff breeze carried the smell of jet fuel. We pulled Finn's suitcases out of the trunk. He gave me the car keys and I helped him carry his luggage inside.

The terminal was bright and airy. Even with all the people around, it didn't feel crowded. The hum of conversation was muted. Finn found the Occidental Airlines counter to our left, just inside the entrance. He took a place at the end of the long line. I queued up with him.

"I'll just get my ticket, go to the gate, and that's it," Finn told me. "All you need to do is keep your mouth shut until I make my connecting flight."

I didn't want to tip him off that I'd deduced his route. "How long will that be?"

He gave me a probing look. "Maybe I should call you when I land."

"Whatever." I glanced around to see if I could read any of the departure monitors. No dice.

Two minutes passed, three. Announcements echoed overhead as

we inched forward. The line grew behind us. At last, when Finn was looking the other way, I took a careful step backward, out of line. He didn't notice. I took one more step, then melted into the crowd.

I walked fast through the thicket of travelers. I imagined Finn's angry eyes boring into my back. When I was far enough away from him, I stopped to check the departure monitors. I was sure Finn was furious with me, but he wouldn't want to give up his place in line to come looking for me. I hoped.

I scanned the list of flights. The only one bound for Salt Lake City was Occidental Flight 789, departing at 5:55.

I checked my watch. 4:48. I had just over an hour to somehow get Elder Finn talking to President Tuttle. It wasn't a lot of time, but it would have to be enough.

If it wasn't—well, I had the glimmerings of a backup plan forming. But that was a contingency I didn't want to think about.

I TOOK AN ESCALATOR TO THE MEZZANINE LEVEL. MY IMMEDIATE goal was to get out of sight before Finn came looking for me, but then I spotted the row of pay phone kiosks near a window overlooking the tarmac. That was my second goal.

I fished a quarter from my pocket. At the second phone from the window, I dialed the mission office. With four stakes in Calgary, there had to be at least a dozen and a half LDS meetinghouses, and I had no idea which one was hosting the leadership conference. I hoped someone at the office could tell me.

The line rang. And rang. Five times, seven. Ten.

"Shit," I said, hanging up. What now? Call every church building in the phone book?

I plugged my quarter back in and dialed Elder Quimby's number, which I knew from helping Elder Snow report our district's weekly numbers. Elder Titus and the others might be back from miniature golf by now. Maybe one of them would know what building to call.

No answer.

Desperate now, I dialed Lienhard and Kopp, but they weren't home either. Of course they were out enjoying P-day, like sensible elders, but I cursed them anyway. I called my own apartment on the slim chance that Snow and McKay might have stopped there on a break from the conference. I tried McKay's too, with the same result.

That exhausted the phone numbers I knew from memory. I tried to dredge up any others I might have dialed at one time or another, but to no avail. A thick phone book hung by a metal cable from a shelf beneath the phone. Maybe I could find a listing for Bishop Tomlinson, or the Blanchard family, where I was due for dinner in a couple of hours . . .

I smacked my head. *Wait.* There was one more number I could try. I shoved the quarter into the slot and dialed the sisters.

One ring. Two.

"Come on," I said, anxiously tapping my foot.

Three.

"Come *on,* Sisters."

Four. The line clicked.

"LDS missionaries, this is Sister Steed. Can I help you?"

My words tumbled out in a rush. "Steed, it's Elder Shunn. I need your help bad. I'm out at the airport, and Elder Finn's about to fly home."

"Not funny, Elder Shunn," Steed said sternly. "Goodbye."

"Wait wait *wait!*" I cried. "Judas Proust, I'm not kidding! *Steed!*"

She didn't hang up, but she didn't say anything to me. A babble of voices argued in the background.

I heard Sister Roper say, "Gimme that!" A clattering sounded as she picked up the receiver. "Elder Shunn? What's this all about? What's going on?"

I nearly sobbed with relief. "Oh, thank goodness. I'm at the airport with Elder Finn. He's flying home."

Whatever reaction I expected, it was not Sister Roper's sad, heavy sigh. "That little turkey. How many times did I talk to him about this? Now he's doing it anyway."

I blinked. "You *knew* this was going to happen?"

"I knew he was thinking about it. I thought I'd talked him out of it, though. I sure didn't know he'd do anything *today*."

My lungs constricted with anger. I felt betrayed, abandoned. I had sat *right* at Roper's lunch table, and she *knew* I was splitting off with Finn, and she hadn't said a *word*. How could she have sat back and let me walk into a trap like this? "Well, it's not a done deal yet."

"Let me talk to him. Put him on."

"I can't," I snapped. "He's downstairs checking in for his flight. I had to slip away to find a phone."

"You let him out of your *sight?*" Roper exclaimed.

"I didn't have a choice!"

"Elder Shunn, that was a mistake. You go find him and get him to this phone. I'm gonna have me a word or two with that boy."

"All right, fine." Fuming, I let the receiver dangle and hurried to the railing near the escalator. I felt like we were wasting time, but I was also relieved to pass responsibility to someone more authoritative. That way, when things went wrong it wouldn't all be my fault.

The crowd in the terminal below had thinned by quite a bit, and I could no longer see anyone waiting at the Occidental ticket counter. As I descended the escalator I saw that a long queue had formed beyond the ticket counters, at the entrance to Customs. Elder Finn with his two blue suitcases was easy to spot. Not without trepidation, I hurried to where he stood and tapped him on the shoulder.

Finn turned his head and did a double take. "Where the hell have you been?" His voice was a slow-burning fuse. "I thought I'd seen the last of you."

I jerked a thumb over my shoulder. "I've got Roper on a phone up on the mezzanine. She really wants to talk to you."

Finn's face twisted like he was either going to cry or bite my head off. "Shunn, you fucking *rat*. I should have known you'd fucking rat me out the second my back was turned. You *fucking* asshole."

People were starting to look. Palms up, I backed away a step. "Roper just wants to say goodbye, that's all. I can save your place in line."

"I don't fucking want to talk to Roper! I just want to—" He stamped his foot. "*Shit!* Just get the fuck away from me, Shunn, okay? Go."

"Elder Finn, if you—"

"Go!"

"Okay, okay."

I turned and walked fast back to the escalator. I felt dozens of eyes on my back. I wondered if security was watching me now. Time was running out.

I found the receiver still dangling and hoped my one quarter had been enough to keep the line open. "Roper, you there?"

"Elder Shunn? Where's Finn?"

I sighed. "He said—well, he was pretty emphatic about not wanting to talk. I'm sorry." When she didn't reply, I said, "Roper? Hello?"

"Yeah, I'm here." It sounded as if the hope had leaked out of her. "For what it's worth."

"You can still help," I urged, galvanized by a manic energy. It was up to me to take charge now. "You can find President Tuttle. He's at the leadership conference, but I don't know where they're holding it. If you track him down, we can maybe get him out here to talk to Finn." I looked at my watch. 5:05. "But you have to do it fast."

"All right," she said, "I can take care of that. How about I see what I can do and call you back in ten minutes?"

"Sounds good. Do you have a pencil?" I read her the number from the strip above the keypad, then had her read it back to me. "Good luck, talk to you soon."

I hung up and went back to the mezzanine railing. The line at Customs had shrunk. Elder Finn was nowhere in sight.

I PACED FOR SEVERAL MINUTES, MY HELPLESS MIND SPINNING OUT of control. There was nothing I could do about anything, not until Sister Roper called me back, and every time I looked at my watch it seemed the second hand had barely moved.

Near the phones sat a change machine and a video game console. My stomach was eating itself. I *had* to think about something else for a few minutes, so I changed a couple of dollars and plugged a quarter into the game.

Trivia questions popped up one by one, each correct answer propelling a little man a few rungs higher up a ladder. After fifteen minutes the little man still hadn't reached any summit, but I had the high score and Sister Roper hadn't rung me back. I checked my watch. 5:25. I went to phone and dialed.

"Shunn, where on earth did you go?" Roper demanded. "I've been calling and calling."

"I've been right here the whole time! Maybe these phones don't take incoming calls. Dammit."

"Never mind. I got hold of Prez. He's on his way."

I had never heard sweeter words. "No kidding? That's great!"

"He's bringing Elder Roland with him from the conference." Roland was now a zone leader in Edmonton. "Finn worshipped that guy."

"Even better," I said. "What do *I* need to do?"

"When does the flight leave, Elder Shunn?"

I glanced at my watch. "A little under half an hour."

"Half an *hour*?" Roper screeched. "Good gravy, Shunn, how's Prez going to make it to the airport in half an hour?"

Things were sliding out of control again. "Finn and I did."

"You weren't in the middle of rush hour."

"Where's Prez coming from?"

"Calgary North stake center. Crap, Shunn, he's not gonna make it. So here's what you need to do. Call the airline. Ask them to hold the flight for a bit, just long enough for Prez to get there and talk to Finn."

I couldn't believe what I was hearing. "Do *what?*"

"Call the airline."

I shook my head. "Roper, airlines don't just hold flights because you ask them to. They've got schedules to keep."

"Elder Shunn, you have to try. Just explain the situation. Say Prez is on the way. What's the airline?"

"Occidental."

"Oh, they do lots of business with the church. They'll listen."

"They won't," I snorted.

"Elder Shunn, do it. You have to do everything you can to keep Finn there."

A knot tightened in my chest. I pressed my forehead against the cool chrome of the phone kiosk. "All right, all right."

"Good man, Elder Shunn. Call me back when you've talked to them."

I STOOD THERE, HEAD DOWN, HANDS ON MY HIPS, FOR AT LEAST A full minute, mulling over my options. There weren't many.

So now it had come down to this. The backup plan. The Hail Mary. The in-case-of-emergency-break-glass final resort.

I assumed the instructions Sister Roper gave me were passed along from President Tuttle, but even so, I had no intention of obeying. A polite request that Occidental Airlines hold Finn's flight would be plain useless, and would only waste time.

But that didn't mean calling the airline was a bad idea. I paced a tight pattern in front of the phones. The only question was whether I had the balls to make them pay attention to me.

I took out a quarter, rubbing my thumb obsessively across the Queen's face. Mormonism has a long tradition of earthly laws broken in pursuit of a higher good. One example is the incident early in the Book of Mormon where God commands Nephi to smite off Laban's head with his own sword. Laban was custodian of the scriptural re-cords that Nephi needed to take with him to America. Laban refused to hand them over, so God set aside the commandment against murder to accomplish a higher good.

This story, of course, sprang from Joseph Smith's imagination, but he certainly never hesitated to break the law in real life when it stood in the way of the cause of righteousness. This tradition had even worked in *my* favor, when the pretty immigration officer at the border bent the rules to let me back into Canada. Obviously a higher purpose had been served in that case.

These rationalizations aside, what I wanted most was to not end up like Elder Dedman—busted for not doing everything in my power to keep Finn from leaving his mission. I could not face that trauma and humiliation too, not on top of everything I'd been through already. I could not face more of President Tuttle's disapproval. And if I wasn't going to listen to my leaders, then why had I stayed out on my mission at all?

Fuck it. The longer I waited, the harder this was going to be.

I ripped the phone book open to the Yellow Pages and swiped through until I found AIRLINES. There were several listings under OCCIDENTAL AIRLINES, but most of them were 800 numbers.

The last listing, though, was definitely local, as I could tell by the area code. OCCIDENTAL AIR CARGO. That was the one I wanted. I dropped a quarter in the slot. My hand shook like an old man's as I dialed the number. I couldn't get enough breath. I tasted copper.

The line picked up on the first ring. "Occidental Air Cargo," said a young man. "How can I help you?"

I took a deep breath. Sister Youtz had complimented my deep, rich telephone voice. I used it now, slowly, clearly, and distinctly.

"There's a bomb in a suitcase on Flight 789."

I hung up.

CHAPTER 39

AS I BACKED AWAY FROM THE PHONE, I REALIZED I WAS GRINNING. I couldn't believe I'd actually done it—conceived and executed such a crazy, brilliant, left-field gambit. I was a giant, a legend, a colossus, pumped up to superhuman dimensions by my sheer reckless audacity. In three strides, I could be through the wall and out on the tarmac, a berserker tossing trucks and planes like medicine balls. *Elder Shunn smash puny humans! Bah!*

But over the next few moments, it dawned on me that I had just broken the law in a serious way. The euphoria drained out of me as I shrank back to normal size. The airline surely traced all incoming calls. The police were no doubt mobilizing now, converging on my location.

A violent spasm shook me. I had to move.

I wanted to run down the escalator, but I forced myself to hold still on that slow conveyance, like a normal person would. My knees quaked. It was all I could do to stand in place, let alone strike a casual pose.

At ground level, I joined the thinning crowd and walked toward the Occidental ticket counter. No one else might have noticed, but I could see how so many of the men who passed me sported mustaches and dark suits, how briskly they were moving while trying to look as if they weren't in a hurry, how many of them were speaking quietly into small radios . . .

Ice filled my guts. Never in my life had I felt so cold. I was not the gamesman I had imagined myself to be, but a common criminal. I was working here without a net, having placed myself outside the bounds of civil society. I was sure my guilt was written on my face. One wrong glance, one misplaced step, would bring every agent in the place swarming down on me.

I wandered the airport in a paranoid fog. I knew I should get in the car and just drive, if the car was even still there and hadn't been towed. The longer I stayed the more likely I was to get caught, but I couldn't make myself leave the terminal. Even at my most confused, I knew I had some kind of duty there. I began to come back to my senses when, wrung out, I found myself at another pay phone speaking to what would have to pass for a friendly voice.

"Elder Shunn, thank goodness!" cried Sister Roper. "Where the hell have you been?"

"Um, just hanging out." I was trying my hardest not to shoot terrified glances in every direction.

"Is President with you?"

I took a deep breath. The police hadn't caught me. They probably weren't going to. How could they know that I, out of all the people at the airport, was the caller they were looking for? "No, I haven't seen him."

"He isn't there yet?"

"I don't know. I mean—I don't know. He could be. I don't think so."

"You don't *think* so? Elder Shunn, I thought you were going to keep on top of things there. Where are you?"

"I—I'm at the airport."

"But *where*? Are you someplace where you'll see Prez and Elder Roland when they get there?"

"I don't know." I rubbed my eyes and looked around. I had somehow ended up far from where Finn and I had entered. "I have no idea. Probably not."

"You gotta meet them when they get there, Elder Shunn. Jiminy Christmas, you're the only one who knows the situation there. So go where you need to go and call me back." She hung up.

Wearily, I sighed. *I might not be fleeing the scene, but common sense was.*

On legs that still wobbled, I headed back toward the Occidental counter. The evening sun streaming through the terminal's high windows made everything look hyperreal. I scanned my surroundings obsessively, but a few straggling travelers were all I saw, no security personnel. Operations were winding down for the evening. I checked my watch—5:51—and wondered what was happening on the tarmac.

I found a pay phone with a good view of the entrance. Roper picked up before the end of the first ring. "Shunn, you in place?"

"Yeah, I'm here."

"And President's still not there?"

"Not that I know."

"All right, keep an eye out. How long until Finn's flight leaves?"

"Less than five minutes."

"Damn. Did you call the airline?"

I hesitated. "Uh, yes. Yes, I did."

"Great! What did they say? Are they holding the flight?"

I hesitated again. "Well, I think I can say they're giving it serious consideration."

"That's good news. And you're keeping tabs on Elder Finn, right? Where is he?"

I held the receiver away from my face and stared at it in disbelief. "No, Sister Roper," I hissed when I put it back to my ear, "I'm not *keeping tabs* on him. I don't know where he is! He went through Customs half an hour ago! He's probably on board already!"

"He's gone through *Customs?*"

"Of course he has! He's flying home to the States!"

"Elder Shunn," said Roper brusquely, "do you think President Tuttle's gonna be able to get through Customs to talk to him?"

Oh, fuck. Of course not. With a sinking feeling, I said, "No. No, I really don't think so."

"Okay, here's what you need to do," said Roper, with an authority not many elders could have summoned. "You need to go to Customs and explain the situation, make sure they'll let President through when he gets there."

"But—"

"No buts, Elder Shunn! Do it. Call me back. Hurry."

I hung up and let out a long, resigned breath.

A STEEL MESH CURTAIN BLOCKED ACCESS TO THE INTERNATIONAL concourse. A door-sized opening in it was flanked by metal detectors and two bored young women in matching polyester. Were these Customs officers? They looked barely out of high school.

"Um, hi," I said, approaching them, "I'm a missionary with the Church of Jesus Christ of Latter-day Saints, you know, the Mormons? And one of our missionaries is, um, you know, flying home early, like, before his time's up? And well, anyway, our, um, minister, I guess, is on his way out here to try to talk this elder, um, missionary, into staying, but he's already gone through Customs. So what I was wanting to see was if, um, when he gets here, the president, I mean, if he could get through Customs so he could talk to this guy. Okay?"

The two women exchanged wary looks. Their expressions of boredom had turned increasingly uneasy during my awkward monologue. "What's that again?" one asked with a confused shake of her head.

I slowed down and tried to explain the situation more cogently, uncomfortably conscious that I was making my church sound like a repressive cult.

They exchanged another look. "Uh, listen," said the first, "we really can't help you. You'll have to talk to our, uh, supervisor."

"Yeah," said the other, "we were just shutting down."

After an apparently telepathic exchange, one of them went to retrieve their supervisor while the other kept a suspicious eye on me.

Two or three minutes later, a bearded man in an orange windbreaker arrived. I repeated my story to him.

"I'm sorry, sir," he said haughtily, "but this is a sterile area and there is no special admittance."

My most abject pleas got me nowhere. Desperate, I asked if there was someone else I could talk to. With a imperious thrust of his chin, the bearded man went to fetch that someone else.

I was by now standing inside the Customs cordon. The two women had wrestled the metal detectors through the curtain, and I watched with some alarm as they shuttered and locked the opening. It was six o'clock, the international concourse was apparently closing down, and there was still no sign of President Tuttle. If Finn's flight was still on schedule, it had departed five minutes earlier.

The bearded man reappeared, accompanied by a sixtyish woman in a blue uniform. She wrinkled her nose as she looked me up and down. "What's going on here, sonny?" she rasped.

I went through the litany again. "Stay there," she said, and walked away with no particular urgency.

I waited in an awkward grouping with the two young women and the bearded man.

"*Mormons,*" the man said derisively. He rocked back on his heels, eyes aimed ceilingward. "I hope this *friend* of yours manages to get away."

The two women stifled giggles, and I felt my face burning. Behind me, the lights over many of the ticket counters in the main terminal went out, though for now the dying sun provided plentiful illumination. I wondered if my ruse had failed and Finn was indeed gone.

The older woman returned, accompanied by a compact man in a

tweed jacket. He stopped several feet from me, standing straight and still with unforced authority. "I'm Constable Vaughan from the Royal Canadian Mounted Police."

I glanced at the people around me. "Elder Shunn."

"Why don't we go back to my office, Elder Shunn." His voice was soft and calming, his eyes sleepy. "Just to chat. It's this way."

After another glance around, hoping to spot some other option, I followed the constable down a nearby corridor. My footsteps sounded somehow muffled. He opened a frosted glass door. I looked back the way we had come. The two young women had already drifted away, but the bearded man and the older woman stood whispering together.

The office we entered was small and gray, cluttered with law enforcement books. A young man in a plaid shirt and tie was just rising from a typewriter stand, but he sat down again as we entered. "I guess *I'm* not leaving on time tonight," he muttered, casting a glare in my direction as he rolled a form into his Selectric.

I began to have a very bad feeling.

Vaughan ensconced himself behind a steel desk. I took the chair across from him.

"Now, Mister Shunn, was it?" asked the constable with relaxed curiosity. His thinning hair was neatly trimmed, his ginger mustache clipped with military precision.

The office was so cold I shivered. Or maybe that was just me. "Um, *Elder* Shunn, actually."

The typewriter clacked. I nearly jumped out of my skin. "How do you spell that?" asked the typist.

"S-H-U-N-N. Two *n*'s."

"That's an unusual name," said Vaughan.

"Shunn?"

"Elder."

"Oh, right. It's a—a title. My name's actually Bill. I'm a missionary with the Church of Jesus Christ of Latter-day Saints."

"The Mormons."

Clackity-clack!

"That's right."

Vaughan settled back in his chair, folding his hands across his flat stomach. "I've seen you young men around town. Never met one of you before, though." He raised his eyebrows, and his heavy-lidded eyes widened a little. "So, I take it there's some kind of difficulty with one of your, er, colleagues?"

The typist eased back from his machine, watching. I sensed a vise tightening but told myself not to be paranoid. This constable had no reason to suspect I was anything but what I appeared to be. I'd done this a million times with bishops and stake presidents. I would be fine.

"That needs a little explaining," I said.

Vaughan spread his hands. "Go right ahead."

The typist poised his fingers.

"Like I told you, I'm a missionary. We get sent out for two years, and we dedicate ourselves to teaching people about our church for that whole time. There's no visits home or vacations or anything like that. The other thing about being a missionary is that you go around in twos all the time, with a—a *partner*, and, well, today my partner decided he wanted to go home."

"Ahead of schedule," said Vaughan, with the typist clacking in the background.

Sweat prickled the back of my neck. "Exactly. He's only been out for four months, so I tried to talk him out of leaving. I told him what a big mistake he was making, why didn't he talk it over with the mission president, and so on, et cetera."

"Why would it be a mistake?"

"Well—" I shrugged. "It's just, I almost did it myself a couple of months ago, and it was a *mistake*. Being a missionary's a big thing to Mormons. It's like, you could end up a pariah if you go home early."

"But he still wanted to leave."

"Yes! So he made me drive him to the airport, and now our mission president's on his way here to try to talk to him before he leaves, and I was supposed to go to Customs to make sure the president could get through to see him before departure time."

Vaughan nodded, squinting a little. "I see. So you've been in contact with your, er, superiors, I suppose. At your mission?"

"That's right."

He picked up a pencil from his desk. "And how did you contact them?"

"Well, I called them."

"By telephone."

"Yes. I mean, I didn't talk directly to the mission president, but I talked to some other missionaries who passed the message along."

"You called them from the airport, here. This afternoon."

"Yes."

"I see." Vaughan tapped the pencil eraser against his cheek. "Tell me, Elder Shunn. Have you made any other telephone calls from the airport here this afternoon?"

THIS CHANGED THE ENTIRE TENOR OF OUR CONVERSATION. I TRIED to swallow, but the saliva turned to dust in my throat. He knew. I didn't know how he knew, or how long he'd known, but now I knew he was on to me. And he must have known that I knew.

Had I really believed the police would never catch up with me? Even if I'd left the airport after the bomb threat, President Tuttle still would have shown up looking for Elder Finn, or one of the passengers in line might have remembered our argument, and the police would have started asking questions.

Still, I told myself I could brazen it out. "No. I haven't made any other phone calls."

"None at all?"

My head swam. "None."

The constable sighed and put down the pencil. "Elder Shunn, perhaps I should inform you that we're conducting a criminal investigation here at the airport—a quite serious one. Now, if there was any way you could help us resolve this investigation, any information you could give us that would help to clarify the situation here, I'm certain that all of us involved would be very grateful, and that the fact you helped us out would be remembered. Now, may I ask you again? Did you make any other phone calls this evening?"

The game was over. I knew it. All I wanted was to go home and go to bed.

"Yes," I said in a small voice. "Yes, I did."

Vaughan's expression didn't change, though the typist's mouth hung open. "How *many* other phone calls?"

"Only one."

He leaned forward in his chair. "May I ask who it was you called?"

I let out a long breath. "Occidental Air Cargo."

"I see. And what did you tell them when you called?"

I gave a bitter laugh. "I think you already know what I told them."

Constable Vaughan shook his head. "That's not good enough. I need to hear it from you."

"All right," I said, feeling like an idiot. "What I said was—" I swallowed. The words were surprisingly difficult to repeat. "What I said was, 'There's a bomb in a suitcase on Flight 789.'"

Vaughan showed neither surprise nor satisfaction. "I see. And is there, in fact, a bomb on that flight?"

"No. At least, not as far as I know."

"Thank you, Elder Shunn." Constable Vaughan leaned back in his chair and steepled his fingers, shaking his head sadly. "You know, if you'd come forward immediately with this information, it might have changed things. But I'm afraid we've gone too far for that. Do you realize that, even as we speak, there's an airplane out on that runway from which over a hundred passengers have been removed, while crews with dogs and bomb detectors go over every square inch of it? There are a dozen police cars out there, a half-dozen fire engines, and I don't know how many men, and even though I'm reasonably certain now that there really *isn't* a bomb, it's too late to call off the search. Most of those passengers are going to miss their connecting flights, and the cost to the airline is going to be massive. *That's* what you've done with your one little phone call."

The typist looked from Vaughan's face to mine and back again, all anticipation. I felt like I'd been nailed to my chair.

Vaughan spread his hands. "I don't really want to do this, Elder Shunn, but now I'm afraid I have to place you under arrest."

CHAPTER 40

I SAT FOR TWO HOURS IN A TINY ROOM THAT WAS MORE LIKE A soundproof recording booth than a cell. The walls were carpeted in soothing shades of lavender and beige. The door had no knob on the inside, only a slot for a key. My chair was plastic.

It was my second cell of the evening. At the airport Constable Vaughan had charged me with public mischief—"willful interference with the lawful use and enjoyment of public or private property valued in excess of one thousand dollars." He had also informed me, under Section 10 of the Canadian Charter of Rights and Freedoms, of my right to know the reasons for my arrest, to retain counsel without delay, and to have the validity of my detention determined by way of habeas corpus. His recitation had the cadence of a Miranda warning but was so unfamiliar in wording that I may as well have entered the Twilight Zone. In the interest of full cooperation, I wrote out a confession at the constable's desk, after which he locked me alone in a cell inside the airport police precinct at the end of the corridor.

An hour later a pair of detectives had arrived to take custody of me. The man had shaggy brown hair and a mustache. The woman was blond and wore a very short skirt under her trench coat. Out of respect for my status as an ordained minister, they did not handcuff me, but they warned me not to try to run as we walked through the silent airport to their car. They drove me to a small police station on the outskirts of the city, and that's where they stuck me in the upholstered room.

Part of that time I spent giving another confession to the female detective, which is when I learned that repeated attempts by the police to reach President Tuttle had failed. Part of that time I spent imagining Katrina taking my confession dressed in that same short skirt. The rest of the time I spent sunk in dark thoughts, guilt, and prayer, none of which gave me any comfort.

At long last the door to the cell flew open. A bear in a blue police uniform towered over me. "Elder!" he exclaimed, sounding amused. "Looks like you got yourself in a little trouble!"

I trembled before the officer, who was roughly the size and shape of a meat locker. "You're—you're a member?"

"Of course I am!" he roared in a tone that suggested I'd just tossed off the most hilarious quip in the history of spoken language. "Terry Wolfe, Calgary Twenty-first Ward. Glad to meet you. I heard what was up on the radio on my way home, and I had to come make sure they were treating you right. How are you holding up, Elder?"

That was the moment when I finally burst into tears.

AFTER I HAD SOBBED MY EYES OUT AGAINST OFFICER WOLFE'S chest, he took me to an empty office, where he looked up President Tuttle's home number.

"Typical that no one thought to try the White Pages." Eyes twinkling, he lifted the receiver from the desk phone. "Now, do you want to tell your mission president what happened, or would you rather I did it?"

"Could you?" I asked timidly.

"Sure thing." He dialed, then listened for a few moments. "President Tuttle! Hello, this is Officer Wolfe of the Calgary Police Department calling. Are you missing one of your elders?" He winked at me. "Well, don't worry. I've got him right here with me. Yes, he's fine, but I'm afraid we've got him in custody. Yes, public mischief. Mm-hmm. Well, it seems he was trying to keep his companion's plane on the ground so you could talk the guy out of—right, so he called in a bomb threat!" His voice bubbled with amusement. "Pretty creative thinking, eh? Yeah, so what's going to happen is, he'll be taken downtown to the Remand Centre to see a bail magistrate tonight. No, there shouldn't be any problem getting him out, as long as someone's there to post bail. No, it doesn't sound all that serious. Mm-hmm. Just a second." Wolfe covered the mouthpiece. "You want to say hello to him, Elder?"

I nodded, not without trepidation, and Wolfe passed me the phone. I winced, ready for the dressing-down of a lifetime. "Hello?"

But President Tuttle only sounded concerned. "Elder Shunn, are you okay?"

"Uh-huh." I managed to say it without starting to cry again, but it was a closed thing.

"Are you scared?"

"Yeah."

"Listen, don't worry about anything. I understand why you did what you did, and it was a good thing you were trying to do. You may have gone about it the wrong way, but I know your heart was in the right place, and we're going to get you out of there. I'll be downtown to bail you out, and I'll bring Elder Snow."

"Okay."

"Oh, Elder Shunn, I'm so glad you're safe. When I couldn't find you at the airport, I thought—well, I just had no idea. We've all been out looking everywhere for you—Elder Snow, your district, the a.p.'s. Everyone's going to be so relieved you're okay."

"Okay."

"You hang in there, Elder Shunn. Say a prayer. You're going to be fine."

I hoped he was right, but somehow I didn't believe him.

THE REMAND CENTRE DOWNTOWN WAS AS GRIM AS ITS ORWELlian name implied—a five-story concrete warren of a jail interleaved with courts and other judicial services. It housed inmates awaiting trial or transfer, and even prisoners serving sentences of up to a year. It was dark out when the two detectives drove me to a back entrance and signed me over to Corrections. In a daze, I was photographed, fingerprinted, and escorted upstairs to a bright white holding cell.

As the bars slammed shut behind me, the half-dozen men slouched on the benches regarded me with the frank inscrutability of zoo animals. Threadbare clothing, dirty faces, greasy hair, unshaven cheeks. Smoke from their half-dozen cigarettes hung in the air, overlaying a miasma decades old. The pads of my fingers were stained black with ink. Soapy water dripped from my hands. I wiped them on the backs of my jeans and took a seat on the bench against the rear wall. I felt like a bleeding lamb among wolves. I had never been more terrified.

Once it became clear that I had no cigarettes or matches to share, though, the others pretty much ignored me. The cell was roomy, with a bench bolted to each of the three walls. In the far corner a metal partition screened a stainless-steel toilet. Patches of mildew and rust merged at the tops of the wall, and two oversized light bulbs in wire-mesh cages blazed from the ceiling. I kept my head down and made eye contact with no one.

I lost track of time as detainees rotated in and out of the cell—aging biker types, swaggering punks, surly teenagers, scowling young Southeast Asians, a wino or two, even a miserable-looking businessman in a rumpled suit. The cops would haul one off to a bail hearing, then drag a fresh replacement in from the street. I couldn't tell how long this went on. There was no clock, no window. Time seemed to skitter and stop.

I waited patiently for my turn to come. More men went out than came in. At some point I looked around in wonder, like waking from a bad dream. I had the cell to myself. I was alone.

I took advantage of the lull to use the toilet. I prayed. I paced. I talked to myself. I wondered aloud if the Blanchards hated me for missing our dinner appointment, if the news of my arrest would drive the Mareks away from the church. And what about my parents? What would my father say? My mission was now messed up even worse than his.

The respite didn't last. I heard a commotion from down the corridor, and within moments four police officers had shoved a thin, struggling prisoner into the cell and locked us in together.

"Fuckers!" the man shouted, launching himself against the door, rattling it like a box of bones. The back pocket of his brown corduroys was torn, exposing a patch of white flesh. "Mother*fuckers!* This is harassment! I'll *sue* your asses!"

The only response was the slamming of a door somewhere far away.

My new cellmate looked right at me, eyes agleam with righteous indignation. "Fuckin' pigs think they're *God*."

I shrugged. My pulse beat loud in my ears.

He started to pace. I swung my feet up onto the bench and watched him, hugging my knees. He moved like a limping windup toy, the spring inside him coiled so tightly it would break if he didn't run it down.

As he paced, cowboy boots clacking, he ranted at great and colorful length about the bastards who'd repoed his mum's TV and how *they* should be in here for assault and battery, not him, being as they jumped him. *Anyone* would have fought back. With the pipe.

I braced myself for the moment he would turn on me.

But that moment never came. When he ran out of steam, he threw himself down on the adjacent bench and pulled a crumpled pack of Kools from the front pocket of his cords. A few quick shakes and he had a cigarette dangling from the corner of his mouth. He squinted into the pack, then turned it upside-down and shook it some more. With a disgusted look, he tossed the empty pack into a corner. The torn paper matchbook he pulled out next did him no better.

"Shit," he said blandly. His cheek was bruised, and his lower lip was split. "You got a light on you, kid?"

"N-no, sorry," I stammered, blinking hard. My contacts were drying out. I looked at my shoes. "I'm not really a smoker."

"Huh." Shoulders hunched, hands dangling between his knees, he peered up at me from hollow eye sockets. "What else is there to do in this hole but climb the walls?" He stood up and went to the bars. "Hey, how 'bout some matches back here, eh?"

To my surprise, an officer appeared and tossed a matchbook into the cell. "Here. Just keep it down."

With a grin full of stained and crooked teeth, my cellmate picked up the matchbook, his cigarette still spit-glued to the corner of his mouth. As he sat down again, he struck a match, puffed his cigarette to life, and waved the flame into oblivion. The fresh tobacco smoke was oddly comforting. It reminded me of my uncle Dale's house from when I was a kid. He too had smoked Kools.

My cellmate took a reflective puff and smoothed his skimpy mustache. "You know," he said, almost philosophically, "this place really sucks."

I must have grinned because he poked his cigarette in my direction. "You think I'm crackin' a joke? Let me tell you, kid, this place sucks like you can't imagine." He took a deep drag and blew it out in a thin, angry stream. "I wouldn't wish this place on my worst enemy. Twenty-nine years old, I been in and out ten years. I got this little girl I don't hardly even know. Those guys that jumped me? When I'm out I might put 'em in the hospital, but I wouldn't ever put 'em in a place like this, no way. I wouldn't do that to anyone."

He leaned forward and rubbed the back of his neck. "Seventy fucking days. That's all I been out this time, man. Probation's fucked." Grimacing as if in pain, he arched his back. His faded Jack Daniels T-shirt lifted to show his belly. "Why am I tellin' you this, anyway? How old are you, kid?"

I huddled more tightly around my knees. "Nineteen."

"Been in before? You haven't, have you."

"Not, uh. No."

"Shit." He squinted up at the lights. "I was doing my first hard stretch at your age. What're you in for?"

My charge seemed so inconsequential and innocuous that I was embarrassed to answer. "Public mischief," I mumbled.

He made a face. "Fuck does that mean? What, did you toilet-paper some rich asshole's house?"

My cheeks grew hot. "I made a bomb threat, okay?" I spat. "I said there was a bomb on an airplane."

"No shit," my cellmate said mildly.

"Yeah." I hadn't meant to sound so vehement, and now my arms shook.

He tilted his head, looking almost impressed. "So why'd you do that?"

I looked away. "It's—" I stopped, trying to work the rough edges out of my voice. "It's a long story. You don't want to hear it."

He studied his vanishingly short cigarette. "I don't know about you, but I got time."

I massaged the bridge of my nose. I didn't want to admit I was a missionary, not knowing how well that might go over. "I have this friend," I said. "We work together. Today he tells me he wants to quit, he wants to fly home to California. He's got a plane ticket, his bags are packed. He wants me to take him to the airport." I closed my eyes. "I tell him he's making a huge mistake, he's only running away from his problems. I try to talk him out of it, but he won't listen. His mind's made up."

"So you call in a bomb threat to stop his plane."

I looked at him, startled. "Something like that, yeah."

"Clever." He was nodding soberly. "What I don't get, though, is how do you know he was making a mistake? I mean, how do you know what's wrong or right for him?"

My eyes burned. Maybe it was the smoke. "I just knew it, okay?"

"You just knew it." He didn't sound convinced.

"Look, I've *been* there. I tried to run away once myself. But it's not worth it. It's just not."

He took a final drag on his cigarette and stubbed it out. "You know, kid, you probably couldn't have done something dumber if you tried. You're in some deep fucking shit."

I nodded miserably.

"But at least your heart was in the right place."

The world grew watery. President Tuttle had told me the same thing, but coming from this guy it pierced me more deeply. "Yeah," I said softly, thinking of Elder Dedman. *His* heart had been in the right place. Mine hadn't. All I'd been trying to do was to stay out of trouble with Prez.

"I mean, you really stuck your fuckin' neck out. I hope your friend appreciates that."

I snorted. "Yeah, me too."

"Well, does he? Did he stick around?"

"I don't have a clue. I got arrested before I could find out."

"I wouldn't have gone. No fuckin' way. Not if someone was willing to go to jail to stop me."

"He doesn't even know what I did."

"He knows. You stopped his plane, didn't you?"

"I guess."

"Man, if someone would've called in a bomb threat on me . . ." He shook his head. "Kid doesn't know how lucky he is, a friend like you."

I swallowed a lump. The silence stretched.

At last my cellmate cleared his throat. "You know, kid, you should gimme a call when we get out. We could get together maybe."

Suddenly nothing seemed as important to me as that. Maybe this all had happened for a reason. "Yeah, okay."

"Can I ask you something? If you don't wanna answer, that's okay, I'm just curious."

"No, go ahead."

He seemed a little embarrassed. "What, uh, is it you do? You never said exactly."

Embarrassed myself, I stared at my hands. "You probably wouldn't believe me if I told you."

"Why wouldn't I? Why would you lie?"

I sighed. "I don't know. I'm a—well, a Mormon missionary."

His eyes widened before a mask of nonchalance descended. "Hey, that's cool," he said, raising his palms. "That's cool, that's okay, I can handle that. You believe in what you're doing. I can respect that. I mean, you know." He shrugged like it was all no big deal. "I think about God sometimes."

I broke out in goosebumps. This was the Holy Grail—the opening every missionary was trained to pounce on. "Lots of people believe in a Supreme Being," I said. "We call him God, the same as you do, and we believe—"

Footsteps and jangling keys interrupted. The door to our cell screeched open. Two officers stood there.

Please, God, not now! My bail hearing couldn't possibly be *now*, not when I was about to teach a discussion in *jail*.

But the name they called wasn't mine. I was so befuddled that I failed to catch what it was.

My cellmate rose wearily. "Yeah, I'm here. Where the fuck else would I be?" He hitched up his torn corduroys. "You give me a call, kid. We'll get together."

A pit yawned in my stomach. "How? What's your number?"

One of the officers snapped handcuffs onto my friend's wrists and shoved him out the door. "This ain't no social club. Let's go."

The door slammed shut. My friend was reciting numbers, but the officers were already hustling him away. "Good luck, kid," he called.

I watched them disappear, and with them my chance of turning my imprisonment into a legend worthy of the greatest missionaries in church history. Now I felt more alone than ever.

CHAPTER 41

THE SOUND OF A KEY RATTLING IN THE LOCK ROUSED ME. "SHUNN, visitors."

Groggily I stood and stretched. I hadn't been asleep, but I hadn't exactly been awake, either. My back was sore from slouching against the cinder-block wall.

The corrections officer escorted me along several echoing corridors. Unlocking a whitewashed metal door, he motioned me into a dim room.

President Tuttle stood up as I entered. His eyes glittered. He caught me up in a squishy hug. "Elder Shunn, are you okay?"

"Pretty much," I said, my voice muffled against his shoulder. I'd forgotten all about that morning's *Playboy* incident.

He let go of me and told me to sit. My brown suit lay over the back of one of the two chairs in the room. A tall, gray-haired gentleman stood nearby. I thought I might have seen him before at church.

"I'm sorry I couldn't bring Elder Snow," said President Tuttle. "He's in the waiting room with Elder Roland. We've been here for *hours*, and then they only let two of us in to see you."

It was Elder Snow I wanted most to see. "What time *is* it?"

The other man looked at his watch. "Half past midnight." His flat, western vowels didn't seem to go with his fine blue suit.

Only two hours since I'd been processed in? It didn't seem possible. "They took my watch. I've been going crazy without it."

"Who did?" asked Tuttle, horrified. "The other prisoners?"

"The police."

He pulled himself together. "Of course, of course. Well, Elder Shunn, you've met President Page before, I believe."

"Fred Page," the man said, shaking my hand. "I've seen you in stake correlation meetings."

"Yes, right. Hello."

"Fred's a counselor to your stake president. He's also an attorney, and he's volunteered his services to help us out."

"Thank you very much," I said. "You're a criminal attorney?"

"Corporate," said Page. "But this is a pretty straightforward case. Go ahead and sit down, Elder. Let me explain the situation. Your bail hearing will be first thing in the morning. It should have been tonight, but the Crown Prosecutor's office has gotten hold of this and won't let go. That's the Crown Prosecutor of *Alberta*, like a state attorney general where you're from."

I shuddered. "Judas Proust."

"He's taken a personal interest in this case, and has, in fact, let it be known that you are not under any circumstances to be released on bail tomorrow. With the Olympics coming up, he wants to send a clear message that Alberta is not soft on terrorism."

"But I'm not a terrorist!" I protested.

"*We* know that. We just have to convince a magistrate. Which we can do."

"And don't worry about the money," said Tuttle. "The mission has that covered."

"We'll get you out," said Page. "But I'm afraid you'll spend tonight in the pokey."

The *pokey?* Had this guy just time-traveled in from *The Music Man?* I tried not to groan out loud. *Yes, I got trouble.*

Page spent a few minutes asking me questions in preparation for the morning's hearing, mostly to get my motive clarified. Then he glanced at the door. "We don't have much more time. You'd better get changed."

President Tuttle lifted my suit from the chair. I stared at it. Until that moment, it hadn't really hit me why they'd brought it.

"But—" I protested, filled with dread. My clean sweater and jeans weren't exactly protective coloration in jail, but they were a damn sight better than a suit.

"You need to look respectable for the hearing tomorrow," said Tuttle. "You need to carry yourself like a representative of the Lord. That's how you'll get out."

He seemed to think I was checking into a hotel for the night. Not even this suit was going to make me look respectable after I'd spent the night sleeping in it.

But if I were the type to disobey my mission president, then I wouldn't be where I was now. Tuttle and Page turned their backs to let me change. I traded my sneakers for thick-soled dress shoes and knotted a cheery yellow tie around my neck. They had even remembered my name tag, which I clipped to my breast pocket as if bolting on my final plate of armor.

President Tuttle turned back to face me. "Oh, when that judge sees you, Elder, there's no chance he'll keep you locked up. Not with all these criminals."

In my mind I saw my friend in the torn corduroys. *Publicans and sinners*, I thought.

The guard knocked on the door. "Two minutes."

"We'd better wrap things up," said Page.

The prospect of abandonment made my bones feel cold and hollow. "Um, before you go?" I said, abashed but urgent. "President, do you think, um, do you think I could get a blessing, please? A really quick one?"

Tuttle glanced at Page. "Certainly, of course. Sit down."

I didn't feel like I deserved a priesthood blessing, or even necessarily believed that it would bring me any solace, but asking for one is something of a reflex for Mormons in dire circumstances. I took a chair, and the two men laid their hands on top of my head. President Tuttle pronounced a short but not hasty prayer over me, promising that the Lord would comfort and protect me throughout the night and see to it that I emerged safely from this period of tribulation.

"Amen," I said as I opened my eyes. I did feel better, but that wouldn't last for long.

THE OFFICER WHO LED ME AWAY DID NOT RETURN ME TO MY HOLDing cell. He escorted me instead up a flight of stairs to a property window, where another officer looked me over and made me take off my belt, tie, and name tag. So much for looking even halfway respectable in court.

As I followed the officer to our next destination, I had to hold my trousers up so they didn't slide down around my hips. I stifled a whimper. I felt like I was being marched into some netherworld of no return. I reminded myself that even a man as great as Joseph Smith couldn't help but despond during his long stretches of incarceration. In Liberty Jail in 1839, he fell into such despair that God tried to cheer him up with these words:

> If thou art called to pass through tribulation; if thou art in perils among false brethren; if thou art in perils among robbers; if thou art in perils by land or by sea;
>
> If thou art accused with all manner of false accusations; if thine enemies fall upon thee; if they tear thee from the society of thy father and mother and brethren and sisters; and if with a drawn sword thine enemies tear thee from the bosom of thy wife, and of thine offspring, and thine elder son, although

but six years of age, shall cling to thy garments, and shall say, My father, my father, why can't you stay with us? O, my father, what are the men going to do with you? and if then he shall be thrust from thee by the sword, and thou be dragged to prison, and thine enemies prowl around thee like wolves for the blood of the lamb;

And if thou shouldst be cast into the pit, or into the hands of murderers, and the sentence of death passed upon thee; if thou be cast into the deep; if the billowing surge conspire against thee; if fierce winds become thine enemy; if the heavens gather blackness, and all the elements combine to hedge up the way; and above all, if the very jaws of hell shall gape open the mouth wide after thee, know thou, my son, that all these things shall give thee experience, and shall be for thy good.

Tough love. I wonder if what came next was for *my* good.

I WAS HANDED OFF TO ANOTHER CORRECTIONS OFFICER, MONSTROUS in size. He prodded me ahead of him down a long, narrow passageway. I imagined his bulk behind me compressing the air like the head of a piston, driving me irresistibly forward. He shunted me into a cold, gray room. A naked light bulb above and a drain cover in the center of the floor were its only features. The room was so claustrophobic I could feel the tons of concrete above pressing down on me. Surely this wasn't where I'd be spending the night . . .

I turned to find the officer two feet from me, plugging the doorway. He loomed over me, mountainous. In a voice like the grinding of boulders, he said, "Strip."

My brain could not quite process what I'd heard. "Pardon me?"

"You heard me!" the officer barked. The overtones reverberated once and fell dead, swallowed by the concrete. "Strip! Now!"

An electric revulsion convulsed my skin. My priesthood blessing had apparently worn off somewhere en route to this room. Civilization was a trillion miles away.

Reluctantly I shrugged off my suit jacket and looked for a place to hang it. The guard snatched it from me, an overgrown playground bully squinting at me through porcine eyes. "Come on, everything! Go, go!"

I untied my shoes while he ran his hands over every panel and seam of my jacket. He took the shoes and pounded the heels against the wall while I removed my pants and socks and shirt. In a moment I stood shivering in nothing but my garments, which gentiles were never supposed to see.

The officer's face flushed a deep scarlet when he looked up from his inspection and saw that I still wasn't naked. His scraggly mustache seemed to bristle. "Do you understand English? I said every-thing! *Now!*"

Cowering, I slipped out of my garments and handed them over. I stood with my arms crossed low in front of my shriveled dick, which was doing its best to crawl backwards into my bladder. I could not stop shaking. More upsetting than my nakedness was the way the of-ficer profaned every inch of my sacred underclothes with his grubby hands. I wasn't supposed to let gentiles *see* my garments, let alone han-dle them. Was that sin now on my head too?

When he'd satisfied himself that I wasn't concealing any drugs, knives, or grenade launchers in my underwear, the officer draped them with the rest of my clothes over the top of the open door. "Face me and stand up straight."

I squared my shoulders. My feet sucked up the cold of the concrete floor.

The officer eyed me like a piece of rotting meat. "Tilt your head for-ward and run your hands through your hair."

I did as he said, though I could barely control my hands.

"Fold down your ears. Open your mouth. Tongue up. Raise your arms."

I felt like a plucked chicken as his eyes worked their way down my body. He pulled a surgical glove from his pocket.

"Turn around and bend over," he said, tugging the latex like sausage casings over his fingers.

I turned around and did as he said, hands on my knees, clenching my eyes shut. I heard the sterile snap of the glove against his wrist.

"Spread your cheeks."

My entire body tensed. I strained and strained my glutes.

"I said spread your cheeks, you dumb hump!"

I opened my eyes. Upside-down through my legs, I could see him crouched behind me like a quarterback, finger poised. "I'm trying, I'm trying!" I cried.

"Not telekinetically, goddammit! Now put your hands on your cheeks and SPREAD 'EM!"

My hands flew back of their own accord and slapped cold flesh. I yanked my cheeks apart like the halves of a peach and closed my eyes. The world slowed on its axis.

But he didn't touch me. "Okay, get dressed," he said contemptuously, peeling off the glove. He threw my clothing at me all in a wad.

I WAS STILL TUGGING MY SHOES ON WHEN THE OFFICER PRODDED me back into the passageway. Careful of my dangling laces, I shuffled after him through a labyrinth of concrete and shadow. Where we stopped, rank after rank of cells crowded the darkness, each visible more dimly through the bars of the next, until it seemed as if the jail must extend to infinity.

The officer unlocked the door of the nearest cell. "Pick a bunk." In that moment he seemed not mean but tired—and, as I realized how shitty his job must be, even pitiable. He locked the bars gently behind me and shambled away.

The air smelled of sweat and antiseptic. I turned in a slow circle. My cell—and every cell I could make out through the gloom—contained five double-decker bunks. Nine of the berths were occupied. In one, a shadowy form turned over, cracked one curious eye, and went back to sleep. I sat down on the last remaining bunk, a thin mattress pressed wearily to metal slats.

I folded my jacket into a makeshift pillow and lay stiffly on my back, buttocks clenched. Around me, a hundred pairs of lungs breathed in and out.

I stared at the bottom of the bunk above me and clamped my throat against the sobs.

CHAPTER 42

I BLAMED MYSELF AND NO ONE ELSE FOR WHERE I'D ENDED UP, though in reality I hadn't landed in that jail cell all on my own. It took ill-considered words, selfish acts, and sheer well-meaning bonehead-edness on the parts of several other people, maybe a dozen or more, to put me behind bars. No one forced me to pick up that phone and make a bomb threat—no one else, I'm sure, would even have dreamed of it—but it took a village to create the conditions under which I would actually do it.

Joseph Smith had this problem writ large. I suppose today we'd call his inner circle "enablers"; certainly they reinforced his delusions and abetted his most self-destructive behaviors. But that makes his enemies enablers too, for how magnificently they brought his perse-cution complex to life. And the greatest enablers of all may have been the Illinois politicians who could have put the brakes on his abuse of the Nauvoo city charters but didn't, out of fear of losing a vastly over-stated Mormon vote.

Without that last factor in play, who can say when or where Jo-seph's story would have ended? Its final punctuation might still have been as violent, but might have come chapters or volumes later. And it likely would have arrived much farther west than Carthage, Illinois.

LILBURN BOGGS, OUTMANEUVERED BY JOSEPH TIME AND AGAIN, had never lost his thirst for revenge. The Mormons had trumpeted their mistreatment in Missouri far and wide, making the state look like a nest of barbarians in the national press. Late in the spring of 1843, Boggs, together with the traitorous John C. Bennett, convinced Governor Thomas Reynolds that the only way to repair Missouri's image was to finally bring Joseph to trial on those treason charges still pending from the Mormon War of 1838. When presented with Missouri's demand for extradition, Governor Ford of Illinois could find no way to deny it.

A sheriff from Missouri and a constable from Illinois set out together to arrest the prophet. They knew they had to apprehend him somewhere far from Nauvoo, or the city court with its extraordinary powers would simply invalidate the warrant. In June, while Joseph was traveling with his family, they tracked him to the town of Dixon, more than halfway across Illinois. Impersonating Mormon missionaries, the lawmen found out the family was staying with Emma's sister in nearby Inlet Grove. Breaking into the house during dinner, they seized Joseph at gunpoint without even bothering to serve the warrant.

The lawmen brought their prisoner into Dixon, where they locked him in the upper room of a tavern, intending to start back for Missouri the next morning. But Joseph, orating from his window, drew a large crowd and easily charmed them into helping him foil his kidnappers. (No love was lost between free Illinois and the slaveholders of Missouri.) While several people went to fetch a judge, one wag in the street requested a sermon on marriage. Joseph was delighted to oblige.

In the end, the two lawmen were arrested for threatening Joseph's life. With Joseph as their prisoner and them as the Lee County sheriff's prisoner, they set off the next morning in a convoy to try to settle the whole mess before a circuit court judge.

Meanwhile, William Clayton—an English convert and another

fourth great-grandfather of mine—rode into Nauvoo with news of Joseph's capture. With no shortage of volunteers, Hyrum Smith dispatched rescue parties in every direction, some even scouring the Mississippi by steamboat in case the lawmen were trying to spirit Joseph away by river.

One party did intercept the convoy en route to Quincy. According to one rescuer's account, Joseph wept with relief as more and more of his men rode up to surround his captors. "I am not going to Missouri this time," he is reported to have said. The convoy turned toward Nauvoo, where the municipal court was sure to set aside his arrest warrant.

Nauvoo greeted Joseph as a returning hero, with a brass band, an honor guard of flower-bedecked horses, and victory cannons all deployed to welcome the convoy. The two lawmen, one of whom had participated in the Missouri persecutions, expected to be killed, but instead Joseph made them guests of honor at a banquet at his home.

The lawmen rode out of the city the next day humiliated but free. Their mission in tatters, they petitioned Governor Ford to send the state militia after the prophet, but, knowing the strength of the Nauvoo Legion, he would not.

The last thing Ford wanted for Illinois was a repeat of Missouri's blunders. He still hoped he could rein the Mormons in peacefully.

FOR HIS PART, JOSEPH EMERGED FROM THIS EPISODE MORE PARAnoid than ever about the forces arrayed against him, and more determined to erect every conceivable defense for himself and his people. He had already declared to the Saints that he considered Illinois state laws unconstitutional. Now, in December 1843, he pushed measures through the city council that made himself effectively immune to prosecution. Anyone trying to arrest him in Nauvoo on old charges from Missouri could be imprisoned for life, and any arrest warrant for a citizen of Nauvoo was illegal unless it was first signed by the mayor—Joseph himself. Finally, in an attempt to nullify the power of Illinois entirely, Joseph appealed to Congress to grant Nauvoo the status of an independent territory, with himself, of course, as governor.

None of this endeared the Mormons to the rest of the state, where their bad press was already on the rise. During the extradition crisis, to prove themselves friends of the Saints, Stephen A. Douglas and a rival Whig judge named Cyrus Walker had vied for the right to hear Joseph's case. In exchange for trying Joseph in Nauvoo, Walker extracted a promise that the Mormons would support him in his upcoming run for Congress. But at the last minute before the election, Hyrum Smith, who had his own political ambitions, announced he'd had a revelation that he should vote for Walker's opponent, Joseph Hoge. Unwilling to call his brother's revelation false, Joseph told the Saints to vote as they liked. Walker lost to Hoge by a narrow margin, and the Whig papers instantly turned on the Mormons.

Early in 1844, Joseph was pursuing a more overtly political agenda himself. With public sentiment in Illinois running against him, he wrote to five of the leading presidential candidates to ask their positions on reparations and federal protection for the beleaguered Mormons. When none of the answers he received were satisfactory, he decided to run for president himself. It's unlikely that he expected to win, but he knew that, once again, the Saints faced danger from suspicious neighbors. He hoped that by mobilizing his missionary force as a campaign machine he could generate sympathy for his people, maybe win them a military escort for their next westward migration. Anything that would allow them to practice their religion in peace, free from harassment, as the Constitution promised.

Joseph had by now modified his conception of Zion. Rather than just Jackson County, Missouri, he used the term to apply to the entire continent. He sent scouts to Oregon and California to identify suitable places to settle, and emissaries entered talks with President Sam Houston, who promised there was plenty of room for the Mormons in the Republic of Texas.

In private, Joseph was laying the foundation for what in his campaign preaching he called "theodemocracy." He failed to see why a man chosen by God could not rule a democratic nation where people were still free to worship as they liked. To him electoral politics, rather than solving the problems of the poor and downtrodden, was what led inexorably to loss of life, liberty, and property.

To that end, in March 1844, Joseph established a Council of Fifty as a shadow government in Nauvoo. Though a few non-Mormons were included, council members were ordained as "princes in the Kingdom of God," and Joseph was voted their king. They may have been preparing to rule a new nation in the west, or to step in when the American government collapsed upon Christ's return, but for the time being the council met in secret to manage Joseph's presidential campaign and plan the migration of the Saints. William Clayton served as their clerk.

Joseph saw himself as the most benevolent of potential rulers. But in the rest of the country, growing numbers saw him as a religious despot with visions of empire—and an army to bring them to pass.

OF ALL THE ENEMIES JOSEPH MADE DURING HIS PROPHETIC CAreer, the most dangerous turned out to be one who loved the church most fiercely.

William Law was an Irish immigrant who joined the church in Upper Canada in 1836. He migrated with his family to Nauvoo in 1839, where he impressed Joseph with his urbanity, his dedication, and, no doubt, his wealth. In January 1841, when Hyrum Smith moved into the position of presiding patriarch, Law replaced him as Joseph's second counselor in the First Presidency.

Law first clashed with Joseph over real estate. He and his older brother, Wilson, were investing in housing and mills for Nauvoo's benefit at a time when the prophet wanted to control and direct all construction in the city. Law thought Joseph was a poor businessman and that he shouldn't be meddling in temporal affairs.

But the real break came over plural marriage. Law had, in all innocence, helped defend the church against rumors of polygamy, and he was shocked when Joseph and Hyrum finally let him in on the truth. He and his wife Jane discussed the matter and ultimately decided not to participate in the practice. (Some sources report that Joseph tried to make Jane one of his celestial brides, but this is a point of much dispute.)

Still, the couple kept their misgivings private until January 1844, when Law found himself expelled from the First Presidency for not accepting the principle of plural marriage. He believed deeply in the Book of Mormon and in Joseph's early teachings but had come to view polygamy and other later doctrines as false. Reluctantly Law decided that Joseph, once a true prophet, had given in to lust and sin, and had fallen.

Law fell in with a small group of fellow dissidents who had all manner of complaints against Joseph, some more justified than others. The ensuing battle of innuendos between them and church leaders occasionally broke out into public confrontations, with accusations of malfeasance and debauchery flung both ways. Despite a few attempts at reconciliation, Law and three other dissenters, including his wife and brother, were excommunicated in absentia on April 18. (A more public hearing had been planned, but Joseph learned that Law was marshaling dozens of witnesses to turn the tables on him.) The men were also expelled from the Nauvoo Legion and from their Masonic lodge.

Though he never claimed to be a prophet, William Law organized a reform church on April 21, taking as his gospel the simpler principles laid out in the Book of Mormon and attracting as many as three hundred followers. Other dissenters were now speaking out publicly and giving their stories to area newspapers, which reported gleefully on the schisms rocking Nauvoo. Joseph responded with character assaults so vicious that some Mormons began to wonder if he really did have something to cover up.

IN THE COURSE OF THIS CHAOTIC SPRING, JOSEPH'S DOCTRINE CON-
tinued to evolve. It was at an outdoor memorial for a city constable
named King Follett that he extemporized for two hours on the topic
of eternal progression—namely, that men could, through faithfulness
in this life and diligence in the next, become gods themselves. Moreover, God the Father, our creator and the object of our worship and ven-
eration, was himself an exalted man who had lived his own righteous
mortal life and thereby achieved godhood. The whole of eternity, Joseph
taught, was one boundless skein of gods, united in mind and purpose,
learning and growing without end, giving rise to numberless spiritual
progeny who then were lifted up to join the ranks of the exalted. Lorenzo Snow, the fifth Mormon prophet, summed up the concept most
succinctly: "As man now is, God once was; as God is now man may be."

By all accounts, the King Follett Discourse, as it became known, was
a remarkable sermon, though we can reconstruct it only through notes
taken by four members of the huge crowd. It was the culmination of
all Joseph's religious thought and American idealism. What, after all,
could be more democratic than the idea that any man might grow to become a god? It was also the end of a radical transformation of what had
begun as a simple American take on primitive Christianity. Mormonism was now something wholly new. As Fawn Brodie writes, "It was a
real religious creation, one intended to be to Christianity as Christianity
was to Judaism: that is, a reform and a consummation."

Joseph himself had become, or always was, a conundrum—an original and daring doctrinaire who preached peace but couldn't help pro-
voking his neighbors, a generous, tolerant, charming bon vivant who
turned scathingly petty when crossed, an "American Mahomet" who
craved political respect, a city planner of this world and an empire
builder of the next, a man of God who was more than ready to roll in
the dirt for his people, both literally and figuratively.

A dictator and a demigod. A prophet and a problem.

No one saw the prophet as a bigger problem than William Law and his dissidents, who suspected Joseph's secret police of plotting to murder them. Joseph for his part harbored the same suspicion of the dissidents. Though violence was probably not one of their primary aims, he was certainly right that they meant to bring down his empire.

In May, from the city of Carthage, the dissidents launched a legal barrage. First they brought suit against Joseph for slander. Later they secured grand jury indictments against him on charges of adultery, polygamy, and perjury. Despite the powers of the Nauvoo courts, Joseph was forced to spend half that month evading arrest.

But this wasn't enough for William Law, who craved a full public accounting of Joseph's many crimes. For this purpose he and his associates purchased a printing press and founded their own paper, the *Nauvoo Expositor*. The first and only issue appeared on June 7. While eschewing luridness, the *Expositor* reported in detail on how plural marriage was practiced by the leaders of the church, and went on to describe, with an insider's eye, the prophet's fiscal, political, and judicial abuses.

The thousand printed copies of the *Expositor* stoked a firestorm like none Joseph had ever faced. He had fought off accusations of polygamy before—differentiating in his mind between the connotations of that lurid term and the holy practice of plural marriage—but this was a far more credible attack. Perhaps with a more tempered response he could have weathered this one too, but he feared these revelations would be what finally brought mob violence down upon Nauvoo.

On June 10 the city council debated all day what should be done about the *Expositor*, finally declaring it a public nuisance. That night Joseph dispatched a posse of about a hundred Nauvoo Legionnaires under the direction of the city marshal to destroy the press in the name of public safety.

The soldiers forced their way into the *Expositor* offices, removed everything inside to the street, and burned it all.

IF JOSEPH THOUGHT THIS MOVE WOULD DEFUSE TENSIONS, HE couldn't have been more wrong. Not only had he handed the dissidents a rock-solid criminal case against him, but he'd given his other detractors proof that he really was the despot they believed him to be. Here he was, a serpent in their midst, brazenly trampling the sacred freedom of the press. Outraged mobs burned Mormon farms, while the *Warsaw Signal*, the region's most incendiary paper, openly called for vigilante action against Joseph and Hyrum.

As the Saints took refuge in Nauvoo, the Legion stockpiled arms and prepared to defend the city. Governor Ford hurried to Carthage when he learned of the trouble and tried to hold the hostile local militias back from action. At the same time, he urged Joseph to turn himself in and stand trial on charges of riot. Otherwise, as he later confessed in *A History of Illinois*, Ford was afraid the troops would sack Nauvoo with or without his approval—and that the Mormons would then turn around and kill *him*.

Nevertheless, Joseph dared not trust himself again to the mercies of an enemy force. Through pouring rain, in a leaky boat, he and Hyrum fled across the Mississippi to the Iowa shore.

CHAPTER 43

THE DOOR OPENED AT THE END OF THE NARROW VESTIBULE.
"Shunn! Donald William!" called a bailiff.

I stood and threaded my way to the door like a red corpuscle navigating a clogged artery. Our waiting room was long but only about five feet wide, with a bench that ran its full length. There must have been twenty of us crammed in there together, each awaiting his turn before the bail magistrate.

"Go, kid!" stage-whispered a fat, bearded guy everyone called Mac. He seemed an old hand at this, our *de facto* elder statesman. "Three hundred's the mark to beat."

I grimaced, exhausted. It had been a long night and a longer morning. I had tossed and turned for what seemed like hours in the darkness, then sprung wide awake when an officer glissandoed the bars of our cell with his baton. Swabbing the floors, picking at breakfast, and shooting the shit were the only activities available to my cellmates and me until noon, when a squad of officers arrived to escort our sizable cohort through a bewildering maze of concrete and steel to this constricted vestibule.

Now, as I passed into the courtroom near the magistrate's bench, I felt like I was emerging into reality from behind the walls of a flat, gray stage set. The world had color and substance again, and so, for a few minutes, did I.

The courtroom was small and warmly lit. As I took my place in the defendant's box, I spotted President Tuttle in the gallery beyond the railing. I hoped for a friendly wave and a smile, but what I saw on his face was shock, disbelief, and anger. I'm sure my disheveled, unshaven, open-collared look wasn't quite what he'd hoped for. Elder Snow was with him, though, and he flashed me a solemn thumbs-up.

The arguments took very little time. A bearded prosecutor made the case that, in light of my gross disregard for the airline, its passengers, and public safety, it was not in the community interest to release me on bail. President Page, looking distinguished, explained that I, a selfless servant of God, had acted only to prevent a fellow missionary from making what I thought was a terrible mistake, and had not taken time to consider the consequences. Cast in such a benevolent light, I felt guilty and transparent.

Before the snowy-haired magistrate could make a ruling, President Tuttle stood up in the gallery and asked to speak. "Go ahead," said the magistrate impatiently.

Tuttle wrung his hands. "Thank you, Your Honor. I just want to plead with you not to keep our missionary locked up any longer. Elder Shunn is a good young man with a good heart, and I promise the court that if he's released on bail, our mission will take full responsibility for seeing that he stays in Calgary until his trial, and that he stays at our office doing only clerical work in the meantime. Please let him go, Your Honor. He doesn't belong in there."

"Thank you for your input," said the magistrate, looking anything but grateful. "Bail is set at one thousand dollars." He rapped the bench soundly with his gavel.

My guard steered me back into the vestibule before I could register anyone's reaction. Liquid with relief, I picked my way to a clear spot on the bench as another detainee was called.

"So, what'd you get?" asked Mac.

Though giddy, I tried to sound nonchalant. "A thousand."

The amount seemed ludicrously small given my crime, but the look on Mac's round face changed from amusement to shock. "A thousand *dollars?* Are you shitting me?"

"I shit you not."

"What did you *do?*"

I shrugged. "Bomb threat. Airplane."

The men around me murmured. I prickled with a strange sense of pride.

NEARLY TWO MORE HOURS PASSED BEFORE I WAS RELEASED. AN OFficer at the property window returned my personal effects and buzzed me through a door to an elevator vestibule.

On a low vinyl-and-chrome couch near the elevator, one of my cellmates sat snugged between two young women in thick makeup and short skirts. I wondered if they'd paid his bail or if they were getting out too. He nodded to me as I pressed the down button, smiling like the cat who ate the canary. He whispered something to one of the women, who giggled nastily. Self-conscious, I didn't look at them again until the elevator arrived.

I stepped inside. Just as the doors were closing, the woman shouted, "Look out! There's a bomb in the elevator!"

Their hysterical laughter stayed with me all the way down to ground level.

IT WAS JUST PAST ONE, ACCORDING TO THE CLOCK IN THE MAIN lobby. No one was there to meet me. I checked all over the cavernous space and even walked around the block in the cold, growing more agitated by the minute. Certainly I understood that President Tuttle had needed to get back to the leadership conference after my hearing, but I'd expected *someone* to be there waiting.

I was not familiar with the public transit system, and I had no idea whether or not I could afford a taxi. Choking back an angry lump, I called the mission office. Elder Farnsworth, one of the senior missionaries, was the only one there. It took some doing, but I finally convinced him to drive downtown in his big Buick and pick me up.

When the apes arrived back at the office from the conference, it was late afternoon. I had ensconced myself in the front room, noodling something dark and downbeat at the piano. On top of the piano lay a copy of the *Calgary Herald* I'd bought outside the Remand Centre. My name was on the front page of the metro section, beneath a full-color photograph of an airplane surrounded by emergency vehicles.

"Elder Shunn!" exclaimed Elder Fearing. "How are you? Are you all right?"

"I'm fine." I stood up from the piano braced for castigation. I hadn't forgotten the last conversation I'd had in this room with Elder Hardy.

I startled when both elders threw their arms around me and pounded me enthusiastically on the back.

"Whew, you smell like a bowling alley," said Fearing, pulling back.

I sniffed my sleeve warily. "Yeah, I guess I do."

"It must have been way scary for you," said Hardy. "I mean, jail and all. What was it like?"

"Yeah, it *was* pretty scary. Pretty intense. Lots of guys you wouldn't want to meet in a dark alley. Scary dudes."

"Did you teach any discussions?" asked Fearing eagerly.

"Almost. There was this guy in my holding cell, and I was just starting on him with the first D when the guards came and moved him."

"Aw, bummer."

"A for effort, though," said Hardy. He gave me a high-five.

I grinned.

"Were you scared, like, the whole time?"

"Pretty much. But not always. I mean, the worst thing about jail isn't being scared. It's not knowing what time it is."

"Didn't you have your watch?" asked Fearing.

"No, they took it away."

"No way!" said Hardy.

"Yeah. They took my tie and my belt and my name tag too."

"You're kidding. Did you get fingerprinted and everything?"

"Sure—fingerprints, mug shots. They strip-searched me, too."

"No joke? You mean they—?" Fearing thrust with his index finger.

"Almost."

Hardy boggled. "You had to get *naked?* G's and everything?"

"Oh, man, let me tell you."

So I related the full story of my strip search, pantomiming the process in excruciating detail. The apes hung on every word. When I got to the part where the officer told me to put my hands on my cheeks, they practically fell down laughing.

"Oh, boy." Fearing wiped his eyes. "You're lucky you didn't get the ol' backdoor burglary."

"Yeah, talk about turning the other cheek!" quipped Hardy, and we all doubled over.

When we'd caught our breath, Elder Fearing said, "You know, Shunn, everyone here's been awfully worried about you. In fact, Sister Tuttle had this big breakfast planned for us at the conference this morning, but everyone voted instead to fast for you to get out of jail. A lot of people here really love you, man."

Mormons believe that fasting makes prayer more effective, so they'll frequently skip a meal or two during times of crisis. That a few dozen of my colleagues had done so on my behalf was bewildering. It embarrassed me how touched I felt.

Elder Snow and Elder McKay walked in then. "Hey, buckfart! How's my favorite criminal mastermind?"

"Snow!" We thumped each other's backs.

"You sure know how to start something, jacko. You straighten out those buggers down at County? Teach 'em some D's?"

Barely able to control his excitement, Elder Fearing said, "Shunn, you *gotta* do the strip search for Snow and McKay!"

I put on a modest show of reluctance, and within moments all four elders were begging me to run through it again. I let them talk me into it, this time refining the story and adding a few flourishes. More elders arrived during the act, until by my third time through I was performing for a laughing, hooting, whistling crowd. If I'd worried that my fellow missionaries were going to hate me for what I'd done, those concerns were gone. If I felt more like a hypocrite than a hero, at least I also felt liked.

I was regaling the group with my further jailhouse adventures when Roper, Steed, and Herzog walked in. Seeing me, they burst into tears in unison and hurried over. I'm sure they would have thrown their arms around me if there hadn't been so many elders around.

"Oh, Elder Shunn, it's true, you're safe!" cried Sister Steed.

"Oh, it must have been so *horrible!*" wept Sister Herzog.

"Oh, Elder, we're so sorry," sobbed Sister Roper, wringing her hands. "This is all our fault. If only we hadn't—" Her words dissolved into blubbering.

"No, no, Sisters," I said, patting the air. "It wasn't your fault. The bomb threat was all my idea. Really. Please, stop, please."

After the sisters had calmed down a little—and after Sister Roper had asked me if I'd taught any discussions in jail—someone mentioned the strip search to them, and I had to go through the whole pantomime again.

Just as I finished, President Tuttle entered the room. "Oh, Elder Shunn, good, you're here. Could you please see me in my office for a minute? Elder Snow, you too. And Elder Fearing and Elder Hardy."

CHAPTER 44

"PRESIDENT PAGE HAS BEEN WORKING HARD ON GETTING THINGS expedited for you, Elder Shunn," Tuttle told us once he'd closed his office door. "You'll be happy to know your initial court date is tomorrow."

I eyed him sullenly. It was petty, I know, but I was still miffed that I'd been abandoned at the Remand Centre. "That's fast."

Tuttle settled himself behind his desk. "The way I understand it, this is simply where you choose how you want to be tried, with a jury or a judge. It's not like back home. But we'll talk that over tomorrow with Fred, I'm sure."

"Okay."

"Meanwhile, gentlemen, we have something of a dilemma. President Page informs me that Elder Shunn's work visa has been suspended pending the outcome of his trial. That means he's not allowed to proselytize. We can't put him back with you, Elder Snow, or you'll have to stay idle too, so for the moment I'm assigning Elder Shunn to a three-leg with the a.p.'s here at the office. He can't do any work, but at least he won't be a hindrance."

"But we have an appointment tonight," I said. "The Mareks. It's their fifth discussion."

"I'm sorry, Elder Shunn, but I can't allow it. You can't risk getting caught working without a visa."

Elder Snow cleared his throat. "It doesn't matter anyway. I talked to the Mareks today, and, well . . . I don't know how to tell you this, Shunn, but they don't want any more discussions."

My mouth fell open, and my heart fell into my shoes.

He grinned. "At least not until you're out of this, bucko. They told me they refuse to take the discussions from anyone but you and me, together."

"Wow." My eyes stung with humility and gratitude.

"That's another reason to pray for Elder Shunn's deliverance," said Tuttle. "Elder Snow, you stick with Elder McKay for the time being. When this mess is over, we'll get the companionships all sorted out."

With that business out of the way, President Tuttle asked if we'd like to hear the details of *his* Monday night.

THANKS TO TRAFFIC, AS HE TOLD IT, PRESIDENT TUTTLE HAD NOT arrived at the airport with Elder Roland until nearly 6:15. As the two of them approached the Customs gate, Elder Roland spotted two figures entering a dim hallway on the far side of the cordon. He thought one of them might have been me.

They shouted for assistance until a bearded man in an orange windbreaker appeared. The man was surly and cross, and his only response to Tuttle's inquiries about two missionaries was to say that another of "you Mormons" had been there but was gone again now.

President Tuttle finally convinced the man to check the departure lounges for Stewart Finn, who may or may not already have boarded a flight. The man returned several minutes later to report that Finn didn't want to talk to *anybody* from the church.

Confirmation of Finn's presence only fueled Tuttle's determination to see him. As soon as the bearded man was gone, he asked Elder Roland to give him a boost. I wish I could have seen this for myself, but

President Tuttle swore he managed to scale the Customs gate, which did not extend all the way to the ceiling, and plop down on the other side. He rushed off in the direction of the departure gates, only to be spotted by the bearded man and escorted back by an armed security guard.

"The man just kept shouting, 'This is a sterile area! This is a sterile area!'" Tuttle told us. Given the circumstances, he was lucky not to have been arrested himself.

Unsure what to do next, President Tuttle and Elder Roland left the terminal. That's when they spotted the Aries K still parked in the loading zone (quite an oversight in a province looking to be tough on terrorism) and began to wonder what had become of *me*. If I wasn't waiting to meet them at Customs, *and* I hadn't taken the car anywhere . . . might I be leaving with Finn?

Meanwhile, Elder Finn was having problems of his own, or so Tuttle learned from phone calls with other church leaders and an angry one with Finn himself. Not only was Finn's flight delayed, putting his connection in Salt Lake City in jeopardy, but the police were interrogating him.

Hoping, presumably, to confirm my confession and rule out the possibility of a conspiracy, a couple of officers had tracked Finn down and hauled him back to the little airport precinct for questioning. They told him they knew he was in this with his Mormon friend and demanded to know what he knew about the bomb. Finn, of course, was clueless. At last, with no reason to hold him, they returned him, shaken, to his departure lounge.

Occidental Flight 789 finally took off after a ninety-minute delay. When it landed in Salt Lake, Elder Finn was one of the few passengers who stood a remote chance of making his connecting flight. But as he exited the plane, someone stepped up to block his path—Milton Farrow, Tuttle's predecessor as president of the Calgary Mission. According to what I'd heard from Elder Fowler, Farrow was a real hardass. In Finn's position, I'd have been peeing my pants.

But Finn, with a plane to catch, pushed past him and took off at a jog, saying if Farrow wanted to talk then he'd have to keep up. President Farrow paced him, barking like a drill sergeant. He offered Finn a return ticket to Calgary. He told him God was disappointed. In return, Finn told Farrow that all the missionaries who remembered him hated his guts and were glad he was gone.

In the end, Elder Finn did make his plane. He arrived home safely in Fresno late that night.

"I'm sorry to be the one to break the news, Elder Shunn," said President Tuttle. "I know you did your very best."

Overwhelmed by my own predicament, I hadn't spared Finn much thought. Hearing that he was home, though, made me queasy. I didn't know whether to feel regret, jealousy, or admiration. In his first attempt, he had pulled off the feat that still eluded me.

Now that we were all caught up, President Tuttle waved the other three elders out of his office. "I have one other piece of news to report," he said to me, "and I think it might make you very happy. Your father's on his way! He'll be here in a few hours."

I WAS PLAYING THE BLACK BABY GRAND IN THE TUTTLES' LIVING room late that evening when I heard the front door of the house open. President Tuttle entered a moment later, smiling broadly as he removed his coat. "Elder Shunn, look who's here!"

A figure lurked in the entryway behind him. I rose stiffly from the piano.

My father stepped into the light. "Hello, son." His lips were pressed together in a somber line. His bald head shone red from the chill.

I took a step away from the piano. Let me not mince words—I was terrified of my father, still. I was long past the age where he could beat me with a belt, but he still had the power to make me feel tiny, sinful, and helpless. That all hung between us in the air, and the conflicts of the past six months as well. Neither of us moved.

I went for humor to puncture the tension. "Um, happy birthday, Dad?"

My father had turned 51 the previous week. He snorted, crossed the room, and wrapped his arms around me. He was a couple of inches shorter than I was, but broader and stronger.

"You're all right, son," he said. All I smelled was the sheepskin jacket he loved. "Everything's going to be okay."

For that moment, at least, I forgot everything else and did nothing but believe him.

My father politely declined Sister Tuttle's offer of chocolate cake, a sure sign he wasn't feeling like himself. President Tuttle showed us downstairs to our two guest rooms, then left us alone to catch up.

"Your mother sends her love," said my father, laying his suitcase out on one of his two twin beds. The room was a tidy little box, warm and plush, decorated in yellow and blue. It smelled of pine shavings and lemon. The house was lousy with small bedrooms like this one, so it could accommodate a dozen incoming greenies.

I hovered near the door. "She's ward Relief Society president now, right? How's she liking that?"

My father laid his hands flat on his folded clothes, mouth compressed tight. "When the bishop announced her calling in sacrament meeting and asked if anyone was opposed, I raised my hand."

"You *what?*" LDS wards maintain the illusion of democracy by asking the congregation to approve new callings with a show of hands, but I'd never seen anyone dissent. "What happened?"

"You can imagine how well it went over, especially with your mother. But like I told that bishop of ours afterwards, I'm the head of the household. I don't care if the Lord gave you a revelation in person. You don't give my wife a church calling without asking me first."

"Wow." I could imagine the gossip at church, but my father was not one to let something like that shut him up. If there was one thing I admired about him, it was that fearlessness. For all that he harped on obedience to church leaders, he often thought the men who held those offices were idiots, and he wasn't shy about saying so.

"Anyway, your mother's thinking about you and praying every minute."

"That's good." That image somehow made me uncomfortable. I was conscious of exactly how little I deserved anyone's prayers. "Did you have any trouble getting time off from work?"

"No, I managed to find a substitute. You remember Cobb Sanders. He's got my classes. He'll cover me as long as it takes."

I grimaced. I hoped my father had enough vacation days for this.

He hung a couple of his shirts in the closet. "So, that girl you used to run around with? What's her name?"

"Katrina?" Knowing him, it was entirely possible that he meant someone else.

"Yeah, Kaneesha, that's the one."

I sighed. "Katrina."

"That's what I said—Kaneesha." He fished a large white envelope from a pocket of his suitcase and handed it to me.

I recognized the looping cursive writing. My heart skipped a beat.

My father tucked his chin down, the way he always did when addressing uncomfortable topics. "I guess your mother must have called her and told her something. The girl came around this afternoon before I left for the airport. Brought you that."

It took all my willpower not to rip the envelope open then and there.

"I don't think she's taking this very seriously," he said, not looking at me.

I huffed. *Of course not, because a felony arrest in a foreign country isn't nearly as serious as jerking off.*

"All the time she was at the house, she couldn't stop giggling. Just like the girls do in my classes."

"Women," I said dryly and turned to leave.

"Are you going to bed?"

"Yes." I made a show of yawning. "I didn't get a lot of sleep last night. You know, in jail."

"Let's say our prayers before we turn in."

He knelt beside the bed, and I reluctantly joined him. Hands clasped behind his back, he closed his eyes and bowed his head. My father sometimes wore his Mormonism like a drill sergeant's uniform, other times like sackcloth and ashes. That night it was the latter. His plea for God to keep me out of prison was so somber it sounded like a funeral prayer.

When I stood up to leave, I gestured awkwardly with the envelope. "Um, thanks. For this. For coming."

I fled before he could respond.

My own room was all blue-and-red plaid, like the inside of a sleeping bag, from the bedspreads to the curtains to the fabric wallpaper. The lamp on the nightstand between the twin beds gave off an intimate, comforting glow. I didn't bother unpacking my overnight bag. I laid the envelope from Katrina on the bed farther from the door and knelt to offer my personal evening prayer.

When that was done I stripped to my garments, hung up my suit, and arranged myself in bed with my plush Opus. Only then, alone in that cocoon of light and darkness, having sufficiently savored the anticipation, did I finally open the card from Katrina.

On the front, pink cartoon hippos offered generic wishes of good luck. (Hallmark, after all, probably didn't make hope-you-stay-out-of-prison cards.) Inside Katrina had written a long note:

My dearest William (The Mad Bomber!)—

Ever since I heard the news I haven't been able to stop laughing. I know I shouldn't, but I think about it and it just sets me off again! You're the only person I know who could get himself into a predicament like this, and that's why I love you so much.

I'll be thinking about you tomorrow, but I'm not going to worry. I know you won't go to prison because Heavenly Father would never let anything bad happen to one of his missionaries.

I know you'll get through this and come home to me safe. Be brave!

Your loving fiancée,
Katrina

I read the note four times, trying to take comfort from Katrina's expressions of faith. From this remove, I think she was trying as hard to convince herself of her own belief as I was, but in the moment all I felt was a mounting dismay. I knew too well that God did *not* always protect his missionaries, and her card only reminded me of that.

A handful of missionaries died every year, the causes ranging from disease to car accidents to murder. The most infamous and upsetting example was the case of Elder Gary Darley and Elder Mark Fischer, who disappeared late in 1974 in Austin, Texas. They were apparently dismembered by a recent convert named Robert Elmer Kleasen, in the taxidermy shop behind his trailer home. I say "apparently" because their bodies were never found. Blood and hair belonging to both missionaries was recovered from the housing of a band saw, while Elder Fischer's bloody watch and a name tag with a bullet hole through it were discovered in Kleasen's trailer. No other traces of the elders ever turned up.

A far more recent incident was fresh in my mind. Only two weeks earlier we'd heard news that an elder in Lisbon, Portugal, Roger Todd Hunt, had been shot and killed by an overzealous security guard while he and three other missionaries were setting off firecrackers.

And from the pages of history came the famous 1879 case of Joseph Standing, a 24-year-old missionary who was shot in the head during a scuffle with a Georgia mob suspicious of the church's phenomenal success among the region's poor hill people.

The point was, bad things *did* happen to missionaries, all the time. There *was* a veil in the world—a scabby, sinister veil behind the fragile fiction of civilization, where expectations of safety, sufficiency, and mercy died torn and bleeding. I'd crossed that veil the moment I called Occidental Air Cargo. I'd been walking in its shadow ever since.

With my record as a missionary, I had no claim on special protection from God anyway. I was the truly wicked and unrepentant one in our relationship, not Katrina. Her childlike faith was touching—and a reproach.

I wasn't sure we were going to make it.

CHAPTER 45

AFTER HIS WIFE HAD FED US A HEARTY BREAKFAST, PRESIDENT Tuttle invited my father and me into his study. "We go to court at two," he said. "We'll meet with Fred Page beforehand to review our strategy, but I thought maybe our best course of action this morning would be a father's blessing. Such a blessing has special power, and if ever the time for one was appropriate, it's now."

I took a seat in an overstuffed leather chair. We could have been in an old-school lawyer's office, except the books that lined the shelves were all gospel-related. For the second time that week, two bearers of the Melchizedek Priesthood stood behind me and laid their hands on my head. When in that somber voice my father invoked his priesthood and promised that angels would watch over me in the courtroom, I prayed he was right.

MY FATHER AND I SPENT A LONG, LONG MORNING AT THE MISSION office. I played the piano while my father, in full avuncular mode, swapped mission stories with the apes. Around eleven we made a brief trip out for copies of the *Herald* and the *Sun*. Both papers had stories about my looming court appearance.

As noon approached, President Tuttle invited us to join him for lunch. He chauffeured us to a nearby Wendy's in his big white Chevy Celebrity.

My father balked at the busy counter when the president tried to pick up the tab. "Please, we don't want to be a burden to the mission."

With a broad smile, Tuttle patted my father on the back. "What else is your tithing money for?"

My father's face darkened. "Tithing funds are consecrated."

I tensed.

"Brother Shunn, that was just a little joke. You came all this way. Please allow me."

But my father dug in his heels, and Tuttle was forced to let him pay for our two meals separately. I think in any other company I would have laughed at the tithing quip, but in the light of my father's offended sense of propriety it took President Tuttle down another notch in my estimation.

(Much later I would learn that mission presidents, while not technically employees of the church, receive generous reimbursements for a broad range of living expenses that they are instructed not to report as taxable income. Our Wendy's combos would have been a molecule in that bucket.)

As we ate in a booth by a window, Tuttle talked about his struggles to keep the mission running smoothly during this crisis. "Honestly, it's been a challenge. Every elder in the city wants to be there with you this afternoon, but I can't let them stop proselytizing, and we really can't afford to have forty missionaries running loose in the courts. How would I keep the reporters away? You just *know* one of those boys will pop off with something dumb, and next thing you know we'll be hearing it on the six o'clock news. I had to send the word out yesterday that the courthouse is strictly off-limits."

A lone infantryman heading into battle with a squad of officers— that's how I felt. "Elder Snow will still be there, though, right? He's my companion. He has to be."

President Tuttle shook his head. "I'm sorry, Elder Shunn. Your companion did come to me last night and ask special permission to go. He made a good case, but if I'd allowed it then I would have had to let Elder McKay come too. Then someone else would have wanted to, and someone else, and pretty soon it would have been a circus."

The words seemed to make sense, strung one after another, but to me they didn't quite add up. If I had a best friend in the mission, it was Snow. McKay could have spent the time with the apes, or joined someone else's companionship in a three-leg.

One friend at my trial, that was all I wanted. President Tuttle was just doing what was easiest for him. I wanted to call him out on it.

I didn't.

He took a swig of his Sprite. "Bless him, though. Elder Snow was disappointed, but he said he understood perfectly and would support my decision. Unlike those pesky sisters."

"What sisters?" asked my father.

I looked out the window, wondering what now. The day was sunny and cool, but gauzy gray clouds haunted the horizon.

"Roper, Steed, and Herzog. They're in your son's district. What is it you call them, Elder Shunn?"

I turned my head. "Um, what? I don't know."

"Yes, you know. You made up nicknames. Elder Snow told them to me once."

I winced. "Oh. You mean, um, Doper, Weed, and Mad Dog?"

Tuttle snorted in amusement. "That's it! Sister Doper, ha. You should have heard them sniveling in my office last night. In they come, weeping and wailing, throwing themselves on the floor, using up my Kleenexes." He put on a mocking falsetto. "'President, oh, President! It's all our fault! You *have* to let us go to the trial! If anything happens to Elder Shunn, we'll *kill* ourselves, oh, *please!*'"

I stirred a french fry in my ketchup.

"That's all we need, is *three* hysterical women blubbering over poor

Elder Shunn in that courtroom. Can you imagine? What a p.r. night-mare. As if we don't have a big enough image problem already." Tuttle shook his head with an aggrieved sigh. "They wouldn't take a simple no. Finally I had to say, 'Sisters, I'm only going to tell you this once, so I hope you're paying attention. If I catch you anywhere *near* that courthouse tomorrow, if you step so much as a toe outside your pros-elytizing area, I will *excommunicate* all three of you, end of story. Are we clear?' *That* shut them up, let me tell you. Those sisters turned as pale as ghosts."

He chuckled and shoved two fries into his mouth.

We sat around a low coffee table in President Page's fifth-floor office downtown. He clasped his hands on his knees, looking di-rectly at me, sparing barely a glance for my father or President Tuttle.

"Now, Elder, let me explain a little about what happens this after-noon. This isn't a trial. It's a *hearing*, where the judge decides whether or not there's sufficient evidence for a trial, and where you get to elect *how* to be tried. You don't always get a jury trial in Canada: only if you're facing a maximum sentence of at least five years. In that case you can choose a judge or a jury trial, whichever you think will be fair-er. Are you with me so far?"

The air smelled faintly of sandalwood. "Yes."

"Good." He tilted his head, and the overhead lights glared off his rimless glasses. "Now for the bad news and the worse news. The bad news is, we've drawn a judge this afternoon named Phil Callahan. Some judges, with a case like this, you know they'd throw it out. Oth-ers, you know they'd lock you up in a heartbeat. But Callahan's hard to predict. You can never guess which way he'll lean. It's a toss-up, tak-ing your case before him. You could walk free, or you could end up in the pokey."

I nodded to show my understanding, but the way he kept using that corny word did not inspire confidence.

"So we have an important decision to make. We can stick with Callahan today and take our chances, or we can ask for a postponement in hope of drawing a more sympathetic judge. Of course, we might draw a worse judge, so that's a risk too. You wouldn't be able to leave Calgary until after the new hearing, which could be four or five months from now, and in the meantime, with your work permit suspended, you wouldn't be able to proselytize."

My father spoke up before I could. "Bill didn't come on a mission to twiddle his thumbs. He's here to work. Let's go ahead with the hearing today. Everything will be okay."

"I agree," said President Tuttle. "Let's get him past this and back to work."

Back to work? That sounded odd. I had started to believe that when all this was over, whichever way it went, I would be sent home. I'd committed a felony on church business. No way would they want me for a missionary after that.

But out loud I said that I agreed too—not that I'd been asked.

"That was my inclination as well," said Page. "I'm glad we're of one mind on this. So now for the worse news. Elder Shunn, I don't know quite how to tell you this, but the prosecution wants to bring a more serious charge against you than public mischief."

Criminy. I closed my eyes. "What's the charge?"

His voice was grave. "Hijacking."

I flew up out of my chair, heart pounding. "What? How can they do that?"

"Let me ask you a question, Elder." Page looked up at me with calm sympathy. "And this is an important question, so please think hard before you answer. Tell me, where was that airplane when you made your bomb threat?"

I sat down, feeling foolish and confused. "Where *was* it? What do you mean? It was on the runway."

"Are you sure?"

"Of course I'm sure." The question didn't make any sense. "Why wouldn't I be sure? Where else would it have been?"

Page crossed to one of his bookshelves. "I'm glad you think so, but you're wrong. In fact, it was still in the air at the time you made the phone call." He located a thick book and began leafing through it. His windows overlooked the Bow River, and the water cast shimmering reflections onto the ceiling above. "The plane was on its way from Edmonton to Calgary, and it was only scheduled to be on the ground for about fifteen minutes, just long enough to load passengers and luggage before continuing to Salt Lake City. The tower didn't even tell the pilot about the bomb threat until the plane was on the ground."

He found the page he was looking for and brought the book over, like Saint Peter opening the Book of Life. "Here's our legal definition of hijacking."

As I read the passage, I felt like throwing up. The law printed there was just ambiguous enough that *any* threat against a plane in the air could be construed as hijacking. It didn't matter whether or not the perpetrator was actually on board.

And according to the statute, hijacking carried a maximum sentence of life in prison.

President Page closed the book. "Based on your understanding of the plane's location, I'm fairly certain we could beat a hijacking charge, but I'd rather we didn't try. The lead prosecutor is Dan Plummer, and he wants to make an example out of you."

I groaned.

Page raised his palms. "Now, I'm going to talk to him before the hearing, and what I'd *like* to do is offer him a plea deal. We'll plead guilty, but only if he agrees to stay with your original charge of public mischief. You *did* confess—three times, in fact—so there's not much we can really do about that. But if he goes ahead and tries to stick you with this hijacking charge, we'll plead not guilty in no uncertain terms, and if we lose then we'll appeal and keep appealing. We'll tie this case up for years if necessary. We'll make him sorry every day." He took a deep breath. "So. What's your preference? Can I offer him this deal, or are you spoiling for a fight?"

It didn't seem like much of a choice to me. I was about to say so when my father spoke up. "Let's plead guilty on the lesser charge."

"Uh, yeah, that," I said.

"I do think that's the right choice. I don't know if Plummer will agree, but I'll certainly press him hard." Page frowned. "But, Elder Shunn, if he takes this deal and we do plead guilty to public mischief, the hearing automatically becomes a sentencing. The question then is whether you get jail time or a fine. We'll be arguing for the fine, of course, but you should expect the prosecution to ask for some pretty stiff time. And I have to warn you, you'll still be in real peril. Public mischief carries a maximum sentence of *ten years*."

I stiffened. For *mischief?* They wouldn't ask for ten years, would they? This was exactly the nightmare Constable Vaughan, as he had told me at the time, had wanted to shield me from when he selected that charge.

"I doubt they'll go *that* high," President Page said, "but you do need to be prepared for what happens when the judge hands down your sentence. If it's a prison term, it starts that moment. You go out the back door of that courtroom and directly into custody." His expression darkened. "Elder, you *must* be prepared to spend time in the pokey."

I wanted to scream.

"It won't necessarily be so bad," Tuttle chimed in. "Have you ever met President Badami? He's my second counselor."

I shook my head. I wasn't aware that mission presidents even *had* counselors.

"Well, President Badami's a dentist. He works at Spy Hill, and he thinks he could get you a job as an orderly."

I shook my head, feeling dizzy. "I'm sorry, what?"

"Calgary Correctional Centre," said Page, shooting Tuttle a strange look. "It's minimum security. They call it Spy Hill. If you do get prison time, we can probably arrange for you to do it there. And it'll be more interesting for you with a job to do."

An awful horror stole over me. These men were already planning my prison agenda. They were *expecting* me to get sent up.

"Now, before we head down to the courthouse," said Page, "let's put together a list. I want to hear every good thing you've ever done in your life. Awards, scholarships, Scout badges, community service, old ladies you helped across the street, *everything*. When that judge looks at you, he needs to see an angel. He needs to know that a bad decision today is going to haunt him."

Sure. But not like it'll haunt me.

CHAPTER 46

"I CAN'T BELIEVE IT," SAID PRESIDENT TUTTLE OVER ICE CREAM. "We were so close."

"It's not over," said President Page.

"So *close*."

We had spent less than an hour in the bright, spacious courtroom. Dan Plummer accepted the plea bargain before the start of the hearing, so I pled guilty to public mischief before Judge Callahan, a balding man with thick glasses. Both sides presented eloquent arguments, Plummer in favor of sixty days in jail, Page in favor of a fine. My father bore tearful witness to my excellent character, though the part about how I'd never given my mother or him a moment of trouble struck me as rank perjury. Callahan seemed to be on the verge of delivering a sentence when he abruptly called a 24-hour recess.

President Tuttle and my father had steered me past the handful of reporters lying in wait outside the courtroom. We took refuge in a vinyl-padded ice-cream parlor a few blocks away. President Page joined us soon after in our snug booth.

"I really thought we had him." My father shoveled a spoonful of burnt almond fudge into his mouth. His side was warm against me. I was glad to see his sweet tooth was back.

"I still just can't *believe* it." Tuttle thumped the table, rattling our water glasses. "Elder Shunn, that judge was *right* on the verge of letting you go. Just like President Page suggested, he was going to let you off with a fine. The words were coming out of his mouth, and then something held him back. The Spirit was working on him, but he hardened his heart. Oh, *rats*, it makes me so upset!"

"The judge is in a difficult position," said President Page. "Morally he knows the right thing to do. What he doesn't know is the right thing to do *legally*."

"What do you mean?" asked Tuttle.

Page set his elbows on the tabletop. "He's about to set a precedent. There's never been a case like this in Canada. I know. I've checked. The next time this happens, that judge will head to the casebooks to see how Philip Callahan decided in *The Crown v. Shunn*. It's an awesome responsibility, and one he can't take lightly."

"My son is not a precedent." My father's lip trembled, and he put down his spoon. "Doesn't that judge understand?"

"He understands, Brother Shunn," said Page gently. "That's what makes the decision so hard." He scooped up a bite of his cherry ripple. "But it's out of our hands at this point. We've done everything we can. All we can do now is pray Judge Callahan talks to the right person tonight."

"What person?" I asked. I hadn't eaten much of my banana split.

"Whoever he trusts enough to ask for advice in situations like this." He took another bite of ice cream. "So like I said, let's pray it's the right one."

I didn't want to pray. I wanted to turn back time and make a different choice.

Different *choices*. A lot of them.

AFTER FLEEING ACROSS THE MISSISSIPPI, JOSEPH AND HYRUM Smith spent all of twelve hours in hiding in Iowa.

It was June 23, 1844. Their plan had been to make their way around

Illinois and on to Washington, D.C., where they would lay their pleas for protection and reparations for the Mormon people before President John Tyler. But in the early afternoon, Porter Rockwell brought them entreaties from Emma and others to come back and stand with the Saints. The people felt abandoned by their prophet in their hour of greatest need, and Governor Ford swore he could provide Joseph safe passage to trial if he would turn himself in. Everyone, including faithful Hyrum, seemed to believe that things would go well if he returned.

Joseph did not share this optimism. By doing as requested, he fully expected to be murdered in Carthage. "If my life is of no value to my friends," he is reported to have said then, in resignation, "it is of none to myself."

And so he climbed back into the boat.

I PILOTED THE HUGE WHITE CELEBRITY THROUGH WIDE STREETS and a waning afternoon. President Tuttle had lent me the unwieldy car so my father and I could get away from things for a few hours. It was a sad inversion of our usual road trips, my father hugging the distant passenger door on the short, meandering drive while I pointed out features of interest. I'm sure he would have felt better behind the wheel, but it was a mission vehicle and I was the one covered under the insurance.

We dropped anchor at a Chi-Chi's—fancy fare by our family standards—where I crunched a chimichanga in taciturn misery. We both knew this could be my last restaurant meal as a free man, at least for a month or two. Worse, the people at the other tables kept talking about me, or at least that's what it sounded like. I kept hearing snatches of conversation that sounded like "Elder Shunn" or "missionary" or "bomb threat" or "airplane" or "prison." The food turned to mud in my throat.

My father awkwardly tried to keep the conversation going, asking about my plans for life after mission service. He didn't bring up Katrina, and neither did I. Between that prospect and prison I wasn't sure which he found more horrifying, and there was no point in spoiling our meal entirely. Also, I wouldn't give him the satisfaction of admitting that he might have been right about her after all.

We got all the sleep we could that night. In the morning my father and I went sightseeing under a sky the color of old meat. I squired him around Calgary in the big Celebrity, steering it like a yacht through the steel-and-glass canyons of the city. We gawked at the Calgary Tower and the Saddledome, and then, grasping for other landmarks to show him, I tried to find the bronze sculptures we missionaries called the Naked Lakers. Actually titled "Family of Man," it was a group of ten thin human figures at play, each 21 feet tall, installed in front of the Board of Education building downtown. I was sure I knew how to find it, but I only managed to get us lost.

Distracted, I accidentally turned right onto a transit-only street. I missed the warning sign, and I only realized what I'd done when I noticed I was following train tracks down the block.

There was no C-Train in sight, but I panicked anyway. "Crap!" I shouted, stomping on the gas.

"What are you doing? Look out!" cried my father, pressing himself deep into his upholstered seat.

I slewed around the next corner with one hand on the wheel and one on the horn. Pedestrians scattered. I was lucky we didn't run anyone down. I braked at the red light a block later.

"What the hell was that?" my father demanded, white-faced.

I tried to calm my breathing as we idled. My hands were shaking. "Transit-only street. No cars allowed, only buses and trains."

I expected my father to rip me a new one, but he didn't say anything in response. I turned my head. His eyes were unfocused, his mouth slack.

"Dad?" Judas Proust, was he having a stroke?

He burst into sobs so suddenly that I jerked. His body shook in great racking shudders. A horn behind us honked, and I pressed the gas.

My heart was racing. "Dad, are you okay?"

He turned a mottled and tear-streaked face toward me. "It's your mother," he said, his voice catching. "She's praying for you right now." He touched his heart. "I can feel it, son, and you're going to be okay. You're going to be okay."

It was early evening when Joseph and Hyrum arrived back in Nauvoo. As part of the deal with Governor Ford, the Nauvoo Legion had been decommissioned and was now ordered to turn in all government-issued weapons. Joseph hoped to avert a war with his sacrifice, but he also refused to leave Nauvoo defenseless. He instructed his troops to comply with the governor's demand—but not until they'd hidden all their personal arms in a central warehouse, where they could be quickly retrieved in case of attack.

Joseph wanted to address the city before his surrender, but preparing a legal defense left him no time. The next morning, June 24, in the company of more than a dozen city councilmen who were also charged in the *Expositor* riot, Joseph and Hyrum made their final ride out of Nauvoo.

What was Joseph thinking as the city he'd grown from nothing to rival Chicago in size vanished behind him? Was he wondering how his life had spun so far out of control? Did he wish he could go back to any particular moment in time, make a different choice, and change his fate? Did he blame himself for the path he now found himself on? Did he blame God, or Satan, or evil men?

One member of that company, John Taylor, who would later become the church's third president, wrote an account of those last days. He quotes Joseph as saying, as they rode toward the frothing, lawless militias in Carthage:

> "I am going like a lamb to the slaughter; but I am calm as a
> summer's morning. I have a conscience void of offense towards

God, and towards all men. I SHALL DIE INNOCENT, AND IT SHALL YET BE SAID OF ME—HE WAS MURDERED IN COLD BLOOD."

After the fifteen-mile journey to Carthage, the party lodged at Hamilton's Hotel. With much talk among the militiamen of lynching the prophet and attacking Nauvoo anyway, Governor Ford tried to ease the hostility the next day by parading Joseph and Hyrum through town. Ford's ultimate goal was to get the Mormons out of Illinois without bloodshed, but he had already miscalculated time and again, starting with his assent to enforcement of the Missouri treason warrant. Then, rather than challenging the Nauvoo charters himself when it still might have done some good, he had waited for the legislature to take action, which it never did. Ford was now hoping, as he later admitted, that Joseph would escape from custody and flee west with his people—not that the governor had done much of anything to encourage this course of action, either.

Worst of all, he vastly underestimated the hatred of the local militias for the Mormons, even as he tried to rein in and reason with their leaders. The McDonough County militia, which guarded Joseph and Hyrum on the march through Carthage, were orderly and well-regimented, but the jeering threats from the other militias were truly ugly and bone-chilling. They promised "Old Joe" would never leave Carthage alive.

At court, the defendants all received bail and were released pending the next circuit court date—all, that is, but Joseph and Hyrum. A fresh charge of treason had been sworn against them by Augustine Spencer—an anti-Mormon from Nauvoo whose family had all converted to the church—this time for calling up the Legion on June 19 to help him resist arrest. Governor Ford recognized the charge had no merit but felt it more prudent under the circumstances to let the courts work out the problem than to intervene.

So it was that, on June 25, Joseph and Hyrum were confined to the upper story of the Carthage Jail, while their friends and fellow conspirators went free.

BACK AT THE MISSION OFFICE, MY FATHER CALLED MY MOTHER AND confirmed that she had in fact prayed for me at some point during the preceding hour. He took this as a miracle and a sign of hope. I can't say I took it entirely as a coincidence myself, but it didn't make me dread the hearing any less.

After a light lunch, President Tuttle drove my father and me to the Provincial Court Building. We met President Page in the courtroom, taking seats directly behind his table. I couldn't help but stare at the provincial seal hanging on the wall behind the bench. Beyond it, through an invisible scabby veil, lurked the pokey. It was calling to me, radiating menace on a frequency only my bones could pick up. When the judge said the word, it would crack its dripping maw and slurp me down.

The courtroom was filling up. President Tuttle tapped me on the shoulder and pointed across the gallery to two newspaper reporters we'd seen the day before, a man and a woman sitting near each other. One of them wrote clear, measured articles for the *Calgary Herald*, the other breathless tabloid drivel for the *Calgary Sun*.

"I can't wait to see what kind of hysterical *fiction* that woman cooks up tomorrow," said Tuttle. "The fellow from the *Herald*, now *he's* on top of things. I think she must nap and then copy his notes."

My father glanced toward the reporters. "I think you may have it backwards, President."

Tuttle's brow wrinkled. "What do you mean?"

"The reporters. I was noticing their bylines this morning. The woman's the one who writes for the *Herald*. The man writes for the *Sun*."

President Tuttle looked at the reporters again, frowning, and back at my father. "Are you sure?"

"He's right," I said. "I noticed it this morning too."

"Huh," said Tuttle in wonder. "Who would have thought?"

"All rise," ordered the bailiff.

My heart jumped into my throat. At the prosecution table, Dan Plummer stood straight as a telephone pole, chin high, devilish black beard bristling. He exuded a worrisome confidence. But President Page was no slouch, I tried to remind myself.

Judge Callahan entered from his chambers, his robe billowing like the wings of a crow. He looked older than he had the day before, bent and bowed, but when we were seated again his voice rang loud.

"This has not been an easy case to decide," he said without preamble, "but I *have* decided. Before I pass sentence, though, I'd like to briefly review the needs this sentencing must satisfy." He cleared his throat and took a sip of water. "First, there is the issue of deterrence. The Crown makes an excellent point when they ask for a sentence harsh enough to discourage others from committing similar acts. This court has no desire to lend support to the impression that crimes of this nature are acceptable, trivial, or even tolerable. This requirement demands that a jail sentence be imposed."

I shivered. My stomach threatened to rebel.

"At the same time, however, this court has no desire to ruin the life of an upstanding young man with no previous criminal record. Mister Shunn has demonstrated a good attitude toward society throughout his life, and it's my considered opinion that he will never see the inside of another court of law, in this country or any other. For that reason, the imposition of a fine would seem to be called for."

I couldn't take any more. He was toying with us now—with *me*.

Judge Callahan favored the courtroom with a portentous scowl. "I therefore find that, in order to satisfy both opposing demands, a fine *and* a jail sentence are in order."

IN THEIR CELL ON THE TOP FLOOR OF CARTHAGE JAIL, JOSEPH MUST have fantasized about the kind of escape he and Hyrum had pulled off in Missouri, but there was little hope of that now. The militias roiled and seethed in the streets, and for any guard he might have bribed there were a hundred gunmen waiting outside for the smallest excuse to open fire.

The only upside was that their sympathetic jailer let friends of Joseph and Hyrum come and go as they pleased. Among the visitors on June 26 was Governor Ford, who talked and debated with the prophet for hours. The major sticking point in their conversation was the destruction of the *Expositor*. Ford could not make Joseph understand the sacredness of the press in America, and Joseph could not comprehend why he should tolerate a paper that put his community at risk of mob violence.

He pleaded with Ford for a change of venue, convinced he could get a fair hearing anywhere but in Carthage. The governor refused, but mentioned his plan to take one militia group to Nauvoo the next day to make a show of searching for rumored counterfeiting equipment. "Joseph begged to be taken along," writes Fawn Brodie, "for he was certain that the Governor's presence was the only thing keeping the militia under control. Ford promised to do so."

The jailer allowed Joseph and Hyrum the use of his own private room adjacent to their large cell. Several friends spent the night with them, Joseph sleeping on the floor between Dan Jones and John Fullmer. The next morning, June 27, Jones went out to assess the mood of the militias. He overheard a stump speech whipping up troops from the nearby city of Warsaw to kill the Smith boys that afternoon, after the governor was gone.

Jones hurried with this report to Governor Ford, who couldn't believe the militias would be so reckless while he was in Nauvoo, vulnerable to vengeance-minded Mormons. He left Carthage despite this intelligence, taking the McDonough militia with him—and he did not honor his promise to take Joseph.

The Warsaw militia marched out of town with the governor far enough to allay his suspicions, then turned and beat hell for leather back to Carthage. By light of early evening, they joined forces with the Carthage Greys and stormed the jail.

JUDGE CALLAHAN STARED STRAIGHT AT ME WITH UNBLINKING eyes. I couldn't seem to catch my breath, and I couldn't look away. He might have been carved from wood.

"I hereby sentence you, Donald William Shunn, to pay a fine in the amount of two thousand dollars, which *must* be paid from monies you have earned yourself, by your own labor. And additionally"—he drew a long breath through his nose—"to serve one day in jail. Case closed."

He pounded his gavel and vanished in a swirl of black.

The noise of the spectators roared in my ears like wind on a mountaintop. I barely understood what was happening as the bailiff seized me by the arm and dragged me to the back door of the courtroom, down the gullet of the jail.

ONLY WILLARD RICHARDS AND JOHN TAYLOR REMAINED UPSTAIRS in the jailer's room with Joseph and Hyrum. The four men heard shouts and shots at the entrance downstairs. Joseph and Hyrum drew pistols smuggled in by earlier visitors. The other two men had only hickory canes with which to protect themselves. All four pressed themselves to the cell's wooden door but were forced back when gunshots pierced it.

Joseph managed to get out of the line of fire as the door was battered open. Hyrum did not. The cluster of gun barrels bristling from the passageway beyond belched fire; four balls hit him, one in the face. Another from the window struck him in the side. "I am a dead man!" he cried as he fell. He did not rise.

Joseph emptied his pistol through the doorway, injuring three members of the mob but killing none. A hail of lead shredded the air, from both the doorway and the window. John Taylor was shot five times, but not fatally. Willard Richards, standing next to the door and thrashing at the guns with his cane, escaped serious injury.

Joseph leapt to the jailer's window. A hundred blackened faces stared up at him in the ruddy twilight, a hundred bayonets upraised. According to some reports, Joseph shouted a traditional plea for assistance to the Masons in the crowd: "Is there no help for the widow's son?"

That's when a ball from inside the jail struck him in the back. Joseph toppled slowly out the window.

I SAT ON A BENCH NEAR THE PROPERTY WINDOW, SURROUNDED BY armed guards and fellow prisoners alike. My jail sentence was to be applied retroactively, but I had to wait for my paperwork to be processed before I could be released. An hour went by, then two, then three, while faces came and went around me. Having a watch, I learned, did not make the time pass any more quickly.

As my fourth hour rolled around, I became aware of two scruffy, scrappy-looking guys sitting at the other end of the bench. One reclined with his head against the cinder-block wall, eyes closed, while the other kept watching me sideways and fidgeting.

Eventually, having seen that I knew he was watching me, the guy scooted a foot or two closer. He pushed tangled brown hair out of his face and flashed an ingratiating smile. "How you doin', eh?"

I eyed him coolly. "Fine. Just waiting to get out."

"No doubt, no doubt. What are you in for?"

Varnishing the truth no longer seemed necessary. "Hijacking."

"No *way*." His eyes widened. "Hijacking? What did you *do*?"

I gave a casual shrug. "I said there was a bomb on a plane."

His eyes lit up. "Oh, hey, you're that guy from the news!"

I nodded. "That's right."

"Oh, man," he said, squirming. "I can't believe it. This is so *great*." He nudged his companion. "Hey, man, Brian, dude, wake up. You gotta meet this fella here, eh? This is the guy who blows up *planes*."

The second man opened his bleary eyes and squinted at me.

"Hey," I said.

"Huh. You're that guy, eh?"

"Yup."

His eyebrows lifted a millimeter. "Cool."

I couldn't help myself. I grinned. It's a heady thing, having fans.

JOSEPH CLUNG BLEEDING TO THE WINDOWSILL FOR SEVERAL LONG moments. Colonel Levi Williams, commander of the Warsaw militia, ordered his men to fire. No one obeyed. In anguish Joseph cried, "Oh Lord, my God!" and dropped half-conscious to the ground.

One militiaman sprang forward and dragged Joseph across the yard. He propped the prophet against the curb of a nearby well, while Colonel Williams organized a firing squad of four men.

Joseph's eyes fluttered open and he stared at his executioners.

Williams gave the order to fire.

All four balls found their mark, and Joseph Smith fell dead to the dirt.

AT SIX O'CLOCK, AN OFFICER AT THE PROCESSING WINDOW CALLED out, "Shunn! Donald William!"

It was finished. I was free.

CHAPTER 47

WHEN PRESIDENT TUTTLE, MY FATHER, AND I REACHED THE MIS-
sion office, Elder Snow was waiting with the apes and the rest of
our district. He caught me in a fierce hug in the cramped entry hall.
"Shazz, yes, you did it, buckfart. You pulled it off."

Next, Sister Roper threw her arms around me, heedless of President Tuttle's disapproving scowl. "I'm so happy you're safe, Elder
Shunn. We've been praying for you every day." I wished there weren't
so many people watching so I could have enjoyed the moment a little
more.

Hugs followed from Sister Steed and Sister Herzog, then from Elder McKay and Elder Hardy and Elder Fearing and Elder Kopp and
Elder Lienhard. The apes recounted the dozens of phone calls they'd
taken that week, from members and non-members alike, expressing
support and good wishes. Sister Herzog tried to count the number of
prayers she'd offered since Monday. Elder Lienhard assured us he'd
never been worried for a minute.

President Tuttle saw my father checking his watch. "Why don't
we move things a little further inside? Give ourselves some breathing
room."

The ebullient little crowd relocated to the bullpen while Tuttle herded my father and me into his office. "You want to get that flight worked out, I suppose, Brother Shunn."

My father heaved a martyr's sigh, shoulders hunched. "You all have important work to do. The longer I'm here, the more I hold it up."

"You're leaving?" I asked. My father had come to Calgary on an open ticket, prepared to stay for however long it took to work things out, but for some reason it hadn't occurred to me that he'd fly home again at the earliest opportunity. I was surprised to find I felt upset.

"First thing tomorrow. Assuming there's a flight."

Tuttle seated himself behind his desk. "I'll get on the phone." I think he wanted my father gone as much as my father wanted to *be* gone.

"I have a question first." My father eased the office door shut and took a chair beside me. "I want to ask you about his, uh—" He nodded in my direction and lowered his voice. "His priesthood. The status of it."

President Tuttle looked puzzled. "What do you mean?"

"You know. There won't be any, uh, repercussions?"

Tuttle barked a laugh but choked it off. "Excommunication? Oh, my goodness, no." He waved a hand. "No, no, no."

"Well, in cases like this, with a felony conviction, you know, I thought it used to be automatic."

I swallowed. I figured my mission was in jeopardy, but I'd never considered that I might actually lose my church membership. Excommunication was a huge deal once you'd had your temple endowment, one you didn't easily bounce back from.

"Please, there's nothing to worry about," said President Tuttle. "I have nothing like that planned, Brother Shunn. Your son here is a fine missionary, and we'd like to keep him that way." He leaned across the desk and squeezed my shoulder, grinning like a jackal. "Now, why don't I see about that flight?"

THAT NIGHT, CLAD ONLY IN HIS GARMENTS, MY FATHER PACKED HIS suitcase in preparation for the morning. "You understand what a lucky young man you are, don't you?"

I was leaning against the door jamb. "Yes," I mumbled.

"How *blessed* you are?"

"*Yes.*"

He stared at me for a long moment. "Son, you've had a very sacred experience this week. The Lord preserved you." His tone was lecturing, but tears sparkled at the corners of his eyes. "Your uncle Douglas was standing over you in that courtroom today. He was your guardian angel."

I didn't ask if this was just a feeling he'd had or if my father had actually seen him. I didn't want to know.

He closed his suitcase, never taking his eyes off me. "Son, this is the kind of experience you don't talk about, ever. It's too sacred."

"You mean about Uncle Doug?"

He blew out his breath. "I mean about everything, *all* this."

"But—" I shook my head as frustration welled up. "It's not like it's a secret. It's all over the news. Mom said it was on the news in *Utah*. People are *going* to ask me about it."

"Then you tell them it's not something you like to talk about."

"But *why?*" I insisted. "That makes it sound like I've got something to hide."

"You *do* have something to hide—a criminal record. That's not something to brag about." He waved a dismissive hand, not looking at me. "Let's say a prayer and get some sleep."

So which is it, sacred or secret?

I sighed and decided to stop arguing.

THE NEXT MORNING, PRESIDENT TUTTLE AND I STOOD IN LINE with my father at the airport as he waited to go through Customs. I glanced around nervously for any faces I might recognize.

"I'll let you know when I've transferred that money from your savings into checking," my father said. "So you can pay your fine."

"Thank you. Remember, it doesn't have to be a full two thousand. With the exchange rate, sixteen hundred will cover it."

"I won't remember that," he snorted. "Oh, by the way, I don't think I told you what your mother said on the phone last night. This should interest you too, President."

"What's that?" asked Tuttle.

"She heard this from our stake president, who also happens to be a pretty high-ranking captain there at Occidental, a pilot. You remember how the airline reported that the bomb threat cost them a couple thousand dollars?"

"Of course," said Tuttle. "My impression was, that's why Judge Callahan set the fine at two thousand dollars. It struck me as quite low, that figure."

"That's because it *was* low." My father gestured expansively, delighting in this tidbit of gossip. "It turns out the total was more like *twenty* thousand. President Clearmountain convinced the airline to lose a zero."

President Tuttle whistled. "Lucky thing, very lucky."

My father cocked his head. "President, we both know luck had nothing to do with it."

"Amen, Brother Shunn." We had nearly reached the head of the queue. "And now I'd better wish you a safe flight."

"Thank you, President," my father said as they shook hands. "For everything. I can't tell you what a blessing you've been."

"Brother Shunn, I'm only doing my job."

"You seem to do it well. Just try to keep my dumb kid out of any more trouble."

Tuttle laughed. "I'll do my best."

My father put a hand on my shoulder and peered into my eyes. "As for you, son, be good. Say your prayers every night, and give thanks to your Heavenly Father for the fact that you're not in jail." He pointed to President Tuttle. "Obey the mission rules, and listen to this man. He's inspired."

My only response to that was a tiny, disappointed nod.

Almost tentatively, he put his arms around me. "I love you, son, and I'm proud of you. Remember that. And don't forget what I told you." He zipped his lips with thumb and forefinger.

That made it easy to hold back my tears. "I'll remember."

As my father's rounded shoulders passed through the gate, I felt guilty at how relieved I was.

THAT EVENING I RODE WITH MY TWO COMPANIONS TO OUR WARD meetinghouse. Elder Finn's absence had left the mission with an odd number of elders, so President Tuttle and the apes had done some shuffling. Since my status was still uncertain, a hirsute little elder named Banks joined Snow and me in a three-leg.

Our ward was having a potluck dinner. The event had been scheduled for weeks, but from the way I was mobbed you'd have thought they planned it just for me. I shook hands with dozens of people, while dozens more pounded me on the back or tousled my hair. Bishop Tomlinson's wife crushed me to her ample bosom and planted a lipstick mark on my cheek. It took fifteen minutes just to cross the foyer to the cultural hall, where dinner was being served. I soaked up the adulation like a sponge.

We'd been tracting all afternoon—always awkward as a threesome—without success. We were tired, hungry, and ready for mounds of fresh, hot home cooking, but the Blanchard family swooped down on us as we were getting in line.

"I'm *so* sorry I missed our dinner appointment Monday," I said.

Sister Blanchard hugged me tightly. "Don't be silly. You're forgiven."

"We'll have to drop in sometime next week and make it up to you," said Snow.

Brother Blanchard vigorously pumped my arm. "Anytime you want, Elders. Come for Sunday dinner!"

Young Louisa shook my hand firmly. "We were all praying for you, Elder. It looks like Heavenly Father heard us." I almost swooned.

Blaine, the fifteen-year-old son, tugged me by the arm. "Come on, Elder Shunn! I brought a couple of non-member friends tonight, and they're *dying* to meet the terrorist!"

"Let the poor elder at least eat something first," Brother Blanchard chided.

"Aw, *Dad*."

I shrugged. "Hey, I'm on the job. I can't very well say no to potential investigators."

After signing autographs for Blaine's friends, I heaped my plate and found Snow and Banks seated with the Marek family. Cherilyn squealed and jumped to her feet. I just managed to set my plate and glass down before she got her arms around me. Dorian in his baby seat waved his spoon.

Sandor shook my hand with unbridled enthusiasm. "We are ecstatic to see you, Elder Shunn. We were telling Elder Snow this week how we wouldn't take another lesson until you were safely out of jail. And now, like a miracle, here you are!"

"So you'd like to pick up again where we left off?"

"Of course!"

"It *has* been a few days. We could start again at the beginning if you feel like you need a refresher."

"No, Elder," said Sandor, smiling and shaking his head. "We would like to get through the last two lessons as quickly as we can. We want to get baptized next week."

SNOW AND I WERE REMINISCING OVER OUR EMPTY PLATES ABOUT the night the Kent family fed us until we nearly burst, when who should approach us but Brother Kent himself. We both stood.

Brother Kent was one of the wealthiest men in the ward, the kind who seemed to prove the conventional Mormon wisdom that true righteousness brings riches in this world *and* the next. He shook my hand.

"So glad to see you well, Elder." His cultured, mellifluous voice commanded if not demanded respect. "You've had many people here very worried."

"Thank you, Brother Kent."

He inclined his head and lowered his voice. "I understand," he said, looking past me, "that you're faced with a rather sizable fine."

Alarm bells clanged in my head.

"Two thousand dollars, I believe?"

I nodded, trying to swallow.

He lowered his voice further. "Well, Elder, some of the high priests here would like to take up a collection and pay that for you."

All I could hear were Judge Callahan's stern words at my sentencing. "I—I can't," I stammered in a panic. I knew I was making an ass of myself, but the words had to get out, and I was helpless to impose any tact. "I can't take your money."

Brother Kent recoiled like I'd slapped his face.

Elder Snow stepped in and took him by the arm. "What my companion means to say," he purred, "is that the judge specifically stipulated his fine was to be paid from his own savings. Your offer is *extremely* generous and *very* much appreciated, but if Elder Shunn lets anyone else pay his fine, he'll be in contempt of court. The Crown might actually press charges."

Brother Kent's expression changed to sympathetic fury. "That's *outrageous.*" You'd have thought I had to clean public restrooms with my tongue. "There must be *some* way we can help, don't you think?"

Snow stroked his chin as if giving the question serious thought. "You know, there just might be. I *suppose* that once the fine is paid and all the legal considerations are out of the way, there'd be nothing to prevent a group of gentlemen from making a small contribution to Elder Shunn's mission fund. Perhaps in care of his father."

Brother Kent nodded with the barest hint of a smile. "I take your point, I do indeed. Thank you, Elder Snow. I'll talk it over with the others. And congratulations once again on your freedom, Elder Shunn." He strode off purposefully.

In the end, Brother Kent and friends donated a total of $2,150 to my mission fund—which meant I made a modest profit on my crime.

I SPENT THE NEXT WEEK ON PINS AND NEEDLES, WAITING TO FIND out whether or not the church planned to send me home. I wasn't sure what I wanted. The long hours of tracting were as hard as ever to get through. I was still homesick. My relationship with Katrina was in a precarious stage, our truer selves having peeped out from behind the masks of courtship. And I had stories to write—God, did I ever. But I also had friends here who loved and appreciated me, and I felt a deep connection now to the people of Calgary.

I'd been free for nine days when I was summoned to a meeting with T. Aldon Ingersoll of the First Quorum of the Seventy, an eminent grayhair who happened to be visiting from Salt Lake City to speak at a local stake conference. It was March 7, a Saturday morning. I joined him in a small office commandeered from a stake president. Grandfatherly at first, President Ingersoll was all business when he questioned me about my time in Calgary.

"Elder Shunn, the church has no plan nor wish to punish you," he told me after five minutes of intense grilling. "But it's the feeling of the brethren that your notoriety here compromises your ability to be the most effective possible missionary. For that reason, you'll be serving the rest of your mission back in the United States." He put up a hand to forestall my protest. "This is no imprudent move we're making. The Canadian authorities will likely ask you to leave the country anyway."

Canada Immigration had scheduled an inquiry for the coming Tuesday. "Can't we wait to hear for sure what they say?" I asked.

Ingersoll shook his moonlike head. "This is the will of the Lord, Elder Shunn. You'll have your new assignment by Tuesday. Now let's kneel together and pray."

It was only then, consumed by bitter disappointment, that I realized something I should have known all along. I hadn't made the bomb threat to stop Elder Finn, or even to save my own skin. I'd done it to get sent home. I had not stopped looking for the magic bullet that could set me free without fear of censure—and despite everything, I still hadn't found it.

Now I found myself in the worst of both possible worlds—not only locked into another eighteen months as a missionary, but sentenced to start over as a "problem elder" in a new territory, with no friends.

Never let it be said that the church failed to punish me.

WE BAPTIZED SANDOR AND CHERILYN THAT AFTERNOON. THREE days later, on March 10, an adjudicator at my immigration inquiry, after hearing my testimony and the report of an investigating agent, issued me a departure notice, which was one step better than deportation. It stipulated that I must leave Canada voluntarily within seven days. One day I might qualify to reapply for admission, but until then I was no longer welcome in the Great White North.

With Snow and Banks, I spent the rest of that day saying goodbye to ward members, investigators, and other missionaries. The Mareks cried. The Blanchards served up a farewell feast fit for a king. We hung out with the sisters until well into the night. At some point it came out that Sister Roper had no idea I'd ever run away from my mission. "Nobody tells us anything," she complained.

The next morning, Snow and Banks accompanied me to the airport. President Tuttle did not come. In fact, he'd been too busy the day before to offer much in the way of a goodbye at all.

At the Customs gate, Snow said, "Take care of yourself, buckfart." It was about as sentimental as he ever got.

I surrendered my Canadian work visa. When I passed through the cordon, the prosecuting agent from my immigration inquiry was waiting to verify my compliance with the departure notice. As he escorted me to my gate, we ran into my old nemesis, the man in the orange windbreaker. Black beard bristling, he said, "I heard you got off."

"Not exactly. I went to jail and I paid a big fine."

He sniffed haughtily and looked away. "So you're leaving now, eh?"

"That's right."

"Where to?"

"Spokane."

"Are you still a missionary?"

"I am."

"Well." He stroked his beard. Then, without saying anything else, he nodded decisively and walked away.

"What was *that* all about?" asked the immigration agent.

I shrugged. "He and I go way back."

Before my flight departed, one other person found me—Constable Vaughan, my arresting Mountie. He shook my hand and congratulated me on my success in court. "Let me wish you the best in all your future endeavors, Elder Shunn."

It felt like Canada itself stepping up, despite everything, to bid me farewell and good fortune.

CHAPTER 48

JOSEPH SMITH DID RETURN TO NAUVOO—IN AN OAK BOX. HE AND Hyrum lay in state as thousands of mourners filed past. Though an interment was staged in the city cemetery, their bodies were secretly buried in the basement of Joseph's mansion, to spare their graves any possibility of desecration.

Urged to calm by Willard Richards, the Saints never sought retaliation for the murders. The state did identify and prosecute five instigators of the mob, including the editor of the inflammatory *Warsaw Signal*, but all were acquitted and resumed ordinary, otherwise productive lives.

Most prognosticators thought the Mormon movement would dry up and blow away with its founder out of the picture, but the church was too well-organized for that, its doctrine too robust, its remaining leaders too forceful and charismatic. And the community of Saints had been through far too much to stop believing now. Joseph's martyrdom only bound them together all the more tightly.

Still, the years after his death were ones of confusion and uncertainty. Joseph had left no clear instructions on the topic of succession, which led to the development of several offshoot and reform sects. The largest of these became known as the Reorganized Church of Jesus

Christ of Latter-day Saints. This sect claims, with some justification, that Joseph intended the mantle of prophet to pass to his son, Joseph Smith III. It also claims polygamy was never practiced with Joseph's sanction—a belief actively encouraged by Emma, who obdurately denied for the rest of her life that Joseph had taken any other wives. The sect thrives to this day, having changed its name in 2001 to the Community of Christ. With headquarters in Independence, Missouri, it claims a quarter-million members worldwide and allows women to enter its priesthood.

The strongest argument for succession, however, was made by Brigham Young, who had become senior apostle upon the death of David Patten at the Battle of Crooked River. Brigham noted that all necessary priesthood "keys" for leading Christ's church on earth had been conferred upon the Quorum of the Twelve Apostles. Sidney Rigdon had organized a conference for August 8, 1844, to present himself as Joseph's "spokesman," but Brigham upset those plans with a fiery speech in which he wryly asked the gathering, "Do you want the Church organized or do you want a Spokesman, Cook, and Bottle Washer?" Many present reported that Brigham's features and voice transformed into Joseph's during the oration.

Sidney founded his own breakaway sect in Pittsburgh and drew some followers, but the main body of the Saints threw in with Brigham, who supported and continued Joseph's doctrinal innovations. Over the next eighteen months, he oversaw completion of the Nauvoo Temple, rushed as many church members through endowment and sealing ceremonies as he could, racked up more than forty plural wives for himself, and finally, as clashes with anti-Mormon mobs worsened, began the church's great exodus to the barren western territory that would one day be called Utah.

In so doing, Brigham Young upheld, honored, and fulfilled as best he could Joseph's vision for the church, and made sure the Saints did the same. Many changes were still to come—such as the official end of polygamy in 1890, and the no-we're-serious-this-time end of po-lygamy in 1905—but the kingdom would only continue to flourish and grow.

Today the church is a polished marketing juggernaut whose hierar-chical structure enforces a worldwide consistency of doctrine and wor-ship. It claims over 15 million members, and currently fields an army of almost 90,000 missionaries. That number exploded when, in 2012, the minimum age for mission service was lowered from 19 to 18 for young men and from 21 to 19 for young women, giving children even younger and less mature than I was the chance to prove their spiritu-al mettle—and less of a chance to stray from the straight and narrow.

Despite this massive expenditure of time, money, and talent, the church has yet to achieve the status Joseph Smith foresaw when he prophesied that it "shall roll forth, until it has filled the whole earth."

If my experience as a missionary is any indicator, it never will.

Unlike Joseph, I resisted buying into my own hype. No mat-ter how many people told me I was a hero for what I'd done in Cal-gary, I reminded myself how wrong they were. I enjoyed the attention, certainly, but never without the keen awareness that mine was hardly a laudable story.

I completed my mission service without distinction, rising to the rank of zone leader on the back of a misunderstanding or two. I broke every possible rule without committing any truly grievous sins, and racked up twenty baptisms along the way—though I never did ful-fill Elder Fowler's dying wish that I give him grandsons. I received an honorable release from my mission on Friday, August 19, 1988, a fort-night shy of my full two years.

Katrina didn't exactly wait for me all that time, but we did try to pick up where we left off when I returned home. That lasted five weeks. I was devastated when she broke up with me, but I can't really blame her. After two years in the field, I had trouble readjusting to normal life. I was clingy, uptight, and demanding, and, despite my less than diligent service, I couldn't help viewing everything through a missionary's gospel-tinted lenses.

I finished college, moved out on my own, went to work as a software developer, and started selling my short stories to science fiction magazines. I drifted away from the church. I finally lost my virginity at the age of 24, and I moved on to my first taste of alcohol at 27. But still, in the back of my mind, I expected that one day I would get my life together, repent of my many sins, and return to the church.

In 1995 I moved to New York City. Or rather, it would be more accurate to say I ran away. Between family pressures, a bleak job outlook, and the pervasiveness of Mormon culture, life in Utah had become nearly intolerable. When the opportunity to hitch a ride cross-country with a new girlfriend presented itself, I jumped. I didn't even tell my family I was leaving. In a way, I think I was completing my abortive Canadian escape from nine years earlier.

If the westward migration of the early Saints strengthened their testimonies and their ties to the church, I found that my eastern migration had the opposite effect. My testimony shriveled and died very quickly outside the nutrient bath of Utah culture. In my little Brooklyn apartment, I read every book on Mormon history I could lay my hands on and at long last learned that the doubts I'd spent a lifetime repressing were anything but wrong. I had sensed the truth as a child, but only as an adult two thousand miles from home could I let myself believe it.

Elder Finn, by the way, left the church too—for a few months. Then he met a nice Mormon woman who convinced him to give it another try, and he married her. I haven't heard from him for almost twenty years, but at last report he was active in the church. I've heard periodically from Elder Snow and Elder Vickers, both of whom remain true and faithful. Elder Fowler has drifted in and out of the church. I don't know about Sister Roper or Sister Steed, but Sister

Herzog popped up recently on Facebook to chide me for my use of foul language. I've never heard from Elder Dedman. My friend Andy Kilmer found his way out of the church before I did, as did several of our high school pals.

So, what was the turning point for me? What diverted me away from the church and onto this more expansive path?

Certainly it helped that I never got seriously involved with a devout Mormon woman in my twenties. I don't think it was my felony conviction, exactly, either, which was more a symptom of the deep war already raging inside me.

It would be oversimplifying, I'm sure, to call out one specific incident, as I probably would have reached this point eventually, one way or another. But if I had to nail it down, I'd say the ship really started turning on Wednesday, March 11, 1987.

PRESIDENT BOYD CLOSED HIS OFFICE DOOR AND WAVED ME TO A chair. "Well, well. Elder Shunn, Elder Shunn." Pear-shaped, he edged behind his desk with a curious sideways motion. "You've had quite an ordeal, haven't you?" He seated himself and bared his teeth, perhaps attempting a smile. "It must feel good to be back in the USA."

The flight to Spokane had taken only an hour. The local apes had picked me up at the airport and driven me directly here, through a city lush with unexpected greenery. In another part of this low-rent building, an orientation session for a pack of greenies fresh from the MTC was in progress.

"I just landed. I haven't really noticed yet."

Boyd's smile wavered like a solid reaching its melting point. "Well, yes."

The office was large and mostly empty. Leafy branches projected their silhouettes onto the half-drawn blinds, which provided the only light. The room smelled faintly of mulch. Neither of us spoke. The moment stretched.

His smile reinflated, puffed by some internal wind of memory. "I spoke to your President Tuttle," he said, as if this merited praise. His voice was as papery as his skin. "He tells me we're fortunate to have you. He says you're eager to put all the unpleasantness behind you and get on with the Lord's work." The wind slackened and the smile sagged. "He has nothing but praise for you. He recommends you as a leader."

My chair was stiff and uncomfortable. My collar chafed. On the wall beside the desk hung a large map covered with push pins. Beside it, dozens of passport-style photos were grouped in pairs.

"Elder Shunn, we mean to find you the best possible fit here, somewhere you'll be happy." Boyd's hands fluttered blindly on the desktop. "But we don't want to call undue attention to anything that might distract your fellow missionaries from the work, or might hamper your ability to help your investigators feel the Spirit." He leaned forward. "President Tuttle and I both agree that your legal difficulties should remain between us. No one here needs to know. You can put it behind you now."

I nodded, but inside I was already going numb. Sweat stippled my forehead and greased my back. I was itching to get out of my suit jacket.

"I expect that's settled, then," President Boyd said with a satisfied nod. His jaunty yellow tie made his skin look sallow. "Of course, you'll need a cover story. We get transfer missionaries from all over, for all kinds of reasons, but no one else who—" The smile faltered again. "Well, the point is, if your companions ask you why you came here, you need to have something to tell them." It took me a moment to realize that the rustle of dry leaves I heard was a laugh. "You can't very well tell them you went to *jail*."

Framed portrait prints of Jesus Christ and Joseph Smith gazed down from the walls. I said nothing.

"Yes, well." President Boyd snuffled and steepled his hands. "My suggestion is that you use *illness* as an excuse in case it comes up—

your transfer, I mean." The steeple flexed. "If you're pressed for specifics, you can call it *mental* illness."

In civilian life, the apes had told me on the way from the airport, President Boyd was a pathologist—a specialist in disease. Another thing the apes told me was, "Prez is great. He's definitely inspired."

I'd heard that one before.

"Well, Elder Shunn," said Boyd, rising, "welcome to the Washington Spokane Mission." His flesh pooled around his hips. I had the eerie sense that he'd wobble if I gave him a shove. "We know you're going to love it here."

I rose slowly to shake hands with this man who, for the next year and a half, would be my moral and spiritual compass. This man who clearly didn't want me here. Who wanted me to lie.

The next day, as I settled into a strange apartment in Yakima, Washington, my new companion, Elder Stockton, asked me why I'd been transferred. I thought hard about what President Boyd had instructed me to say.

And then I told Stockton the truth.

POSTLUDE

12/13/2003

NEARLY SEVENTEEN YEARS LATER, I FIND MYSELF TAKING KA-
trina's coat in the front hall of the apartment I share with my wife,
Laura, in Queens. Katrina's a little heavier than when we were kids,
and so am I. I've seen her several times over the years, including at my
Las Vegas wedding in 2001, but this is my first time meeting her second husband, Bernard.

Katrina's first husband, Dick, joined the church for her, but by the
time their first anniversary rolled around they had decided Mormonism was a crock and dropped out. In fact, Katrina was one of the first
people to ask me, before I ever thought of moving to New York, why I
still clung to the church, since it was so obviously making me unhappy.

I met Laura, a recovering Catholic, in 1998, and when we tied
the knot it was in the presence of an Elvis impersonator, not a temple officiator. Katrina's first marriage, in the meantime, broke up badly. She went back to school for a master's degree in chemistry, which
was where she met and married Bernard, a Belgian doctoral candidate. When they finished their degrees, they went to work for the
same Connecticut pharmaceutical company. Which is how it works

out that they're here, now, together, in my home. Bernard seems like a nice enough guy, if a little reticent.

Our apartment is loud, crowded, and well-stocked with booze. I spend some time catching up with Katrina, small talk mostly, with a helping of news about our parents and siblings back in Utah, none of whom have given up hope that we'll someday come back to the church. This, in fact, may be the reason we've stayed friends all this time—our mutual exile from church and country. It's one of those things only another survivor can really understand.

An hour later I'm talking in the kitchen with a small group of friends when Bernard saunters over and inserts himself into the conversation. "You know what I just found out that I did not know before?" he says to the group in a slurred accent. Our liquor cabinet seems to have loosened—and thickened—his tongue considerably. "I found out in the car on the way down here. This guy here"—he indicates me with the wineglass in his hand—"he used to be engaged to my wife."

I glance around the circle of five or six people. "Well, *this* is awkward."

"Yeah," Bernard continues. "He, like, got engaged to her at some airport."

I don't like the intent look on Bernard's face, nor his belligerent tone. I haven't been in a fight since junior high, but I can still sense the inexplicable threat of violence in the air. I try to play it casual. "That was a really long time ago. We were kids. I was nineteen."

"Yeah. And my wife was twenty."

"Time to change the subject, Bill," my friend Bob Howe says quietly. I've known him since before I was a missionary. "You're only digging yourself in deeper."

"Can you believe this?" Bernard says, spreading his arms and sloshing some of his wine onto the floor. "I only just found out. That's a pretty big thing."

"Not really, it's not." I try to make it sound offhand. "It didn't mean anything. To Mormons, getting engaged is a pastime. It's a sport. It's just what you do."

Unfazed by my commentary, Bernard looks around the circle, unsteady on his feet. "You know what else I found out? There was something about a ring, this ring—made out of wrapping paper?"

I look around the group again. "Foil. It was the foil wrapper from a stick of chewing gum."

Bernard wags a finger at me. "Yeah, yeah, that was it. A gum wrapper. And you know what else?" He leans in close enough for me to gag on his breath but doesn't lower his voice at all. "She still has it. She still has that ring."

I don't know why this comes as such a shock. I never considered how that time of our lives might have been as important to Katrina as it was to me. I do my best to keep a neutral expression. The tension is almost unbearable.

"That's nothing, Bernard," I say, patting him on the shoulder. "I still have the gum."

For a moment he looks like he believes me. Then everyone laughs good-naturedly, and so does he, and the tension washes away. With a couple of dips of his head, Bernard wanders away in search of other entertainment.

"You dodged a bullet there, pal," Bob says.

I rub a hand across my face and blow out my breath. I'm thinking of those six months in Canada, which have all come flooding back.

"That's my superpower," I say, and I go looking for a drink.

ACKNOWLEDGMENTS

THIS BOOK WOULD HAVE BEEN A FAR MORE ARDUOUS PROJECT without the generous encouragement and support of many people, some of whom may not even know how or when they helped—or may be mortified beyond words to see their names here. To anyone whose contributions I've overlooked, please forgive me. A book that has been in the works for as many years as this one accrues a mountain of debts, and sometimes the ledgers, sadly, get misplaced.

District leader promotions go to Cynthia Babak, Brad Beaulieu, Steve Benson, Chris Bigelow, Michael Bishop, Libba Bray, Scott & Lynne Bronson, Mark Bullock, Jotham & Kristin Burrello, Bob Carlson, Al & Sharon Chavoen, Tom Chavoen, Jessica Silver Concepción, Chris & Vivian Connolly, Brenda Cooper, Amy Davis, Terry Deru, Norm & Rachel Doucet, Jon & Amy Doyle, Scott Edelman, Craig Engler & Victoria Marano, Ken Ficara, Paul Fischer, Fawn Fitter, Geoff & Naomi Fowler, Jim Freund & Barbara Krasnoff, Eileen Gunn, Jacob Haller, Mette Harrison, Craig & Laura Horowitz, Andrew Huff & Cinnamon Cooper, Stan Jensen, Kevin Kartchner, Maggie Kast, Mike & Sarah Kelly, John & Shai Klima, Dan Kois, Matt Kressel, Ron Kuby, Pat Libling, Grá Linnaea, Kristi Long, David MacKenzie, Bob McAllister, Todd McAllister, Shawna McCarthy, Farah Mendlesohn & Edward

James, Lis Mitchell, Joe Monti, Brian Murphy, Steven Naifeh & Gregory White Smith, Remy Nakamura, Resa Nelson, Patrick & Teresa Nielsen Hayden, Mike Norton, Richard Packham, Hallie Gordon Palladino, Paula Peterson, Alison Pitt, Colin Poellot & Barbara Lynn Cantone, Tim Pratt & Heather Shaw, Jenn Reese, Joe Regal, Jana Remy, Eden Robins & Kyle Thiessen, Michael Roper, Will Rosenthal, Kris Rusch, Greg & Betty Ryberg, Shana Ryberg, Aaron & Diana Schnuth, Erika Skougard & Jenna Helf, Dave Slusher, Martha Soukup, Kelly Swails, Scott Swanson, Chris Sweet, Alice Taylor, Paul Thomas, Laura Tiebert, Greg van Eekhout, Greg Wands, Johnny Wider, Gregory Wilson, Sara Ross Witt, Tina Woelke, and Rob & Cindy Ziegler.

Zone leader appointments for service above and beyond the call of duty go to Cory Doctorow, Bob Howe, Vincent Jørgensen, Eleanor Lang, Michael Libling, Barry Malzberg, Holly McDowell, Jim Minz, Paul Witcover, and especially to my wise editor, Juliet Ulman, and my tireless agent, Barry Goldblatt.

Special member-missionary citations to those intrepid, anonymous dissidents who secretly recorded and transcribed the pre-1990 temple endowment ceremony, which allowed me to quote from it accurately.

And more than everyone else put together, I owe thanks to my brilliant wife, Laura Chavoen, who has lived with this book for the full duration of our relationship, and without whom writing it would have been an impossible mission. I love you, and I'm proud to call you companion.

BIBLIOGRAPHY

I FOUND MANY BOOKS INVALUABLE DURING THE LONG PROCESS OF researching and writing *The Accidental Terrorist*. First and foremost was the second edition of *No Man Knows My History*, by Fawn M. Brodie. Originally published in 1945, Brodie's work was the first important piece of scholarship on the life of the prophet. Despite flaws, it changed the game for Mormon historians, and it still casts its shadow over the field 70 years after its initial appearance. No study of the Latter-day Saints is complete without considering this book—though to some Mormons, simply having read it is tantamount to admitting apostasy.

The first serious challenger to Brodie's position in the field is 2005's *Joseph Smith: Rough Stone Rolling*, by Richard Lyman Bushman. This more thorough work, though written by a historian who takes Joseph's claims literally, gives both sides of the debate around the prophet equal consideration. It was crucial to me in painting a fuller picture of the church's founder.

Here is a complete list of the works that helped me write about Joseph Smith and the Mormon experience, and which in some cases helped me navigate my own passage out of the church:

Inside the Mind of Joseph Smith: Psychobiography and the Book of Mormon, by Robert D. Anderson (Signature Books, Salt Lake City, UT, 1999)

Reconsidering No Man Knows My History: *Fawn M. Brodie and Joseph Smith in Retrospect*, edited by Newell G. Bringhurst (Utah State University Press, Logan, UT, 1996)

No Man Knows My History: The Life of Joseph Smith, the Mormon Prophet (Second Edition, Revised and Enlarged), by Fawn M. Brodie (Alfred A. Knopf, New York, NY, 1971)

Historical Atlas of Mormonism, edited by S. Kent Brown, Donald Q. Cannon, and Richard H. Jackson (Prentice Hall, New York, NY, 1994)

The Mysteries of Godliness: A History of Mormon Temple Worship, by David John Buerger (Signature Books, Salt Lake City, UT, 1994)

Joseph Smith: Rough Stone Rolling, by Richard Lyman Bushman (Alfred A. Knopf, New York, NY, 2005)

Evil Among Us: The Texas Mormon Missionary Murders, by Ken Driggs (Signature Books, Salt Lake City, UT, 2000)

Shot in the Heart, by Mikal Gilmore (Doubleday, New York, NY, 1994)

Secret Ceremonies: A Mormon Woman's Intimate Diary of Marriage and Beyond, by Deborah Laake (Island Books, New York, NY, 1993)

History of the Mormons; or, Latter-day Saints, by Henry Mayhew (Derby and Miller, Auburn, NY, 1852)

Mormonism and Masonry (Second Enlarged Edition), by E. Cecil McGavin (Bookcraft, Salt Lake City, UT, 1949)

New Approaches to the Book of Mormon: Explorations in Critical Methodology, edited by Brent Lee Metcalfe (Signature Books, Salt Lake City, UT, 1993)

The Mormon Murders: A True Story of Greed, Forgery, Deceit, and Death, by Steven Naifeh and Gregory White Smith (Weidenfeld & Nicolson, New York, NY, 1988)

Mormon America: The Power and the Promise, by Richard N. Ostling and Joan K. Ostling (HarperSanFrancisco, New York, NY, 1999)

Orrin Porter Rockwell: Man of God, Son of Thunder (Second Edition), by Harold Schindler (University of Utah Press, Salt Lake City, UT, 1983)

History of the Church of Jesus Christ of Latter-day Saints, by Joseph Smith, Jr. (7 vols., edited by B. H. Roberts) (Deseret Book, Salt Lake City, UT, 1948-1950)

Brigham Young: Pioneer Prophet, by John G. Turner (The Belknap Press of Harvard University Press, Cambridge, MA/London, England, 2012)

Mormon Polygamy: A History (Second Edition), by Richard S. Van Wagoner (Signature Books, Salt Lake City, UT, 1989)

I have also, of course, referred frequently to what Mormons call the Standard Works—their four canonized books of holy scripture. Besides the King James Version of the Bible, these include the Book of Mormon, the Doctrine and Covenants, and the Pearl of Great Price. These last two books are compiled primarily from Joseph Smith's revelations and other writings in the years after the founding of the church.

There is much wonderful and contradictory material out there about the lives of Joseph Smith and the early Saints. Any errors of historical fact in this book you may blame on me alone, though I make no apologies for the conclusions I've drawn.

ABOUT THE AUTHOR

SINCE HIS FIRST PUBLICATION IN 1993, WILLIAM SHUNN'S SHORT fiction has appeared in *Salon, Storyteller, Bloodstone Review, Newtown Literary, Asimov's Science Fiction, The Magazine of Fantasy & Science Fiction, Science Fiction Age, Realms of Fantasy, Electric Velocipede,* and various anthologies and year's-best collections. His work has been shortlisted for the Hugo Award, the Nebula Award, and the Theodore Sturgeon Memorial Award. His chapbook *An Alternate History of the 21st Century* appeared from Spilt Milk Press in 2007, and his novella *Cast a Cold Eye,* written with Derryl Murphy, from PS Publishing in 2009.

He is a former producer and host of the acclaimed Tuesday Funk literary reading series in Chicago. He currently lives in New York City with his wife, Laura Chavoen, and their soft-coated wheaten terrier, Ella the Wonder Dog.

For more information, visit www.shunn.net or follow @shunn on Twitter.

The new name is Noah.

CPSIA information can be obtained at www.ICGtesting.com
Printed in the USA
BVOW08*1707170915

418324BV00001B/3/P